D1070423

DRUGS AND FOOD FROM THE SEA
FROM THE SEA
Myth or Reality?

Copyright© 1978 by The University of Oklahoma

DRUGS AND FOOD
FROM THE SEA

Myth or Reality?

Edited by:

Pushkar N. Kaul

University of Oklahoma
Health Sciences Center
College of Pharmacy
Oklahoma City, Oklahoma

and

Carl J. Sindermann
U.S. Department of Commerce
National Oceanic and Atmospheric Administration
National Marine Fisheries Service
Sandy Hook, New Jersey

The University of Oklahoma
Norman, Oklahoma
1978

PREFACE

Since the beginning of civilization two basic needs for human survival have been food to provide energy to sustain life and drugs to alleviate pain. These needs have never been fully satisfied, and 20th century man continues to search for better ways to satisfy them. The oceans, which cover more than two-thirds of the planet, have been and are being examined for contributions to the satisfaction of these basic human needs.

This book is based on an international symposium on drugs and food from the oceans, held at the University of Oklahoma, Norman, in September, 1977. Participants in the symposium were drawn from two distinct but interacting disciplines—marine biomedical research (including chemistry, pharmacology, and physiology) and marine fisheries (including aquaculture). In the past, similar groups of discussants have met under the aegis of the Marine Biological Resources Committee of the Marine Technology Society every two or three years during the past decade.

The book has two major divisions: drugs and food. Included in the drugs section are topics ranging from biochemical taxonomy through preliminary studies of many bioactive substances from marine organisms, to elaborate pharmacological and toxicological evaluations of novel chemical substances of marine origin, which may have potential pharmaceutical value. Included in this division are also chapters which deal, for the first time, with a totally new concept of marine biomedicine which essentially suggests that some of the lower forms of marine life may provide simple systems for understanding various physiological and pathological processes in man. It has also been demonstrated that some of the marine animals may be useful in pharmacological testing of chemical substances usually carried out in much more expensive mammalian systems.

The food division contains sections which constitute a critical appraisal of the status and potential of food production from the sea—from natural as well as aquaculture populations. Outstanding investigators in the field of marine fisheries have addressed the problem of current production and future projections, as well as some of the constraints on marine food production. Present contributions of marine aquaculture and its future potential have been discussed by experts from government, universities, and industry.

We hope that the contents of this book will not only provide insights about the status of research in the fields of both marine biomedicine and marine food, but will also stimulate future exploration and exploitation of the world's oceans as a source of drugs and food to sustain human life.

It would be difficult to name all the individuals who contributed in various ways to make this volume possible. However, we are indebted to the Symposium Session Chairmen: Kenneth L. Rinehart, Jr., James S. Kittredge, George D. Ruggieri, George B. Whitfield, Leon S. Ciereszko, Francis J. Schmitz, Alfred J. Weinheimer, Conrad Mahnken, George F. Greene, Jr., William N. Shaw, and John P. Wise, all of whom provided the necessary leadership and stimulus for productive discussions. Our special gratitude goes to Charlene Burns for her artwork and other contributions, and to Shrinivas K. Kulkarni, Linda Stevens, R.R. Salmon, Marla Johnson Chess, Venita Kaul and Jerry Laizure without whose contributions the production of this book would have been impossible. We are deeply indebted to the management and staff of the University of Oklahoma Journalism Press and the University Printing Services for their priority attention which made it possible to produce this book in a relatively record time.

We gratefully acknowledge the financial contributions and other support for the Symposium received from the University of Oklahoma, Northeast Fisheries Center of the National Marine Fisheries Service (National Oceanic and Atmospheric Administration, U. S. Department of Commerce), the Upjohn Company, Hoffmann La Roche Inc., Abbott Laboratories and G.D. Searle & Company.

Norman, Oklahoma

January, 1978

P.N. Kaul

C.J. Sindermann

TABLE OF CONTENTS

PART I
DRUGS FROM THE SEA

(cont'd)

(cont'd)

INTERLUDE

PART II
FOOD FROM THE SEA

PART I

DRUGS FROM THE SEA

SECTION I

Simple Pathophysiological
Models in Marine Organisms

Another dimension
of marine biomedicine

Biomedical Potential Of The Sea

Pushkar N. Kaul

University of Oklahoma Health Sciences Center, College of Pharmacy
Oklahoma City, Oklahoma.

Natural products of terrestrial origin have always served as a rich source of drugs for mankind. In ancient medicine most remedies were derived from either powders or extracts of plants, animals and minerals. The modern allopathic system of medicine, on the other hand, has advocated the use of pure chemical substances possessing pharmacologic activity, rather than the crude extracts of unknown composition. Most of these pure substances were initially isolated from the terrestrial organisms, but as the knowledge and skill in chemistry evolved the drugs of synthetic origin began to appear. However, the molecular prototype with activity always came from the natural sources.

Medicinal plants and soil microbes from various parts of the world have been explored for potential drugs fairly extensively during the past half a century. As a result, series of so called "wonder" drugs,such as antibiotics and tranquilizers, were introduced into medical practice in the early fifties. Since then, however, there have been no major introductions from the terrestrial sources. It is, therefore, perhaps timely that our attention has now turned toward the sea for further and new leads.

Man's awareness of the possible biomedical benefits from the sea is not actually new. It is not uncommon, for example, to find prescriptions in the ancient systems of medicine, which contained sea weeds or powdered shells or parts of marine animals. What is relatively new and exciting, however, is the exploration of marine life forms and environment with the help of modern tools and approaches characteristic of our times. This effort has in fact just begun.

Perhaps one of the catalysts for exploration of the sea for new drugs was the discovery, by the University of Oklahoma marine research group (Spraggins and Weinheimer) in 1968, relative to the presence of epimeric forms of prostaglandin derivatives in the gorgonian, *Plexaura homomalla*. Since then, a number of reports have appeared in the literature describing the presence of antimicrobial, cytotoxic, cardiovascular and psychotropic activities in the extracts or pure isolates of marine origin. These relatively few but firm reports clearly indicate the vast potential of marine world as a source of drugs for years to come.

Further and more recent evidence in support of the promise the sea offers is documented in this volume. The cardiotonic peptides from the species of *Anthopleura* described by Norton *et al.*, the hypotensive urophysial peptide from a fish reviewed by Lederis, the cardio-active toxins of Beress from sea anemones, and a novel drug metabolism inhibitor from *Aplysia dactylomela* described by Kaul *et al.* are but only some of the examples of useful pharmacologic agents derived from marine animals. Although none of the marine derived substances has become a "wonder" drug yet, there is every indication that some will be forthcoming in due course. It must be recognized, however, that it takes three to ten years for a new drug to evolve from the time its pharmacologic activity is first discovered. Furthermore, only one out of several hundred active compounds may survive all of the safety and efficacy tests required prior to human consumption.

In spite of the optimistic picture I have painted, it is discouraging that the overall effort and money being spent on marine biomedical research is negligible in comparison with the massive effort and funds expended by the industrial and federal agencies around the world on the exploitation of terrestrial plants during the past half a century. The time is now right when the drug industry, the academia and the federal agencies must make a commitment to the biomedical exploration of the sea.

One of the fascinating aspects of marine biomedicine, brought to light by some of the contributions in this volume, relates to a challenging concept that marine life forms may provide simple physiological models for understanding the mechanisms of function and pathophysiology of various organs and systems in man. We may expect a great deal of research activity in this area in years to come. In this regard, it is gratifying to note that the National Institute of Environmental Health Sciences (U.S.A.) has started to specifically encourage this type of research through the newly instituted Marine and Freshwater Biomedical Core Center Grants.

In yet another front, we may witness an increase in the use of marine animals for pharmacologic and toxicologic studies generally employed in screening chemical substances for useful biological activity. This should have a significant impact on the economics of drug development on one hand and the technology of laboratory aquaculture and mariculture on the other.

These are some of the aspects of marine biomedicine we will witness developing and expanding within this century, paving way for the twenty-first century when man will not only go to the Moon and Mars for satisfying curiosity but will also dive into the sea for sustaining his life.

Contributions Of The Sea To Medicine[1]

Stewart G. Wolf

The Marine Biomedical Institute
University of Texas
Medical Branch
Galveston, Texas

I am grateful for the privilege of addressing this distinguished group. I must acknowledge, however, that I know very little about food and drugs from the sea. I gather that Dr. Kaul thought it might be of interest to you to hear of the Marine Biomedical Institute and of contributions of the aquatic environment to medicine other than food and drugs.

The Marine Biomedical Institute has been in existence little over seven years and is still unique as the only marine institute in the world located on a medical campus and "owned and operated" by a Health Sciences Center.

Lawrence J. Henderson recognized the great potential of the marine environment a good many years ago when he said, "No philosopher's or poet's fancy, no myth of a primitive people has ever exaggerated the importance, the usefulness, and above all, the beneficence of the ocean for the community of living things." The beneficence may surprise you a bit, as it did me. The ocean is conventionally referred to as a hostile environment, but on close examination, this appears to be an undeserved label. It may seem hostile to man, but to its proper inhabitants the ocean has been remarkably hospitable. Not only is the world of the sea older and more productive than that on land, but its inhabitants have solved many problems that we are unhappily still struggling with— food supply, population control, conservation of species and social relations, for example. The food chain in the sea is just as predatory as that on land and yet not only is there enough nourishment to go around but weak species do not become altogether consumed. Indeed species all along the phylogenetic scale are preserved in the sea, even from the most ancient times, the counterparts of which on land have long become extinct.

The rationale for tapping the sea for the benefit of medical research and medical practice was clearly recognized by a distinguished series of investigators working at such institutions as Woods Hole and Mt. Desert over the past 50 years or more.

Realizing the need to focus our efforts we elected to pursue primarily two lines of inquiry: (i) the adaptation of man to the marine environment including the associated problems of decompression sickness and hyperbaric medicine; (ii) the study of simple marine organisms to unravel the complex mechanisms of mammalian systems, including those of man.

Such a strategy is feasible and useful because Nature has, over hundreds perhaps thousands of millions of years of biological evolution, used the same or closely similar molecular structures, hormones, enzymes, and neural transmitters, and essentially identical cellular structure and cellular metabolism. We elected to focus on the neurobiological aspect of the bodily economy, neuronal interactions and the organization of neural function, starting with simple marine invertebrates such as the *Aplysia* and extending through the vertebrate and mammalian forms to man. Throughout this broad phylogenetic spectrum the basic structure of the neuron, the mechanisms of firing and neurotransmission and the strategies of organized function have remained essentially unchanged, although there have been vast increases in numbers of neurons and in their elaboration.

There are many other organ systems that lend themselves to profitable study by medical researchers. I would like briefly to describe some of the aquatic models of human physiologic mechanisms and even of disease. The findings have stemmed from the work of others in various parts of the world.

Physiology and Pathophysiology

Monumental contributions to the understanding of osmo-regulation and kidney function resulted from the intelligent exploitation of marine organisms by Homer Smith and his colleagues at Mt. Desert. Through their work with fishes much of the complex behavior of the human kidney has been elucidated.

Our understanding of the functions of the human liver is not so complete, but again marine organisms appear to be providing important leads. Especially promising have been studies of the liver of the shark, an organ whose design and function have apparently remained unchanged for approximately four hundred million years. The liver of the shark, architecturally similar to that of man, appears to perform more of a storage than a metabolic processing function.

Some of the biosynthetic activities carried out in the enormously complex human liver are undertaken by the stomach and intestine in the shark. Thus the shark liver offers a somewhat simpler chemical laboratory for study. Nevertheless, what biochemical transformations do take place in the organ seem to be similar to those that occur in the human liver. The

8

shark liver synthesizes trimethylamine (TMA) oxide, a substance with an apparent osmo-regulatory function. This is accomplished via TMA oxidase, a system closely akin to the detoxifying mechanisms of human liver for foreign nitrogenous compounds (2). Unlike the human, the shark liver is capable of excreting unconjugated bilirubin in the bile, however (3,4). It stores large amounts of fat, some (containing squalene) apparently used to control buoyancy and some (containing triacyl glycerols and wax esters) to support energy requirements (5). An understanding of the regulatory processes involved in these functions, will have important relevance to human pathophysiology.

The liver of the shark in his normal sea water environment synthesizes urea but not albumin in more than trace amounts. A high concentration of urea is retained in the blood to effect osmotic balance. The shark can be acclimatized to a fresh water environment, however. In fresh water the concentration of urea in the shark's blood falls because of increased urea clearance, not of a decrease in urea synthesis. Amazingly, the liver thereupon begins to manufacture a significant amount of albumin. The study of this capability through experimental manipulations would certainly have great relevance to human hepatic disease.

Endocrine Functions

Several published reports suggest that a phylogenetic strategy may be productive in the study of endocrine regulation as well (6-8). The traditional approach to the understanding of hormonal inter-relationships has been to cut away or poison certain cells in mammals in order to simplify the picture and reduce the number of forces acting at one time. The comparative approach, on the other hand, finds simplicity in the normal regulatory mechanisms of animals low on the phylogenetic scale, animals in whom only parts of the complex mammalian machinery have evolved.

One excellent review describes studies pertinent to the phylogeny of thyroglobulin (9). Evidence on early precursors of the thyroid gland has been obtained from studies of ascidians and *Amphioxus*. The subpharyngeal glands of the primitive vertebrates, hagfish and lamprey have been studied before and after metamorphosis. Conveniently the thyroid precursor in the lamprey larva and the thyroid gland in the adult prior to spawning are not dependent on pituitary TSH stimulation (10). Other studies were of the air-breathing fish, *Polypterus* (11).

The relationship of thyroid to other glandular functions, especially with respect to sexual maturation has been studied in several teleosts including the Indian Catfish, *Heteropneustes fossilis*, and during seasonal and temperature changes in other teleosts (12, 13).

Calcitonin production has been studied in lung fishes. Lung fishes have also provided an insight into the very exciting area of neurohormonal interaction and neural regulation of endocrine activity in the estivation of these hibernating fish (14).

Brain and Behavior

One of the richest yields from the study of marine organisms is available to the neurobiologist. The classical studies of the giant axon of the squid and studies of neuronal organization in the Aplysia are well known. From the rapidly accumulating data on interneuronal relationships the circuit diagrams of certain simple behaviors are beginning to take shape. Ultimately some of the complex interactions of neurons, glia and neurotransmitter systems that spell psychiatric and neurologic disease in man may be unravelled through systematic study of the simpler circuitry of marine invertebrates and fishes.

Disease Models

Aging—Spectacular neurohormonal relationships have been described in the migrating Pacific salmon by O. H. Robertson, Wexler and Miller (15). During migration from the ocean to fresh water up-river for spawning, the fish developed a rapidly progressive adrenal hypercorticism with many features of Cushing's disease, hyperlipidemia and extensive arteriosclerosis. After spawning all the fish died. The arterial lesions contained very little lipid but resembled closely the fibrous plaques of human arteriosclerosis. Interestingly, the males were as much affected as the females. Castrations appeared to protect both males and females against the fulminating arteriosclerosis. In 1966, Van Citters and Watson described the development of similar arterial lesions in steelhead trout (*Salmo gairdnerii*) as they swam from the sea to fresh water to spawn (16). In contrast to the salmon, however, not all of them died. Some of the trout were able to swim back to the sea. In these the arterial lesions regressed and disappeared. It should be possible, by maintaining this fish in a controlled environment, to manipulate the process of arteriosclerosis development and its reversal.

Diabetes—Not only do marine organisms offer a potentially rich source of models of human disease, but so also do the fresh water fish. For example, Sekoke, a nutritionally induced syndrome virtually identical to diabetes mellitus, has been identified and extensively studied among carp in Japanese fish farms (17,18). The "clinical" features of the disease include hyperglycemia and glycosuria that is relatively insulin resistant, decreased glucose tolerance and occasionally ketonuria. The pathology includes most prominently a waxy degeneration of skeletal muscles and a vascular proliferative retinopathy (19). Yokote, who made extensive histological studies, demonstrated lesions of the pancreatic islets, the renal glomeruli (Fig. 1), vitreal vessels (Fig. 2 and 3), and peripheral nerves (Fig. 4), that closely resemble those found in human diabetes (20). In addition, he observed defective gonadal development in affected carp of both sexes.

Other workers discovered that the causative agent was an excess of oxidized unsaturated fatty acids in the diet of the carp derived from feeding them silk worm pupae (21,22). The investigators were able to induce the disease experimentally by feeding the fish a diet containing 10% oxidized saury oil for 60 days, and could prevent the disease by prophylactic treatment with *alpha* tocopherol.

A detailed study of the interplay between peroxidation of unsaturated fatty acids and total endocrine metabolism, especially focusing on glucagon and pituitary function, may turn out to be highly profitable. There is strong evidence, recently derived, that the fundamental lesion in

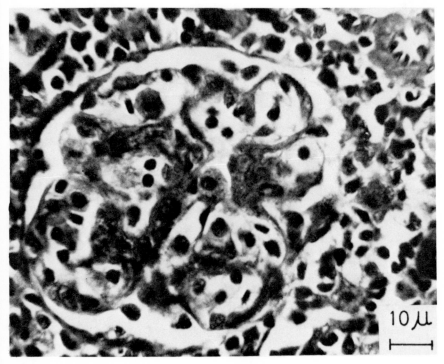

10 μ

FIGURE 1. A glomerulus of the kidney from a Sekoke carp. Noteworthy is PAS-positive thickening of capillary wall and mesangial region. PAS stain, 600.

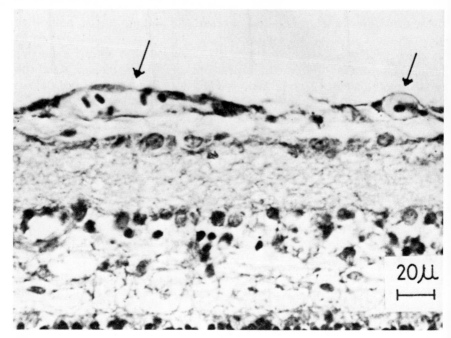

FIGURE 2. Retina from a normal carp. Arrows indicate vitreous capillaries. PAS stain, 150.

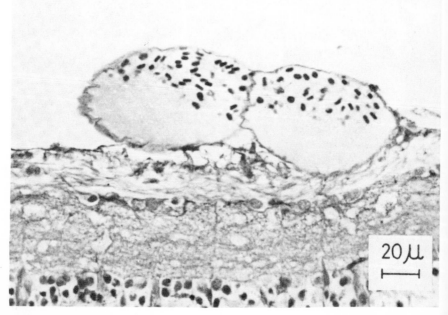

FIGURE 3. Retina from a Sekoke carp showing extremely dilated capillaries. PAS stain, 150.

a   b

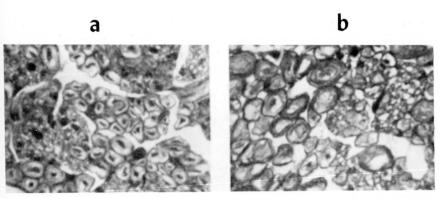

FIGURE 4(a). Lateral line nerve bundle from a normal carp. (b) Lateral line nerve bundle from a Sekoke carp. Dilatation of axons, demyelination, and thickening of Schwann's sheath are observed. Levi fixation, Azan stain, 1000.

diabetes mellitus involves a disorder of cell to cell communication between *alpha* and *beta* cells of the islets of Langerhans (23). Hence it would be important to establish, as a base-line, the insulin regulatory mechanisms that obtained prior to the appearance of glucagon in the course of biological evolution. *Alpha* cells and glucagon first make their appearance among teleosts. Thus, fundamental information on diabetes may be available from the study of more primitive marine forms such as the cyclostomes that appear to possess insulin secreting *beta* cells but no *alpha* cells and no glucagon. Conveniently, their endocrine and exocrine pancreas are completely separated.

While glucagon and its sister hormone, secretin, are relatively new molecular structures in the long perspective of biological evolution, Nature has for the most part used the same substances and the same strategies of molecular interaction throughout most of the span of phylogenetic development. It is therefore often feasible, through the study of relatively simple organisms, to elucidate regulatory mechanisms that operate in the complex systems of man. Few would doubt that the understanding of regulatory processes is the key to understanding the fundamental mechanisms of disease.

Immune Mechanisms

Finally, a deep living teleost, the angler fish, may provide a model for the study of problems of human organ transplantation and tissue rejection. Living at depths from one to several thousand feet in a thinly populated, light-poor environment, the angler fish meets the challenge to perpetuate the species in a striking way When he encounters a female, the male angler fish bites into her flesh, ultimately making a permanent bond with her. The male is nourished through a sort of placental arrangement that develops at the site of the bite. Thereupon his unneeded digestive and respiratory and circulatory organs start to atrophy, eventually leaving little of the male body but the gonads which have hypertrophied and which provide an always available source of spermatozoa. Female angler fish have been caught with as many as three or four males attached. As far as is known, the male body, essentially a homograft, is never rejected.

I think it is fair to conclude that the marine environment constitutes for the biomedical researcher, a veritable gold-mine that has only just begun to be exploited.

References

1. Presented in part at the 88th Meeting of the American Clinical and Climatological Association, Bermuda, October 26-29, 1975.
2. Goldstein, L., Dewitt-Harley, S. (1973). Trimethylamine Oxidase of Nurse Shark Liver and its Relation to Mammalian Mixed Function Amine Oxidase. *Comp. Biochem. Physio.* **45B**, 895.
3. Arias, I. M. (1962). Studies of Bile Pigment Metabolism in the Dogfish (*Squalus acanthias*) and the Goosefish (*Lophius piscatorius*). *Bull. of the Mount Desert Island Biological Laboratory.*
4. *ibid.* (1966). The Jaundiced Newborn Infant and the Dogfish. *Postgrad. Med.* **39**. No. 6
5. Malins, D. C., and Robisch, P.A. (1972). Biosynthesis of Triacyglycerols in Dogfish (*Squalus acanthias*) Liver: Incorporation of (14C)Palmitic Acid into Acyl Chains. *Comp. Biochem. Physiol.* **43B**, 125.
6. Wattez, C. (1973). Effet de l'ablation des Tentacules Oculaires sur la Gonade en Crossance et en Cours de Regeneration chez Arion Subfuscus Draparnaud (*Gasteropode Pulmone*). *Gen. and Comp. Endocrine.* **21**, 1.
7. Godet, R., and Dupe, M. (1965). Quelques Aspects des Relations Neuroendocriniennes chez Protopterus Annectens (*poisson dipneuste*). *Arch. Anat. Microscop. Morphol. Exptl.* **54**, 319.
8. Fujita, H. and Nanba, H. (1971). Fine Structure and its Functional Properties of the Endostyle of Ascidians, *Ciona intestinalis.* (A part of Phylogenetic Studies of the Thyroid-Gland). *Zellforsch.* **121**, 455.
9. Suzuki, S. and Kondo, Y. (1973). Thyroidal Morphogenesis and Biosynthesis of Thyroglobulin before and after Metamorphosis in the Lamprey, Lampetra Reissneri. *J. Gen. Comp. Endocrinol.* **21**, 451.

10. Pickering, A.D. (1972). Effects of Hypophysectomy on the Activity of the Endostyle and Thyroid Gland in the Larval and Adult River Lamprey, *Lampetra fluviatilis L., J. Gen, and Comp. Endocrinol* **18**, 335.

11. Thomopoulos, A. and Wolff, E. (1971): Naissance et individualisation de l'ebauche thyroidienne chez *Polypterus senegalus* Cub. (*Poisson-Brachiopterygien*). *C. R. Acad. Sc. Paris* **273**, 2134.

12. Singh, B. R., Thakur, R. N. and Yadav, B. N. (1971). The Relationship Between the Changes in the Interrenal, Gonadal and Thyroidal Tissue of the Air Breathing Fish, *Heteropneustes fossilis* (Bloch) at Different Periods of the Breeding Cycle. *J. Endocr.* **61**, 309.

13. Wiggs, A. J. (1974). Seasonal Changes in the Thyroid Proteinase of a Teleost Fish, the Burbot, *Lota lota* L. *Canadian J. Zoology.* **52**, 1071.

14. Pang, P. T., Clark, N. B., and Thomson, K. S. (In press). Hypocalcemic Activities in the Ultimobranchial Bodies of Lungfishes, Neoceratodus Forsterio and Lepidosiren Paracoxa and Teleosts, *Fundulus heteroclitus* and *Gadus morhua.*

15. Robertson, O. H., Wexler, B. C. and Miller, B. F. (1961). Degenerative Changes in the Cardiovascular System of the Spawning Pacific Salmon (*Oncorhynchus tshawytscha*). *Circulation Research.* **9**, 826.

16. Van Citters, R. L. and Watson, N. W. (1966). Coronary Artery Disease in Migratory Steelhead Trout. *Circulation.* **34**, 33.

17. Saku Branch of Nagano Pref. Exp. St. (1957). On Sekoke Disease. (in Japanese). Pamphlet.

18. Yokote, M. (1967). Note on the Pathological Studies of Diabetic Carp, So-called Sekoke Disease. (Review, in Japanese). *Fish. Path.* **1**, 54.

19. Murachi, S. W., and Karakawa, Y. (1967). Symptoms Appearing in the Eye Fundus of the Carp Fed on the Containing oxidized Oil. *J. Fac. Fish. Anim. Husb.* Hiroshima University, **7**, 89.

20. Yokote, M. (1970). Sekoke Disease, Spontaneous Diabetes in Carp, *Cyprinus carpio,* Found in Fish Farms, I. Pathological Study. *Bull. Freshwater Fish. Res. Lab.* **20**, 1, 39.

21. Murakami, K. (1964). Study on Sekoke Disease (in Japanese). *Hiroshima Pref. Hokubu Tansuigyo Shidosho Jigyo-Kenkyo.* **4**, 42.

22. Hahimoto, Y., Okaichi, T., Watanabe, T., Furukawa, A., and Umezu, T. (1966). Muscle Dystrophy of Carp Due to Oxidized Oil and the Preventive Effect of Vitamin E. *Bull, Jap. Soc. Sci. Fish.* **32**, 64.

23. Wolf, S. and Berle, B. Eds. (1975). *Dilemmas In Diabetes.* Plenum Press, New York City.

Invertebrate Mucus: Model Systems For Studying Diseases In Man

Robert E. Hillman

Battelle
William F. Clapp Laboratories
Duxbury, Massachusetts

A little over 10 years ago, Dr. Sophie Jakowska (1966) wrote:
"A better understanding of the basic nature of mucus will bring eventual relief to scores of children with cystic fibrosis, to men and women of all ages afflicted with bronchial conditions, to those who live in air polluted by respiratory irritants, and to couples suffering the consequences of their fertility or infertility. The fact that mucus plays an important part in many natural processes in man and animals and represents a complicating factor in a number of diseases is a further inducement for such studies."

She continued further on:
"We cannot help concluding that, even with some 900 pages of newly assembled printed matter on this subject contributed by some of the most prominent scientists, we have gained relatively little understanding of the basic nature of mucus production and transport. As a biological product mucus continues to defy scientific inquiry."

Since that time, there has been a considerable amount of work done on mucus, particularly in invertebrates (1-10), yet much remains to be learned of mucus production, of the role of different mucosubstances in invertebrate physiology, and about the relationship of the function of mucocompounds in invertebrates to that of similar compounds in vertebrates.

It is quite possible that the mucus production in the mantle of the hard clam, *Mercenaria mercenaria*, bears similarity, in mechanisms involved, to the mucus production in certain human disease processes, such as arthritis and cystic fibrosis.

Our interest in mucus developed when we described an interesting characteristic of the hard clam mantle edge (Fig. 1), an enlarged fourth

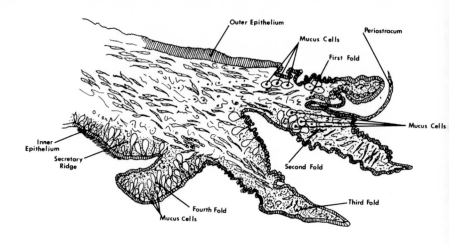

FIGURE 1. Schematic drawing of a cross section through the mantle margin of the hard clam, *Mercenaria mercenaria*, showing mucopolysaccharide-producing cells.

fold containing an unusually large amount of mucus (11,12). Generally, the mantle of bivalve mollusks terminates in three folds. The outermost fold, next to the shell, is primarily secretory in function; the middle fold is considered to be a sensory structure and the inner fold is thought to be a muscular flap controlling the flow of water into the mantle cavity. In the superfamily *Veneracea,* however, the free mantle margin (distal to the attachment by the pallial muscles to the shell) is divided into four folds. The fourth fold in the hard clam appears to be unique because of its relative size and the presence in it of the large amounts of mucus. It was the presence of this material in the fourth fold which led us to the overall investigation of the mucopolysaccharides in the rest of the mantle as well.

Mucopolysaccharides in the Hard Clam

Intensive histochemical analyses revealed some very interesting properties of hard clam mantle mucus. Of particular interest for this monograph are the mucosubstances in the first and the second marginal folds (2,3).

There was a strong alcianophilia in the mucus cells of the first fold, and there was no apparent difference in the intensity of staining when the sections were reacted at pH 1.0 or 2.5 (2). In addition, when the tissues were exposed to alcian blue at pH 2.5 and safranin at pH 1.0 these cells retained their alcianophilia, indicating that the material was possibly either a weakly acidic sulfated mucosubstance, a sialomucin, or hyaluronic acid. However, a dark purple coloration due to an aldehyde fuchsin reaction followed by alcian blue and non-digestion of the material by testicular hyaluronidase tended to eliminate the possibility of the mucus being a sialomucin or hyaluronic acid. A black coloration produced by a high iron diamine reaction was a further indication that the material was sulfated. Alcianophilia persisted in magnesium chloride concentrations as high as 0.6 M, expected of such strongly acid sulfated mucopolysaccharides as chondroitin sulfate, keratin sulfate, or heparin.

It is interesting that none of the mucus in the first fold or outer epithelium of the mantle reacted with dilute Azure A at any pH, whereas both orthochromatic and metachromatic reactions were produced in other areas of the mantle. The first fold mucus, however, produced a metachromatic reaction following 0.1% aqueous toluidine blue 0. Furthermore, this material was periodic acid-Schiff (PAS) positive following diastase digestion and colored purple following an alcian blue-PAS reaction.

Small amounts of calcium, as demonstrated by von Kossa reactions, were present in the mucous cells of the first fold, but not to any great extent. The outer epithelium of the mantle margin also did not show a strong positive von Kossa reaction, and it is in this area that the calcium carbonate shell is secreted. Preliminary electron microprobe studies, however, indicated that the mucus contained considerable quantities of calcium, but these data were only from initial studies and were not conclusive.

Results of all histochemical procedures described above indicate that the material in the first fold of the hard clam mantle is a moderate to strongly acidic, sulfated mucosaccharide. When the reactions of vertebrate mucosubstances to the same reagents as used in this study are compared with the reactions previously described, the results are quite interesting. For example, it is unusual to find strongly acidic connective tissue sulfomucins giving such an intensely positive PAS reaction. Pearse (13) feels that the presence of certain acid groups in periodate unreactive substances, e.g., chondroitin sulfate, exhibit in some way the formation of the complex between the periodate-engendered dialdehydes and the Schiff reagent. Perhaps in the mucopolysaccharide of *M. mercenaria,* these acid groups are not as numerous along the polysaccharide chain, or the molecular construction is such that even though a bond may form between the Schiff reagent and the aldehydes, the molecular resonance is dampened and no coloration is produced.

From the juxtaposition of the material with shell secreting area of the mantle, it might be assumed that this material plays some role in calcification, much as dermatan sulfate might. The presence of calcium, although not demonstrable in large amounts, tends to support this idea. If this is so, the molecular structure of this material would be of considerable interest since it resembles dermatan or chondroitin sulfate in some respects, and is so different, at least histochemically, in others. An analysis of the structure, and its similarities to those acid mucosubstances associated with calcification in other organisms, may provide more information on the function of glycosaminoglycans in the process of calcification.

Results of histochemical reactions for mucosubstances in the second fold (3) indicated that there are probably two types of mucous cells present. The first cell type produces a mucopolysaccharide of varying acidity, depending upon factors which have not yet been determined. It was thought at first that there were a number of different mucopolysaccharide-producing cells in the second fold, but the morphology of the cells is quite constant, so the variations in staining results will have to be explained in another way.

With Azure A, at both pH 1.0 and pH 4.0, the reactions showed the metachromatic purple color, indicating that the mucus was rather strongly acidic. The material was also quite intensely alcianophilic at both pH 1.0 and 2.5—a further indication of its acidity. Alcianophilia tended to be extinguished as the magnesium chloride concentration was increased, but the fact that there was intense alcianophilia in magnesium chloride concentrations as high as 1.0 M indicated that some of the material was very strongly acidic. The mixed reaction with high iron diamine confirmed that some of the material was strongly acidic and sulfated while much of it was not quite as strongly acidic, and some was non-sulfated.

There was no change in the intensity of alcianophilia following testicular hyaluronidase digestion eliminating the possibility of the material being hyaluronic acid. Methylation completely blocked alcianophilia, but the alcianophilia was partially restored following saponification. This is further proof that some of the acidic groups on the mucopolysaccharides were probably sulfate esters. The trace of red coloration following the alcian blue-PAS reaction indicated that a very small amount of the material was a neutral, or non-sulfated periodate-reactive mucosaccharide.

The results of the various PAS combinations on the second cell type revealed a granular, probably neutral mucosubstance, which was not digested by diatase. The cells secreting this material were mixed in with the acid mucopolysaccharide-producing cells so that the second fold is like a gland, and the two secretions, rather than having separate functions, may be working together.

The function of this material can only be speculated upon at this point. Usually the role of invertebrate mucus is in organismal protection, lubrication, and in food ingestion and capture. A portion of the mucopolysaccharide exhibits histochemical reactions similar to heparin, as evidenced by persistence of alcianophilia through at 1.0 M magnesium chloride concentration, and the positive reactions for safranin, aldehyde fuchsin, and high iron diamine. As mentioned previously, the amount of the material exhibiting these reactions seems to vary from sample to sample. The cause for the variation seems to be in the degree of sulfation of the mucopolysaccharide. The more highly sulfated, the greater amount of al-cianophilia persisting at high magnesium chloride concentration, or the greater amount of safranin staining, etc. The variation in the degree of sulfation appears to be seasonally independent and there is little in-dividual variation among clams.

From the results of the histochemical reactions, it would seem that a portion of the material secreted by the second fold cells is similar to heparin. This would not be surprising since heparin-like compounds have been isolated from marine clams (14-16). Love and Frommhagen (14) suggest the possibility that the heparin-like material might aid in the handling of calcium by the clam. Perhaps the material is also affected by the presence of other ions such as sodium and chloride. Its quality and quantity may therefore depend on salinity, which can vary considerably in an estuarine environment. The remainder of the acid mucopolysac-charide material could be a heparin precursor in varying degrees of acidi-ty and sulfation. The neutral mucosubstance also varies in quantity, possibly in relation to variation in the mucopolysaccharide. The mucus secretions in the second fold are distinctly different from that in the first fold (2), suggesting a completely different function and adding support to the theory that the materials are playing far more sophisticated roles in the life activity of the clam than previously suspected.

Relationship to Disease Processes in Higher Organisms

How do the results of the histochemical studies on mucus in the hard clam have any relevance to diseases in higher organisms? The idea of us-ing invertebrates as models for studies of calcifications in higher organisms is not new. As far back as 1948, Bevelander and Benzer (17) investigated the relationship of shell deposition in the hard clam to tooth formation.

Calcium is important in metabolism throughout the animal kingdom, and in general there is an acid mucopolysaccharide present at or very near the sites of calcium deposition. However, the function of acid mucopolysaccharides in calcification is not fully understood (18), but in general, throughout the animal kingdom, they resemble chrondroitin sulfate in mammalian systems. It is interesting to speculate that the molecular configuration of the mucus in the first fold of the hard clam might represent an evolutionary step toward acid mucopolysaccharides which aid in calcification processes in higher organisms, and that dif-ferences in structure, as well as similarities, might be important in how the mucopolysaccharides function in calcification. it could well be that in cases of abnormal calcification, such as in certain forms of arthritis or in metastatic calcification, the pathological condition and associated mucosubstances are similar to normal conditions and normal mucosubstances in lower organisms, and that greater knowledge of the calcification process in the lower animals would lead to greater understanding of pathological calcification in mammalian systems.

Cystic fibrosis is a hereditary (genetic recessive) disease of children, adolescents, and young adults affecting the mucus-producing and other exocrine glands (19). There are generally three characteristic symptoms involved in cystic fibrosis. The most visible is the production of an abnormally large amount of viscous neutral mucosubstance by most, if not all, of the mucus-producing tissues. It becomes a particular problem when it clogs the respiratory tract and secondary bacterial infections develop. Secondly, there is an abnormally high efflux of sodium and chloride ions from the sweat glands, and this has become the diagnostic feature of the disease. Thirdly, a turbid saliva is produced due to a defect in the salivary glands which allows for large amounts of calcium to be present in the saliva. Pancreatic fibrous cysts are common, but are not now considered necessary for establishing the disease.

As far as I know, these three symptoms have not been related to one another, and no one has yet found the one basic metabolic key to the disease. Also, there is no good lower animal model to study all aspects of the disease. There is no known cure for the disease, and it is almost always fatal, with the average age at death being in the teens.

Earlier, I discussed the mucus produced in the second fold of the hard clam mantle. Certain cells produce a highly sulfated mucopolysaccharide which reacts histochemically like heparin. This material appears to be formed in conjunction with a neutral connective tissue mucosubstance, possibly a glycoprotein. The amount of both of these mucus materials, and the degree of sulfation of the mucopolysaccharide appear to vary from sampling period to sampling period. A seasonal variation has been ruled out. I now think that the variation might be related to salinity at the time the clams were fixed for study.

We know that many marine invertebrates osmoregulate by producing free amino acids, especially taurine (2-aminomethanesulfonic acid), to act as osmoregulatory particles (20) as salinity increases. I am now hypothesizing that the variation in the degree of sulfation of the mucopolysaccharide in the second fold is due to osmoregulatory processes as the salinity changes. As salinity increases, sulfate groups may be removed from the acid mucopolysaccharide to be used in the production of taurine and related compounds, and the mucus tends to become neutral. Taurine concentrations in the tissues, of course, rise. As salinity decreases, the reverse takes place and the mucopolysaccharide increases in degree of sulfation. Since the acid mucopolysaccharide in its most sulfated state resembles heparin (which is also invloved in handling calcium ions), it would possibly lose the ability to handle calcium when it loses the sulfated groups, and there would, therefore, tend to be an increase in calcium ions in the tissue fluids.

I have just discussed the possibility of normal mucus secretions in the clam being related to ionic balance and osmoregulation. Consider now, in the case of cystic fibrosis, a disease caused by a recessive gene, that the gene is a back mutation to a sort of wild type gene which would cause certain cells, tissues, or organs to react to the body's natural salinity much like an osmoregulating marine organism might.

Suppose that the abnormal efflux of sodium and chloride ions, which raise the normal body salinity, also results in a desulfation of an otherwise sulfated mucopolysaccharide. Indeed, Roberts (21) has suggested that the degree of N-sulfation of heparin sulfates may be lower in cystic fibrosis patients than in normal subjects. And suppose also that those heparin sulfates lose their ability to handle calcium ions, which then show up in excess, particularly in the salivary gland. One might then expect an increase in free amino acids in the body. A recent article indicates that twice the normal amounts of amino acids, particularly taurine and methionine, were excreted by the majority of patients with cystic fibrosis than by healthy children (22).

If some mucopolysaccharide production in the quahog is related to osmoregulation, and if cystic fibrosis turns out to be a disease associated with cellular osmoregulation, then the formation and function of mucopolysaccharides in the hard clam may prove to be a good lower animal model system for studying the pathology of cystic fibrosis.

Conclusion

I have speculated a great deal on some specific cases where studies of invertebrate mucus formation, especially in marine invertebrates like the hard clam, *Mercenaria mercenaria*, might provide valuable information on the pathology of a few diseases. There is probably a wide range of pathological conditions, such as the various collagen diseases associated with tooth and bone formation and, as Dr. Jakowska has mentioned (23), bronchial and pulmonary conditions where greater knowledge of invertebrate mucus production would aid the medical researcher.

According to most theories, life originated in the sea. Since the complex biochemical mechanisms that give life to organic matter are essentially similar to all organisms, it is only fitting, therefore, that we look to life in the sea for answers to some of our most important medical questions.

References

1. Quintarelli, G. (1968). *The Chemical Physiology of Mucopolysaccharides.* Little, Brown and Company, Boston, p. 240.
2. Hillman, R.E. (1968). Histochemistry of Mucosubstances in the Mantle of the Clam, *Mercenaria mercenaria* I. A glycosaminoglycan in the first marginal fold. *Trans. Amer. Microsc. Soc.* **87**, 361.
3. *ibid.* (1969). *ibid.* **88**, 420.
4. Hunt, S. (1970). *Polysaccharide-protein Complexes in Invertebrates.* Academic Press, New York. p. 329.
5. Wada, K. and Furuhashi. T. (1970). Studies on the Mineralization of the Calcified Tissue in Molluscs—XVII. Acid polysaccharide in the shell of *Hyriopsis schlegeli Bull. Jap. Soc. Sci. Fish.* **36**, 1122.
6. *ibid.* (1971). *ibid.* **37**, 13.
7. Rahemtulla, F. and Lovtrup, S. (1974). The Comparative Biochemistry of Invertebrate Mucopolysaccharides—I. Methods. Platyhelminthes. *Comp. Biochem. Physiol.* **49**, 631.
8. *ibid.* (1974). *ibid.* **49**, 639.
9. *ibid.* (1975). *ibid.* **50**, 627.
10. *ibid.* (1975). *ibid.* **50**, 631.
11. Hillman, R.E. and Shuster, C.N. Jr. (1962). Observations on the mantle of the northern quahog, *Mercenaria mercenaria* (L.). *Proc. Nat. Shellfish. Assoc.* **51**, 15.
12. Hillman, R.E. (1964). The functional morphology of the fourth fold of the mantle of the northern quahog, *Mercenaria mercenaria* (L.). *J. Elisha Mitchell Sci. Soc.* **80**, 8.
13. Pearse, A.G.E. (1960). Histochemistry, Theoretical and Applied, 2nd ed. Little, Brown, and Company, Boston. p. 998.
14. Love, R. and Frommhagen, L.H. (1953). Histochemical studies on the clam *Mactra solidissima. Proc. Soc. Exptl. Biol.* **83**, 838.
15. Thomas, L., Jr. (1954). The Localization of Heparin-like Blood Anticoagulant Substances in the Tissues of *Spisula solidissima. Biol. Bull.* **106**, 129.
16. Burson, S.L. *et al.* (1956). Isolation and Purification of Mactins, Heparin-like Anti-coagulants from Mollusca. *J. Amer. Chem. Soc.* **78**, 5874.
17. Bevelander, G. and Benzer, P. (1948). Calcification in Marine Molluscs. *Biol. Bull.* **94**, 176.
18. Balazs, E.A., and Rogers, H.J. (1968). The Amino Sugar-containing Compounds in Bones and Teeth. In *The Amino Sugars* Vol. IIA. Eds. E.A. Balazs and R.W. Jeanloz. Academic Press, New York. p. 281.
19. di Sant' Agnese, P.A. and Talamo, R.C. (1967). Pathogenesis and

Pathophysiology of Cystic Fibrosis of the Pancreas. *New Eng. J. Med.* **277**, 1287, 1343, 1399.

20. Allen, J.A. and Garrett, M.R. (1971) Taurine in Marine Invertebrates. *Adv. Mar. Biol.* **9**, 205.
21. Roberts, R.M. (1975). Heparin Sulfates in Normal and Cystic Fibrosis Fibroblasts. *Cystic Fibrosis: Quart. Annot. Ref.* **14**, 32.
22. Filipovic, D. and Hajdukovic, R. (1974). Aminoacids in the Stools of Patients with Cystic Fibrosis *Srp. Arh. Celok. Lek.* **102**, 779.
23. Jakowska, S. (1966). The Challenge of Research on Mucus. *Ann. N.Y. Acad. Sci.* **130**, 871.

The Maryland Blue Crab: An Experimental Animal For Cardiotoxicological Investigations

Gary J. Calton, Joseph W. Burnett, and Leah M. Staling

From the Division of Dermatology, University of Maryland School of Medicine and the
Department of Physiology, University of Maryland School of Dentistry,
Baltimore, Maryland

One problem with the pharmacological approach to marine tox-icological investigations is the lack of appropriate organisms which might naturally be the receptors to such toxins. This situation arises because many marine specimens are difficult to obtain in quantity while other well studied models are already in use. The difficulties associated with developing a new laboratory model prevent the investigator from utilizing these animals. However, the increasing cost of biological specimens will stimulate a search for a variety of experimental models. With this thought in mind, the blue crab, *Callinectes sapidus*, a common inhabitant in the Chesapeake Bay was studied to determine the suitability of this animal as an acceptable experimental model. The pulse rate and EKG characteristics of the *in situ* crab heart were investigated before and after systemic injection of toxins derived from animals or plants having en-vironmental habitats similar to those of blue crab.

Materials and Methods

Adult blue crabs and sea nettles *Chrysaora quinquecirrha* were netted from Meredith Creek near Annapolis, Maryland during the summers of 1975 and 1976. Crabs were maintained in bay water aquaria at ambient temperatures until used.

To prepare the crabs for electrocardiographic recording, all periopods were immobilized and two holes were drilled in the carapace with a 26 gauge explorer. Two silver pin electrodes were inserted through the shell bilaterally into the heart. A storage oscilloscope, (sensitivity 100-200 mcV, sweep 0.1-1 sec./cm), (Tektronix Inc., Beaverton, Ore.) was used for all recordings. Data were recorded with a #107 Polaroid camera.

Inocula (0.2-1.0 ml) were injected into the hemocele by introducing the syringe through the coxopodite of the posterior periopod. The animals were blindfolded with a moist paper tower (1). The lethal dose of all toxins or venoms was determined by intravenous assay on 25 g adult mice or by injection into the hemocele of 1 g fiddler crabs *Uca pugilator.* Several two fold dilutions of each venom were prepared and inoculated into four animals per dilution. The titers of these toxins or venoms were then quantiated at 100% lethal doses.

Sea nettle venom from mixed fishing and mesenteric tentacles was prepared as previously reported (2). The concentration of the venom was quantitated and regulated for predictable lethal activity. The blue crab inocula contained sufficient venom to kill 90 mice or 200 fiddler crabs per injection unit.

Tadpoles *Rana heckscheri,* collected in western Florida in 1975, were macerated and extracted sequentially in methanol and water. The methanol soluble fraction was dried and 200 mg was suspended in 0.5 ml distilled water and clarified by centrifugation (1500 rpm, 5 min). Inocula used on the blue crabs contained dosage that was 25% of that which was lethal when injected i.v. into mice, and was also lethal for 100 fiddler crabs.

Berries from the pokeberry plant *Phytolacca americana* were macerated and suspended in water. Hydrochloric acid (1N) was added to pH 4 and the solution was extracted with n-butanol. The solution was then brought to pH 9 with sodium hydroxide (1N). The alkaloid fraction was removed by extraction with *n*-butanol. The presence of alkaloid was confirmed by both Meyer's and Wagner's tests (3). The absence of saponins was confirmed by the stable foam technique (4). One hundred mg of butanol soluble extract was suspended in water and clarified by centrifugation before inoculation into the blue crab. This amount of alkaloid extract was lethal for 650 fiddler crabs as well as for 19 mice.

Results

The normal heart rate of the blue crab spans a range of 20 to 99 beats per minute. The EKG configuration differed depending upon the location of the electrodes. The rhythm of the blue crab heart was altered by intermittent cardiac arrest in response to visual, vibratory or tactile stimuli. Removal of the blindfold produced bradycardia following transient cardiac arrest of variable duration.

Insertion of the needle into the hemocele had no effect upon the EKG but injection of a 1-ml sample of either distilled or bay water (1.2% salinity) produced intermittent cardiac arrest followed by slight tachycardia. Insignificant changes were observed in the EKG tracing after injection of

0.6 ml bay water. After multiple 1 ml injections over a 30-min period, the repolarization wave became slightly diphasic with terminal inversion (Fig. 1). The interval between contraction and depolarization became prolonged in spite of an increase in cardiac rate signifying an intraventricular conduction delay. This defect and an abnormal and prolonged repolarization wave was more pronounced as more bay water was introduced into the circulation.

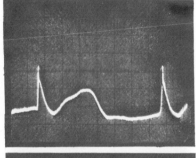
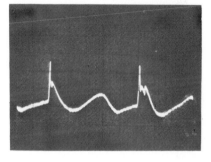

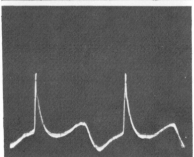

FIGURE 1 -Blue crab control electrocardiogram. Upper left tracing normal crab; lower left tracing-crab received 1 ml bay water every 5 min., 1.5 ml min after second injection; right tracing 4 ml after fourth injection. Scale = 100mcV/ver-division; 0.1 sec./horizontal division.

The same volume of tadpole toxin injected into the crab hemocele induced a prologation of the contraction wave and an abnormal repolarization wave similar to but more severe than that produced by bay water (Fig. 2).

One minute after injection of the pokeberry alkaloid, the contraction wave was adversely affected in the terminal repolarization phase. In the tracing shown, the notching of the contraction complex had diminished (Fig. 3). The repolarization phase was more negative and was prolonged. Later, a slow, irregular beat appeared with intermittent periods of cardiac arrest indicating suppression of the cardiac ganglion pacemaker function.

Sea nettle venom changed the repolarization phase and caused marked changes in the normal time relations. The heart rate increased, then decreased, became irregular, chaotic and finally suppressed. Death occurred within 60 min after injection (Fig. 4).

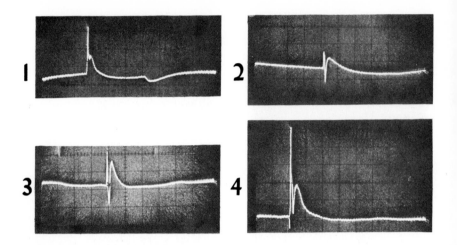

FIGURE 2 -Electrocardiogram of blue crab injected with toxic extract of tadpole. Tracing 1-before inoculation, tracings 2-4 were taken at intervals of 9, 11, and 13 min. after injection. Scale-200 mcV/vertical division and 0.1 sec./horizontal division.

Discussion

The electrocardiographic examination of blue crabs is a practical and reproducible technique useful for cardiovascular research. When functional instrumentation has been calibrated, this examination would require less than five minutes and test animals could be examined serially since the survivors did not appear to be adversely affected by the procedure. Control inoculations of bay water or distilled water produced only temporary cardiac irregularities. In order to insure reproducible results, however, it is necessary to eliminate tactile, vibratory and visual stimuli and maintain constant temperature and oxygen supply during the assay (1,5).

Sea nettle venom contains a cardiotoxin which is lethal to many different animals. It produces ST changes and AV conduction abnormalities in the rat and affects the Purkinje fiber in the dog (6,7). This venom also exerts a lethal effect on single chamber arthropod hearts such as that of the blue crab and fiddler crab *Uca pugilator* (8). The action of nettle venom on the blue crab is identical to that of the Portuguese man-o' war *Physalia physalis* on the land crab *Cardiosoma guanhume*. In their paper describing this cardiotoxic effect of *Physalia* venom, Lane and Larsen (9) do not describe the changes we have observed in the present experiment. However, an examination of their published figures reveals that the man-o'war venom prolongs the contraction complex and depresses the repolarization segment of the land crab's EKG. These changes are in-

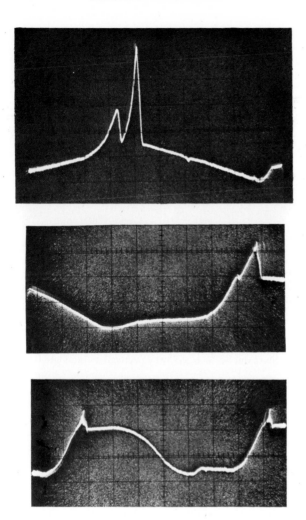

FIGURE 3 -Electrocardiogram of blue crab injected with crude sea nettle venom. Upper tracing was takin before inoculation and the bottom tracing was recorded 28 min. after inoculation of 90 LD100 rat intravenous doses. Scale = 200mcV/vertical division and 0.2 sec/horizontal division.

dicative of intraventricular conduction blocks and an abnormal repolarization of the cardiac muscle.

Crabs in contact with jellyfish toxins exhibit the same electrocardiographic abnormalities as those exposed to tadpole pokeberry toxins. This observation may be a reflection of the limited number of abnormal responses available to unichambered heart.

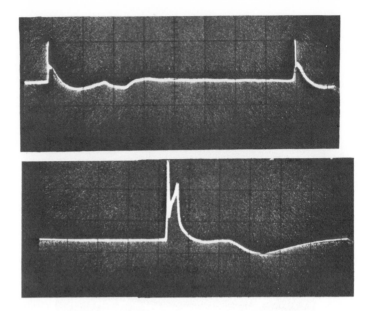

FIGURE 4- Electrocardiogram of blue crab injected with pokeberry toxin. Top tracing was recorded before injection. The middle and bottom tracings were recorded 13 and 45 min. after inoculation of this toxin. Scale = 200mcV/vertical division and 0.05 sec./horizontal division.

Summary

A technique for electrocardiographic examination of blue crabs is described and the normal tracings are demonstrated. Toxins derived from the sea nettle, pokeberry and tadpole induce ventricular conduction and repolarization abnormalities in the crab heart. The electrocardiographic examination of the blue crab is a simple, inexpensive technique to employ when screening substances for cardiotoxic activity.

Acknowledgments

We would like to acknowledge the technical assistance of Miss Helene Rubinstein and Mr. Robert Miller. We are grateful to Mr. Clive Longden for collection of the *Rana heckscheri* tadpoles and to Mr. David Cargo of the Chesapeake Biological Laboratory, Solomons, Maryland for assistance with the crabs. Dr. Leonard Scherlis, of the University of Maryland School of Medicine assisted with the electrocardiographic interpretation.

References

1. Florey, E. and Kriebel, M.E. (1974). The Effects of Temperature, Anoxia and Sensory Stimulation on the Heart Rate of Unrestrained Crabs. *Comp. Biochem. Physiol.* **48A**, 285.
2. Burnett, J.W. and Calton, G.J. (1976). "A Comparison of the Toxicology of the Nematocyst Venom from Sea Nettle Fishing and Mesenteric Tentacles." *Toxicon.* **14**, 109.
3. Smolinski, S.J., Silinis, H. and Farnsworth, N.R. (1972). Alkaloid Screening I. *Lloydia.* **35**. 1.
4. Basu, N. and Rastogi, R.P. (1967). Triterpenoid Saponins and Sapogenins. *Phytochemistry.* **6**, 1249.
5. Hume, R.I. and Berlind, A. (1976). Heart and Scaphognathite Rate Changes in a Euryhaline Crab, *Carcinus maenas*, Exposed to Dilute Environmental Medium. *Biol. Bull.* **150**, 241.
6. Burnett, J.W. and Goldner, R. (1969). Effects of *Chysaora quinquecirrha* (Sea Nettle) Toxin on the Rat Cardiovascular System (34213). Proc. Soc. Exp. Biol. Med. **132**, 353.
7. Klinehaus, A., Cranefield, P.F. and Burnett, J.W. (1973). The Effects on Canine Cardiac Purkinje Fibers of *Crysaora quinquecirrha* (Sea Nettle) Toxin. *Toxicon* **11**, 341.
8. Burnett, J.W. and Calton, G.J. (1973). Purification of Sea Nettle Nematocyst Toxins by Gel Diffusion. *Toxicon.* **11**, 243.
9. Lane, C.E. and Larsen, J.B. (1965). Some Effects of the Toxin of *Physalia physalis* on the Heart of the Hand Crab, *Cardisoma guanhumic* (Latreille). *Toxicon* **3**, 69.

SECTION II

Cardioactive Substances of Marine Origin

Anthopleurin A, B, And C, Cardiotonic Polypeptides From The Sea Anemones
Anthopleura xanthogrammica (Brandt) and A. elegantissima (Brandt)

Ted R. Norton, Midori Kashiwagi and Shoji Shibata

Pacific Biomedical Research Center
University of Hawaii
Leahi Hospital, Honolulu, Hawaii
Department of Pharmacology
University of Hawaii
Honolulu, Hawaii

While examining extracts of coelentrates for antitumor activity (1,2) and central stimulant action (3), the high intravenous toxicity of many of the extracts stimulated interest in examining their effects on smooth muscle. Extracts of nine of 12 species of anthozoans and the one scyphozoan examined showed varying degrees of positive inotropic effect on isolated spontaneously beating rat atria (4). Crude extracts of *Anthopleura xanthogrammica* and *A. elegantissima* were particularly effective at very low concentration. Pretreatment with adrenergic receptor blocking agents, propranolol, metalol, and phentolamine, did not affect the response of the atria to the extracts indicating the adrenergic system was not involved in the mechanism of action. Also, the high potency and margin of safety indicated the possibility of the agents being useful in a practical way in the control of congestive heart failure.

About 70 of some 9,000 known species of coelenterates have been reported capable of causing intoxication in man either from contact with the nematocysts (stinging organelles common to all members of this phylum), or ingestion of uncooked tissues (5). Many workers have examined the chemical nature and pharmacology of these toxins noting such effects as muscle contraction, ECG abnormalities, neurotoxic effects, and hypertension. Beress *et al* (6) isolated three polypeptides from *Anemone sulcata* showing neurotoxicity to crayfish and cardiotoxicity to guinea pig. In their patent case (7), they claim enzyme inhibitory properties as the utility for the polypeptides. The three toxins were described as being basic and having molecular weights of 4702, 4197, and 2678. Romney *et al.* (8) studied the effect of one of these, purified Toxin II (ATX$_{II}$), on the inactivation of the Na + channel in crayfish giant axons, and Wunderer *et al.* (9) reported the sequence of ATX$_{II}$ possessing 47 amino acids. Alsen *et al.* (10) reported on studies of the positive inotropic effect of ATX$_{II}$ in the 2-100 nM range.

Since the introduction of digitalis about 190 years ago, the cardiac glycosides have remained the most important therapeutic agents for congestive heart failure. However, since there is a very high rate of incidence of digitalis toxicity, the necessity for caution and careful clinical judgement in the use of cardiac glycosides cannot be overemphasized. The various cardiac glycosides have among the lowest margins of safety of all drugs prescribed in the U.S. (11). At doses very close to the therapeutic dose, they produce toxic symptoms of cardiac arrhythmia, nausea and vomiting. The use of sympathomimetic agents such as isoproterenol are limited by associated arrhythmia, tachycardia, tachyphylaxis or altered peripheral resistance.

Results

After the initial study of the pharmacological effects of crude extracts of *Anthopleura xanthogrammica* and *A. elegantissima* (4) the results were interesting enough to encourage us to attempt the isolation and characterization of the active agent(s) involved, and to further explore their pharmacology.

Anthopleurin-A— *A. xanthogrammica* was studied first. Dr. Cadet Hand, Director of the Bodega Marine Laboratory (Univ.of Calif.), was invaluable to our work, supplying most of the specimens necessary for the work herein described. He preserved the anemones in 95% ethanol, refrigerated them, and air-shipped them to Hawaii.

The anemones were homogenized with the preservative and additional ethanol, such that the final ethanol concentration was 30%. The extract was centrifuged and the supernatant solution was flash evaporated to remove the alcohol. The remaining aqueous solution was extracted with chloroform to remove the oils as well as other lipophilic impurities. The aqueous solution was then subjected to gel permeation chromatography on Sephadex G-50. This fraction was then put on the cation exchange resin, CM-Sephadex. Using gradient elution with phosphate buffer at pH 7.5, a fraction was isolated containing the active substance in about 65% purity along with the salts. The drug at this purity was used for most of the pharmacological studies (12, 13). For chemical studies this material was desalted with Sephadex G-50 (for phosphate) and Sephadex G-10 (for NaCl) and then rerun through the CM-Sephadex, Sephadex G-50 and G-10 steps. This final material was determined to be a polypeptide. Based on acid disc gel electrophoresis, gel isoelectric focusing, SDS disc gel electrophoresis, and amino acid analysis, it was judged to be pure. It was given the name anthopleurin-A (AP-A) (14).

However, when sequencing studies were started both at the University of Hawaii in Dr. Yasunobu's laboratory, and in collaborative research at the Merck Institute for Therapeutic Research at West Point by Dr. Carl D. Bennett (Personal communication) it was found that the AP-A was about 65% pure when produced as described above. It was found that a phenylalanine containing impurity could be removed using SE-Sephadex and additional impurities were removed in the reduction and carboxy-methylation steps prior to tryptic digestion (15).

In collaboration with Dr. Bennett the following procedure was developed to produce greater than 95% pure native AP-A: The AP-A was prepared as previously described (14). About 50 mg portions of this AP-A were then subjected to ion exchange chromatography on a 2.1 x 39 cm column of Cellex-SE-cellulose equilibrated with 0.05 M pyridine in 25% acetic acid (pH 2.6). Using a 250 ml stirred reservoir of the 0.05M pyridine, a gradient with 0.2M pyridine in 25% acetic acid (pH 3.2) was produced by allowing the latter to flow into the former as it was used in elution. The AP-A was eluted at about Ve/Vo = 2.8-3.5 and after lyophilization was found to be about 85% pure AP-A (Fig. 1).

The final step involved chromatographing the 85% purity material on a 1.1 x 58 cm column of Sephadex G-25, fine, equilibrated with 6% 1-butanol in distilled water. Using a 500 ml stirred reservoir of the 6% 1-butanol, a gradient with 0.05 M NH$_4$OAc in 6% 1-butanol (pH 6.0) was produced by allowing the latter to flow into the former as it was used for elution. Under these conditions, the column acts as an adsorption chromatography column. The AP-A was eluted at about Ve/Vo = 2.5 and after lyophilization was greater than 95% pure AP-A (Fig. 2).

Anthopleurin-B—In the second step of purification of AP-A (CM-Sephadex, pH 7.5 phosphate buffer) the AP-A eluted at about Ve/Vo = 3.2. A second active fraction eluted at Ve/Vo = 6.6. This was called anthopleurin-B (AP-B), and after desalting as with AP-A and rerunning the CM-Sephadex, Sephadex G-50, and Sephadex G10 steps, isoelectric focusing indicated one peak at pI = 9.05 (see Fig. 3). This material was later determined to be about 50% pure AP-B. The purity has been raised to 80% by adding the final two steps described for AP-A, the only difference being in the SE-cellulose step. For AP-B, the gradient was 0.05 M to 1.0 M pyridine (because of the higher basicity of AP-B) and it eluted at Ve/Vo = 2.0.

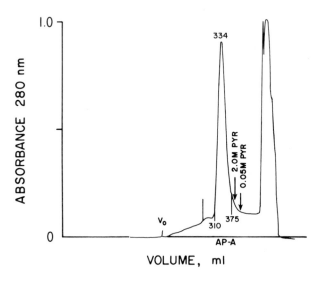

FIGURE 1. AP-A ion exchange chromatography on SE-Cellulose using .05M pyridine gradient to 0.2M pyridine in 25% acetic acid. U.V. (280 nm) absorbance tracing *vs.* eluted volume.

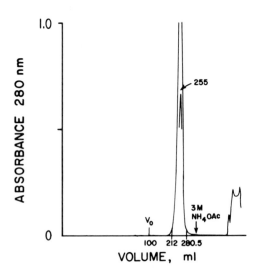

FIGURE 2. AP-A adsorption chromatography on Sephadex G-25 using 6% 1-butanol gradient to 0.03M NH4OAc in 6% 1-butanol. U.V. (280 nm) absorbance tracing *vs.* eluted volume.

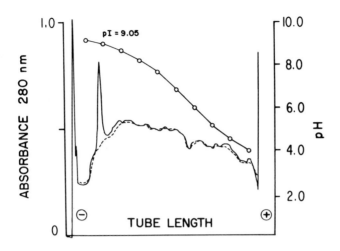

FIGURE 3. AP-B isoelectric focusing. Abscissa is tube length. Solid line is u.v. (280 nm) absorbance of sample, dashed line is absorbance of blank ampolytes, and -o-o-o- is pH of segments of sample gel.

Anthopleurin-C—The third cardiotonic substance, anthopleurin-C (AP-C), was isolated from *Anthopleura elegantissima*, also supplied by Dr. Cadet Hand from the Bodega Marine Laboratory (Univ. of Calif.) as well as Dr. J. J. Gonor of the Oregon State University Marine Science Center. A partial purification has been reported (16).

We have recently discovered with AP-C that we can obtain several times as much drug from the anemones if they are not homogenized. Immersing the whole live anemones in 95% ethanol and isolating the AP-C from the ethanol gives two to three times as much drug as when the anemones are homogenized with the preservative and additional alcohol. A second alcohol leaching of the whole anemones provides an additional 25% of the AP-C.

The ethanol leachate was flash evaporated to an aqueous solution, extracted with chloroform, and centrifuged. The aqueous portion was concentrated to about 250 mg/ml solids content and subjected to gel permeation chromatography on a 2500 ml (53 x 8 cm) column of Sephadex G-25, using water saturated with chloroform as the eluant. The active fraction was eluted at $Ve/Vo = 1.2$-1.6, and 0.63 g was obtained from 11.1 g of crude dry extract (Fig. 4).

The second step was carried out with CM-Sephadex in the same manner as AP-A except that the pH was lowered to 6.5 for both the 0.03M phosphate and the 0.3M phosphate plus 0.3M NaCl, and the active frac-

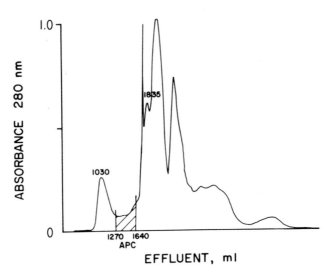

FIGURE 4. AP-C gel permeation chromatography on Sephadex G-25 using H₂O as elutant. U.V. (280 nm) absorbance tracing *vs.* effluent in ml.

tion was eluted at about $Ve/Vo = 6$. In figure 5 fractions C and D showed equal positive inotropic effects indicating the u.v. absorption peak corresponded to the activity. The active fraction was desalted with Sephadex G-10 and rerun through the CM-Sephadex and desalting steps. Isoelectric focusing gave a pI = 8.03 and is shown in figure 6. To obtain 98% pure AP-C, SE-Cellulose and Sephadex G-25 were used just as described for AP-A. The amount isolated corresponded to a concentration of about 30 ppm AP-C based on wet weight of anemones.

The amino acid analyses of AP-A (15), AP-B and AP-C (Bennett, personal communication, 1977), and Toxin II (9), are shown in table I. Figure 7 shows the sequences of AP-A, AP-C, and Toxin II. The regions of identical residues are squared off. A summary of the properties of the anthopleurins is shown in table II.

Because of concern that anemones from different locations might have different AP-A content, the marine biologists listed in Table III were kind enough to supply specimens collected from British Columbia down to Southern California. A range of 10-48 ppm AP-A was found based on wet preserved weight of the anemones using the homogenizing isolation procedure.

We also had some indications that size might affect the AP-A content, so Dr. J.J. Gonor of the Oregon State University Marine Science Center sent us collections sorted as to size. Size apparently is not a factor (see Table III). Dr. Gonor has also been of great aid in supplying sizeable collections of *A. xanthogrammica* to allow us to prepare the research needs for AP-A.

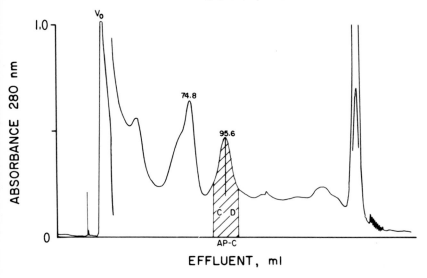

FIGURE 5. AP-C ion-exchange chromatography on CM-Sephadex at pH 6.5 with 0.03M phosphate gradient to 0.3M NaC1. U.V. (280 nm) absorbance tracing *vs.* effluent in ml. Shaded peak is AP-C.

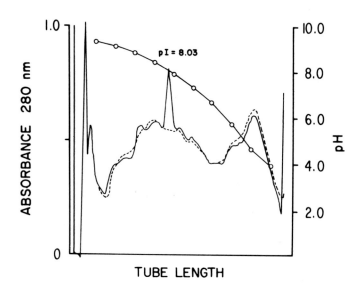

FIGURE 6. AP-C isoelectric focusing. Abscissa is tube length. Solid line is u.v. (280 nm) absorbance of sample, dashed line is absorbance of blank ampholytes, and -o-o-o- is pH of segments of sample gel.

43

Table I
The Amino Acid Analyses
of Anthopleurins.

	AP-A(15)	AP-B*	AP-C*	TOX. II(9)
ASP	4	5	4	4
THR	3	1	2	2
SER	6	3	4	4
GLU	1	1	1	1
PRO	4	5	4	4
GLY	8	6	8	8
ALA	1	1	2	1
CYS	6	4	6	6
VAL	2	1	2	1.5
ILE	1	2	2	3.5
LEU	4	2	4	3
TYR	1	1	0	0
PHE	0	1	0	0
LYS	2	3	2	3
HIS	2	2	2	2
ARG	1	2	1	1
TRP	3	2	3	3
NH_3	3	(?)	3	3
TOTAL	49	42	47	47

*Carl D. Bennett (1977), private communication.

Discussion

Although the sequencing of AP-B has not been carried out at this writing, it is interesting to note that AP-A, AP-C and Toxin II all have the functional ASP-SER-ASP triad at the 7, 8, and 9 positions. It is also known that muscle contraction involves calcium transfer. It is therefore possible that the 7 and 9 aspartic carboxyls could chelate calcium and with the assistance of the 37-lysine amino group, the 39-histidine imidazole group, and possibly the 8-serine hydroxyl group, this moiety could be an important cation exchange group (Fig. 8). If the 6-cysteine and 36-cysteine are connected, the 37-lysine and 39-histidine lie in juxtaposition to the 7-aspartic and 9-aspartic. On the other hand this moiety could well have nothing to do with the mechanism of action.

Anthopleurin-A had a strong selective positive inotropic effect on the

```
                        10
Tox. II[1]  |GLY - ILE/VAL| - PRO - |CYS - LEU - CYS - ASP - SER - ASP - GLY - PRO - SER - VAL - ARG - GLY -
AP-A[2]     |GLY - VAL    | - SER -  =  =  =  =  =  =  =  =  =  =  =  =
AP-C*       |GLY - VAL    | - PRO -  =  =  =  =  =  =  =  =  =  =  =  =

                    20                                                        30
Tox. II   ASN - THR - LEU - SER - GLY| - ILE - ILE - |TRP - LEU| - --- - --- - ALA - |GLY - CYS - PRO|
AP-A       =    =     =     =     =   -  =   - |THR - LEU| -  TYR - PRO - SER - |  =    =    =  |
AP-C       =    =     =     =     =   -  =   - |ILE - LEU| -  --- - --- - ALA - |  =    =    =  |

                                              40
Tox. II   SER - GLY - TRP - HIS - ASN - CYS - LYS - LYS - |HIS - GLY - PRO - THR - ILE - GLY - TRP|
AP-A       =    =     =     =     =     =     =   - ALA - |  =    =     =     =     =     =    = |
AP-C       =    =     =     =     =     =     =   - ALA - |  =    =     =     =     =     =    = |

                  49
Tox. II   CYS - CYS - LYS - |GLN|   47
AP-A       =    =     =   -  -       49
AP-C       =    =     =   -  -       47
```

[1,2] References (9) and (15), respectively.
* Carl D. Bennett (1977), private communication.

FIGURE 7. Amino acid sequences of AP-A, AP-C, and Toxin-II. The regions of identical residues are squared off.

Table II

Properties of Anthopleurins.

	AP-A	AP-B	AP-C
M.W.	5,183	∿ 4,590	4,875
#AA	49	42	47
pI	8.2	9.05	8.03
Rf (pH 3.6)	0.46	0.64	0.49
Rf (pH 8.9)	0	0	0
ED-50	1.5×10^{-9} M	2×10^{-9} M	2×10^{-9} M
CONC/anemone	10-40 PPM	3 PPM	25-30 PPM

cardiac muscle of different animals in both *in vitro* and *in vivo* experiments but no effect on the heart rate, blood pressure, and vascular smooth muscle. This cardiotonic effect was not mediated by the adrenergic mechanism. The potency of AP-A was much greater than ouabain (a cardiac glycoside). AP-A also improved the cardiac performance of induced failing heart. The cardiotonic effect of AP-A was not accompanied by any effect on Na-K ATPase, monoamine oxidase, catechol-O-methyltransferase, phosphodiesterase and c-AMP content. The cardiotonic action of AP-A is observed at appreciably lower calcium concentration than when ouabain is used. AP-A treated cardiac muscle showed much stronger resistance to hypoxia and low and high temperature stress. AP-A increased action potential duration, maximum rate of rise and conduction velocity of cardiac muscle (13).

At Merck, Sharp and Dohme Research Laboratories, AP-A was infused i.v. in anesthetized dogs at 0.2 and digoxin at 2.8 mcg/kg/min, the endpoint of infusion was ventricular fibrillation which was observed in all animals. Table IV summarizes the results.

Table III

Miscellaneous Data Relative to *Anthopleura xanthogrammica.*

SUPPLIER	LOCATION	AP-A CONTENT, PPM	BASIS	SPECIMENS, WT., KG
C. HAND	BODEGA BAY, CA	10	ISOLATION	36
M. BOYD	TRINIDAD HEAD, CA	10	ABS.	0.48
R. TERWILLIGER	COOS BAY, OR	48	ISOLATION	0.16
K. SEBENS	TATOOSH ISL., WA	2	ABS.	0.36
J. GONOR	BOILER BAY, OR	(12.9 AVE.)	ISOLATION	(7.7)
	LG. 6-10 CM	12.7	ISOLATION	2.7
	MED. 4-6 CM	13.5	ISOLATION	3.0
	SMALL 2-4 CM	12.3	ISOLATION	2.0
I. LAWN	BAMFIELD, B.C.	15	ABS.	0.08
N. HAVEN	HOPKINS M.S., CA	31	ABS.	0.44

Table IV

Therapeutic Index of AP-A and Digoxin

Substance	ED-25, mcg/kg (Contractile Force)	Lethal Dose, mcg/kg	Therapeutic Index
AP-A	3.1 ± 0.8	19.8 ± 1.8	6.4
Digoxin	111.0 ± 11	269.3 ± 21.8	2.4

Unlike digoxin, AP-A produced no ventricular extrasystoles prior to fibrillation. At one-third of the lethal and higher doses, AP-A reversed the T-wave in the EKG. As measured by left ventricular (LV) pressure telemetry, AP-A, 2 mcg/kg i.v. single dose, increased LV dp/dt max in conscious dogs; the duration of action exceeded two hours (17).

All the pharmacological work so far indicates AP-A is a good candidate for clinical study in the treatment of the failing heart with potential for considerable advantage over currently used drugs. AP-B and AP-C need to be more thoroughly investigated, but also appear to have good potential. AP-C has the advantage that it comes from *A. elegantissima* which is a tidal sea anemone and readily undergoes asexual reproduction in the laboratory. This allows an essentially unlimited supply of drug. *A. xanthogrammica*, the source of AP-A and AP-B, is a sub-tidal anemone and has not been known to reproduce in captivity, limiting the supply to what can be harvested without damage to the local ecology. Fortunately, both of these species are quite common on the west coast from Alaska to Southern California.

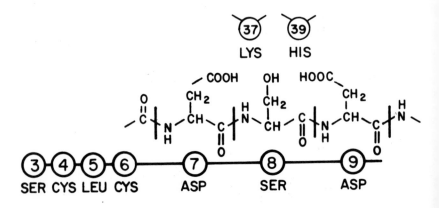

FIGURE 8. Possible active site in AP-A.

Acknowledgments

This work was supported by N.I.H. grant HL-15991from the National Heart, Lung, and Blood Institute.
I would like to thank Ms. Priscilla Searl, Mr. David Seriguchi, and Mr. Dennis Mead for technical assistance in the new work described here.

References

1. Tabrah, F.L., Kashiwagi, M. and Norton, T.R. (1972). Antitumor Activity in Mice of Four Coelenterate Extracts. *Int. J. Clin. Pharmacol., Therap. & Tox.* **5**, 420.
2. Norton, T.R. and Kashiwagi, M. (1972). Purification of a Potent Antitumor Agent from a Tahitian Sea Anemone and Methods of Administration Studies with Ehrlich Ascites Tumor in Mice. *J. Pharm. Sci.* **61**, 1814
3. Turlapaty, P. *et al.* (1973). A Possible Mechanism of Action of a Central Stimulant Substance Isolated from the Sea Anemone, *Stoichactis kenti. Eur. J. Pharmacol.* **24**, 310.
4. Shibata, S. *et al.* (1974). Cardiac Stimulant Action of Extracts of Some Coelenterates on Rat Atria. *J. Pharm. Sci.* **63**, 1332.
5. Baslow, M.H., (1969). Marine Pharmacology. The Williams and Wilkins Co., Baltimore; republished with update, Robert E. Krieger Publishing Co., Huntington, N.Y., 1977, pp. 100-115.
6. Beress, L., Beress, R. and Wunderer, G. (1975). Isolation and Characterisation of Three Polypeptides with Neurotoxic Activity from *Anemonia sulcata. FEBS Letters* **50**, 311.
7. Behringwerke A.G. (1975). Polypeptides from Aq. Extracts of Sea Anemones — As Polyvalent Isoinhibitors for Proteases, Esterases and Peptidases. Patent Case BE-817-370.
8. Romey, G. *et al.* (1976). Sea Anemone Toxin: A Tool to Study Molecular Mechanisms of Nerve Conduction and Excitation-secretion Coupling. *Proc. Natl. Acad. Sci.* **73**, 4055.
9. Wunderer, G., Machleidt, W. and Wachter, E. (1976). Toxin II from *Anemonia sulcata* — The First Sequence of a Coelenterate Toxin. Hoppe-Seyler's Z. *Physiol. Chem.*, **357** 239.
10. Alsen, C. *et al.* (1976). The Action of a Toxin from the Sea Anemone *Anemonia sulcata* upon Mammalian Heart Muscles. Naunyn-Schmiedberg's *Arch. Pharmacol.* **295**, 55.
11. Moe, G.K. and Farah, A.E., 1975, Digitalis and Allied Cardiac Glycosides. In The Pharmacological Basis of Therapeutics, Eds. L.S. Goodman and A. Gilman, The Macmillan Co., New York, N.Y., Chapt. 31.

12. Shibata, S. *et al.* (1975). A Polypeptide (AP-A) from a Sea Anemone, *Anthopleura xanthogrammica* with Potent Cardiotonic Action. *The Pharmacologist* **17**, 218.

13. Shibata, S. *et al.* (1976). A Polypeptide (AP-A) from Sea Anemone (*Anthopleura xanthogrammica*) with Potent Cardiotonic Action. *J. Pharmacol. & Exp. Ther.* **199**, 298.

14. Norton, T.R. *et al.* (1976). The Isolation and Characterization of the Cardiotonic Polypeptide, Anthopleurin-A, from the Sea Anemone *Anthopleura xanthogrammica. J. Pharm. Sci.* **65**, 1368.

15. Tanaka, M. *et al.* (1977). Amino Acid Sequence of the *Anthopleura xanthogrammica* Heart Stimulant, Anthopleurin-A. *Biochemistry* **16**, 204.

16. Quinn, R.J. *et al.* (1974). Antitumor Activity and Cardiac Stimulatory Effects of Constitutents of *Anthopleura elegantissima. J. Pharm. Sci.* **63**, 1798

17. Scriabine, A. *et al.* (1977). Cardiotonic Activity of Anthopleurin-A (AP-A), a Polypeptide from Sea Anemone (*Anthopleura xanthogrammica*), in Dogs. *Fed. Proc.* **36**, 973.

Pharmacological Actions In Mammals And Therapeutic Potential Of The Fish-Urophysial Peptide Urotensin I

Karl Lederis and K. L. MacCannell

University of Calgary
Calgary, Alberta T2N 1N4, Canada

The caudal neurosecretory system of fishes, consisting of neurosecretory cell bodies (Dahlgren cells) in the caudal spinal cord and the neuroheamal storage-secretion organ, the urophysis, has been the subject of numerous studies, in search of an endocrine role for this system and its putative hormones. A broad spectrum of pharmacological effects of urophysial extracts have been described in fishes and other vertebrates (1,2).

Acidic extracts of carp urophyses were reported to elicit a lowering of blood pressure in the rat (3). This observation was confirmed employing mild extraction procedures, and a peptidic nature of the active agent was indicated (4).

One problem associated with the search for the neurosecretory products (putative hormones) of the urophysis was the absence of common criteria and standards which would enable the evaluation and comparison of observations from different laboratories. Bern and Lederis (5) proposed that urophysial biological activities be given the name of urotensins and that the following tentative classification of urotensins be adopted:

Urotensin I — blood pressure influencing activity
Urotensin II — fish smooth muscle contracting activity
Urotensin III — Na^+ movement influencing activity
Urotensin IV — hydrosmotic activity.

A unit of urotensin activity was defined as "the activity present in 1 mg of acetone-dried urophysis powder of the *Gillichthys mirabilis*, extracted in 0.25% acetic acid and heated for 3 min in a boiling water bath".

At that time it was not known whether these activities were associated with one or more chemical substances, other than that the urotensin II activity was a property of a low molecular weight substance which may be a peptide, and which may or may not exhibit the other urotensin activities (6–8).

Isolation, Identification and Purification of Urotensin I

Isolation of urotensin I by gel filtration chromatography was achieved by Zelnik and Lederis in 1971 (9). The separation of urotensin I and II (U_I and U_{II}) and their peptidic nature were established in 1973 (10).

Estimations of the molecular weights of the urotensin peptides by gel filtration and SDS-polyacrylamide gel electrophoresis lead to the conclusions that U_I may be isolated in two molecular size ranges, 1200–1700 and 2300–3000 Daltons, and U_{II} likewise in 1100–1400 and 2000–2400 Daltons (11).

In subsequent experiments, purification of U_I was attempted by a variety of procedures. Isoelectric focussing was found to give a high resolution peak of U_I at pI 5.5. However, this procedure could not be utilized for purification of the peptide owing to a similarity in size between U_I and the ampholytes in the focussing system. From various gel filtration and ion-exchange chromatographic systems, ion-exchange chromatography in SP-Sephadex C_{25} columns was adopted as giving high yields of a highly purified peptide in appropriately selected buffer systems (Letter and Lederis, unpublished observations). This system routinely yielded three active peaks of U_I. In parallel experiments employing high voltage electrophoresis in various buffer systems, in the pH range of 2.0–10, again three active U_I peptides were separated, their isoelectric points were estimated at pI 5.5, 6.3 and 8.0, and these peptides labelled as *c, b* and *a*, respectively.

In excess of 80% of the total U_I activity, as measured by assaying on the isolated hind limb of the rat (12), was associated with the C-peak (pI 5.5). Amino acid analysis of the hydrolysate of this peptide gave the following amino acid composition: Asx[5], Thr, Ser[2], Glx[5], Pro[2], Gly, Ala[2], Val, Met[2], Ileu[2], Leu[5], Tyr, Phe, His, Lys[2], Arg[3] (2). Amino acid sequence studies, now in progress, reveal U_I to be a straight chain peptide which, after cleavage at the Met residues yields peptide fragments with unchanged pharmacological activity either on the isolated hind limb or on the isolated tail artery of the rat.

Because of the remarkable structural similarity between the caudal neurosecretory system of fishes and the hypothalamo-neurohypophysial system, it has been postulated that urophysis-specific, peptide-binding proteins, urophysins, may be found in urophysial extracts (5). By using cold acidic extracts of urophyses, so as not to denature proteins, four such proteins, urophysins A, B, C and D, have been isolated from urophysial extracts of *Catostomus commersoni* (13). In subsequent experiments, it was observed that urophysin A invariably exhibited urotensin I activity, suggesting that this protein may contain the U_I peptide within its structure or that the protein and peptide are tightly bound to one another (14). Partial amino acid sequence analysis of the urophysin A protein has revealed an identical (partial) N-terminal U_I peptide sequence (residues 1-12) after the first three N-terminal residues of urophysin A. Subject to completion of the sequence analysis of urophysin A, it is tempting to speculate that this protein may be a form of a precursor of the U_I peptide, with a further possibility that the native urotensin I in fish may be a relatively large molecule (protein!) and that the peptide U_I, which is routinely extracted in our experiments, with its interesting pharmacological properties in mammals, may be an extraction artifact.

Pharmacological Properties of Urotensin I

The observation by Kobayashi *et al.* (3) that hot hydrochloric acid extracts of carp urophysis caused a lowering of blood pressure in the rat, was investigated further by applying milder acidic extraction of teleost fish urophyses (in 0.25% acetic acid). Such extracts were found to cause a pronounced and prolonged lowering of arterial blood pressure after intravenous administration in urethane anaesthetised rats. These effects were dose-related both in extent and duration, lasting up to six hours after an i.v. injection of a small quantity of an extract (4).

Following the isolation and partial purification of the U_I peptide (10) more extensive pharmacological investigations were initiated in the rat and in other mammals.

The long duration of action of the U_I administration in the intact rat necessitated an assay preparation that would enable investigations on the site(s) and mechanism of action of this peptide. The isolated hind limb of the rat was found to be a convenient and sensitive preparation for the assay and pharmacological studies of U_I. The effect of a lowering of perfusion pressure by U_I, in the presence of noradrenaline to maintain vascular tone, in the isolated hind limb was utilized to establish that (a) small quantities of the peptide (about 1 mU amounting to less than 1 ng of peptide) produced measurable and reproducible effects lasting 5–20 min, (b) the effects of U_I were not mediated by cholinergic, adrenergic or histaminergic receptors or the corresponding agonists, or by any other known endogenous vasoactive agents, (c) that U_I caused direct relaxation of vascular smooth muscle probably in the resistance vessels (15). Repetition of such investigations in the intact rat (conscious or anaesthetised) confirmed the above observations and conclusions except that the duration of effects was prolonged and ranged from 20 min to more than 2 hours in proportion to increasing doses. Moreover, monitoring of cardiac function showed that an increase in heart rate invariably accompanied the hypotensive effect. The increase in heart rate could be prevented by previous administration of propranolol, indicating that the effects on the heart rate were probably reflex in nature (15).

In spontaneously hypertensive rats, in which blood pressure was measured by tail plethysmography, the extent of the blood pressure lowering was more pronounced: a constant dose of 10 mU U_I/100 g body weight produced a lowering of mean arterial pressure by $12.4 \pm 1.28\%$ in normotensive controls, $17.9 \pm 1.46\%$ in hypertensive female rats and by $28.9 \pm 1.06\%$ in hypertensive males (16).

In chronic experiments, after once daily subcutaneous administration of 100–200 mU/100 g body weight to spontaneously hypertensive male rats (17), dramatically prolonged and persistent effects were observed:

(i)   after the first dose of s.c. administered U_I (100 mU/100 g), mean blood pressure fell by more than 20 mm Hg and remained low until the next injection 24 hours later;

(ii) during days 5–8, when U_I administration was discontinued, blood pressure only increased by less than 10 mm Hg; and

(iii) during the subsequent 4 days (i.e. days 9–12) when 200 mU/100 g of U_I was administered once daily, blood pressure remained at more than 20 mm Hg below control levels and only returned to normal on day 17 of the experiment (i.e., at 5 days after cessation of s.c. injection).

The pronounced effects of U_I in the rat, especially the extremely long duration of action in contrast to the usually short duration of action of any other known vasoactive peptides, prompted the question as to the effects of this peptide in other mammals. Doses of U_I, comparable to those used in the rat, were administered (i.v.) to conscious dogs, sheep (10 day old lamb) and a primate (squirrel monkey). In all cases, a lowering of arterial blood pressure was observed, with a similar (or greater) duration of action as that observed in the rat (15).

Studies were initiated to further elucidate the sites of action of U_I, with particular reference to effects in different vascular beds in the rat and dog. In the rat, an indirect method for measuring regional blood flow was applied, utilizing ^{51}Cr-labelled rat erythrocytes (18). A pronounced increase in blood space, suggesting increased blood flow was found mainly in skeletal muscle and the mesenteric region, with a less pronounced increase in skin and kidney. An increase in inulin space in these vascular beds was proportional to the increase in erythrocyte space, but mobilization of extracellular fluid from liver, lung, spleen and skin was indicated.

A more detailed study of the regional vascular effects was undertaken in the anaesthetized dog where electromagnetic flow probes were placed around major blood vessels in most vascular beds (19). The responses in the dog to low doses of U_I (not exceeding 20 mU/Kg), in terms of systemic hypotensive effects, were similar to those observed in the other mammalian species. However, a striking selectivity of regional effects was observed after intravenous or close arterial injections; unlike in the rat experiments, a highly selective, and probably exclusive, vasodilation was observed in the mesenteric region. Indeed, vasodilation occurred only in the vascular beds of the cephalic (superior) and caudal (inferior) mesenteric arteries, and not in the vascular bed supplied by the adjacent caeliac artery. It was concluded that the lowering of systemic blood pressure in the anaesthetized dog was produced by vasodilatation at an undetermined site in the mesenteric arteries. Only minimal and inconsistent cardiac effects (increases in heart rate and left ventricular dp/dt) were observed. These could be prevented by prior *beta*-adrenergic blockade in a similar manner as was observed previously in the rat. Direct vascular action of U_I in the dog was confirmed and the mesenteric vasodilator responses were not prevented by the blockade of adrenergic, histaminergic or muscarinic receptors.

Evaluation of general cardiovascular effects of U_I, resulting from the mesenteric vasodilatation, indicated a number of interesting consequences: (i) total peripheral resistance was decreased, while increasing left and right ventricular cardiac output, (ii) the above, coupled with increased portal vein flow, and without an increase in inferior caval flow, indicated an augmentation of venous return by virtue of diversion of blood through a dilated mesenteric circulation.

The ability of U_I to reduce afterload in the absence of pronounced direct cardiac effects was tested in an experimental model which would simulate acute myocardial injury without the production of cardiogenic shock.

Coronary arterial thrombosis was produced by injecting thrombin into the left anterior descending coronary artery in the anaesthetized dog (unpublished). In such dogs, U_I decreased afterload (decrease in elevated left and right end-diastolic ventricular pressure) and cardiac work without an increase in heart rate. The experimentally elevated left and right atrial pressures were significantly reduced by U_I, indicating a parallel decrease in preload. Some of these effects were modest but more pronounced effects may be expected when larger quantities of U_I become available for prolonged infusions.

In preliminary experiments in chronic dogs in failure secondary to an aortico-left atrial shunt, urotensin I infusions markedly reduced both preload and afterload, indicating that the peptide may also be of value in volume overload.

Therapeutic Potential of Urotensin I

The major mechanism of the hupotensive action of urotensin I, as seen in the dog and monkey, appears to be a highly selective vasodilatation in the mesenteric vascular bed, accompanied by a decrease in afterload and, except at very high doses, no direct cardiac effects.

By increasing venous return, U_I causes right and left ventricular cardiac output to increase. Because of the increased venous return and decreased afterload, stroke volume is increased. It would be expected, therefore, that unless U_I were to constrict coronary arteries, some increase in coronary flow would occur. In fact, preliminary experiments suggest (MacCannell and Lederis, unpublished observations) that U_I produces a moderate dilatation of coronary and carotid vessels. Low doses of U_I, having virtually no systemic hypotensive effects, were found to increase flow in left anterior descending coronary artery by 7.1% (decrease in resistance by 6%).

Similarly, increases in carotid flow of 4.9% and 3.7%, respectively, were observed in two dogs, with corresponding decreases in resistance of 5.5% and 13.7%. Two related conditions, in which there is considerable need for improvement in therapeutic intervention, are cardiogenic (or haemorrhagic) shock and intractable heart failure. Urotensin I appears to be more promising than the drugs presently in use for these conditions.The two commonly used catecholamines, isoproterenol and dopamine, while having beneficial effects in terms of increasing cardiac output, can both produce cardiac arrhythmias, and both agents can also increase cardiac work (20–22).

In left ventricular failure, the use of various nitrates, or other vasodilators (e.g., hydralazine, prazosin, minoxidil) will produce the desired decrease in preload and afterload. However, all these drugs also cause nonspecific vasodilatation and, therefore, have the potential for decreasing venous return, cardiac output and coronary flow.

The pharmacological properties of urotensin I, according to present day knowledge, would appear to make it a superior experimental tool, and a potentially useful drug in cardiogenic shock and intractable heart failure. Moreover, if the gut circulation is indeed central in the generation of clinical shock, as is held by many, an agent which dilates the mesenteric circulation selectively and specifically, as appears to be the case with urotensin I, would not only be a useful agent to establish the physiology (or pathogenesis) of shock, but it may also prove to be a significant drug for the therapy of clinical shock.

Urotensin I may also be of value in the diagnosis and treatment of intestinal angina, if its mechanism of action is the same in man as in the dog and monkey. It might also prove to be a useful agent in the medical management of dissecting aneurysms and in establishing whether the mesenteric vessels are involved in such dissection.

Acknowledgments

The investigations reviewed in this presentation were supported by M.R.C. (Canada) to K.L. and Alberta Heart Foundation (to K.L. and K.L. MacC.). K.L. is an Associate of the Medical Research Council of Canada.

References

1. Fridberg, G. and Bern, H.A. (1968). The Urophysis and the Caudal Neurosecretory System of Fishes. *Biol. Rev.* **43**, 175.
2. Lederis, K. (1977). Chemical Properties and the Physiological and Pharmacological Actions of Urophysial Peptides. *Amer. Zool.* **17**, 823.
3. Kobayashi, H. *et al.* (1968). Vasopressor Substance in Fish Urophyses. *Annot. Zool. Jap.* **41**, 154.
4. Lederis, K. (1970). Active Substances in the Caudal Neurosecretory System of Bony Fishes. *Mem. Soc. Endocrinol.* **18**, 465.
5. Bern, H.A. and Lederis, K. (1969). A Reference Preparation for the Study of Active Substances in the Caudal Neurosecretory System of Teleosts. *J. Endocrinol.* **45**, 11.
6. Bern, H.A. *et al.* (1967). The Urophysis of Teleost Fish. *J. Endocrinol.* **37**, 40.
7. Geschwind, I.I. *et al.* (1968). Purification of Bladder Contracting Principle from the Urophysis of the Teleost *Gillichthys mirabilis. Amer. Zoologist* **8**, 758.
8. Lederis, K. (1969). Teleostean Urophysis: Stimulation of rhythmic contractions of the bladder of the trout *(Salmo gairdnerii). Science* **163**, 1327.
9. Zelnik, P.R. and Lederis, K. (1971). Chromatographic Isolation of Rat Hypotensive Activity from the Urophysis. *Proc. Can. Fed. Biol. Soc.*, Abstr. No. 93.
10. Zelnik, P.R. and Lederis, K. (1973). Chromatographic Separation of Urotensins. *Gen. Comp. Endocrinol.* **20**, 392.
11. Moore, G. *et al.* (1975). Studies on Molecular Weights of Two Peptide Hormones from the Urophysis of White Sucker *(Catostomus commersoni). Can. J. Biochem.* **53**, 242.
12. Lederis, K. and Medakovic, M. (1974). Effects and Assay of Urotensin I on the Perfused Hind Limb of the Rat. *Gen. Comp. Endocr.* **24**, 10.

13. Moore, G., Burford, G. and Lederis, K. (1975). Properties of Urophysial Proteins (urophysins) from the White Sucker *(Catostomus commersoni)*. *Mol. and Cell. Endocr.* **3**, 297.

14. McMaster, D. *et al.* (1977). Separation and Molecular Weight Estimates of Urophysial Peptides and Proteins. *Proc. Can. Fed. Biol. Soc.* **20**, 271.

15. Lederis, K. and Medakovic, M. (1974). Pharmacological Observations on the Hypotensive Action of Extracts of Teleost Fish Urophysis (Urotensin I) in the Rat. *Br. J. Pharmacol.* **51**, 315.

16. Medakovic, M. and Lederis, K. (1975). Pharmacological Effects of Urotensins: IV. Blood pressure-lowering effects of urotensin I in spontaneously hypertensive rats. *Pharmacology* **13**, 435.

17. Medakovic, M., Devlin, A. and Lederis, K. (1975). Blood Pressure and Renal Effects of Prolonged Daily Subcutaneous Administration of Urotensin I Peptide in Spontaneously Hypertensive Rats. *Proc. West. Pharmacol. Soc.* **18**, 384.

18. Medakovic, M., Chan, D.K.O. and Lederis, K. (1975). Pharmacological Effects of Urotensins: I. Regional vascular effects of urotensins I and II in the rat. *Pharmacology* **13**, 409.

19. MacCannell, K.L. and Lederis, K. (1977). Dilatation of the Mesenteric Vascular Bed of the Dog Produced by a Peptide, Urotensin I. *J. Pharm. Exp. Ther.* **203**, 38.

20. MacCannell, K.L. *et al.* (1966). Dopamine in the Treatment of Hypotension and Shock. *New. Eng. J. Med.* **275**, 1389.

21. MacCannell, K.L. (1976). Pharmacological Role of Dopamine in Catecholamine Therapy. In *Dopamine in Clinical Use.* Excerpta Medica, Amsterdam, p. 7.

22. Goldberg, L.I. (1976). Use of Dopamine in the Treatment of Refractory Congestive Heart Failure. In *Dopamine in Clinical Use.* Excerpta Medica, Amsterdam, p. 19.

Biologically Active Polypeptides, Toxins and Proteinase Inhibitors From The Sea Anemones
Anemonia sulcata and Condylactis aurantiaca

Laszlo Beress
Marine Research Institute
University of Kiel
Kiel, W. Germany

Toxins

Sea anemones contain highly toxic compounds which are utilised for the capture of prey and for defence (1,2). Although the stinging ability of the sea anemones was already reported by Aristotle, the first attempts to purify these toxins were made only at the beginning of this century (3,4). Subsequent investigations were concerned with the elucidation of the chemical nature and the physiological function (5-7).

The first paper on the partial purification of a sea anemone toxin from *Condylactis gigantea*, a polypeptide of molecular weight from 10,000-15,000 Dalton was published by Shapiro (8). The potent action of this toxin on crustacean neurons gave rise to further neurophysiological studies concerning the mechanism of its action (9-12).

Chemistry—A systematic study devoted to the isolation and characterisation of sea anemone toxins, especially those from *Anemonia sulcata* was initiated in 1966/67 at the Zoological Station in Naples. This led to the discovery and partial purification of two of its toxins, Toxin I (ATX$_I$) and Toxin II (ATX$_{II}$). Both are polypeptides and have potent paralysing effect on crustaceans and mammals (13). It was later shown that a third toxin, Toxin III (ATX$_{III}$) was also present in *A. sulcata*. Improved methods (14,15) resulted in complete purification of the three toxins on a preparative scale (Table I, Fig. 1 and 2). With slight modifications of these techniques four toxins from *C. aurantiaca* (CTX$_{I, II, III}$ and $_{IV}$) were also prepared (Table II, Fig. 4). The amino acid composition of the seven purified toxins are presented in table III. The molecular weights of these toxins range from 2678 to 5630 Daltons.

Table I

Purification Steps for Toxins I, II, and III.

Five kg *A. sulcata* + 5 l EtOH homogenization, warm up to 65°C, centrifugation. Total toxicity 45 x 10^6 carcinus units (CU)

SUPERNATE I	SUPERNATE II	SUPERNATE III	RESIDUE I
+ 150 g CM-Cellul. pH 6.5 Conductivity 4mS x cm⁻¹	+ 150 g CM-Cellul. pH 5 Conductivity 4mS x cm⁻¹	+ 500 g SP-Seph. (wet) pH 3 Conductivity 2mS x cm⁻¹	Reextration with 50% EtOH Centrifug. supnt. added to supnt. I
			Residue II discarded
Batch I (CM-Cellul.) + 2 l 1M NaCl/0.05M Tris-HCl pH 8	Batch II (CM-Cellul.) + 2 l 1M NaCl/0.05M Tris-HCl pH 8	Batch III (SP-Seph.) + 2 l 1M NaCl/0.05M Tris-HCl pH 8	
Eluate	*Eluate*	*Eluate*	*Batch III*
Concen. to 70ml gel filtration on Seph. G. 50	Concen. to 70ml gel filtration on Seph. G. 50	Concen. to 70 ml gel filtration on Seph. G. 50	III Seph. G 50 Fr6 Concen. to 10ml Chromat. on Seph. G 25.
Batch I Seph. G 50 Fr.3 Concen. to 20ml desalting with Seph. G 25 lyophilization Chromat. on SP-Seph. C 25	*Batch II* Seph. G 50 Fr.3 Concen. to 20ml desalting with Seph. G 25 lyophilization Chromat. on SP-Seph. C 25	*Batch III* Seph. G 50 Fr.3 Concen. to 20ml desalting with Seph. G 25 lyophilization Chromat. on SP-Seph. C 25	Fraction 3 = Toxin III. Concen. to 3ml. Chromat. on Seph. G 10 Fraction 2 = Toxin III Concen. to 0.1 ml. Chromat. on Biogel P2
Fraction 5 = *Toxin II*	Fraction 3 = *Toxin II*	Fraction 2 = *Toxin I* Fraction 7 = *Toxin II*	Fraction 2 = pure *Toxin III*
62 mg Toxin II *(30,000 CU/mg)*	**270 mg Toxin II** *(30,000 CU/mg)*	**300 mg Toxin I** *(25,000 CU/mg)* **412 mg Toxin II** *(50,000 CU/mg)*	**7 mg Toxin III** *(2,000 CU/mg)*

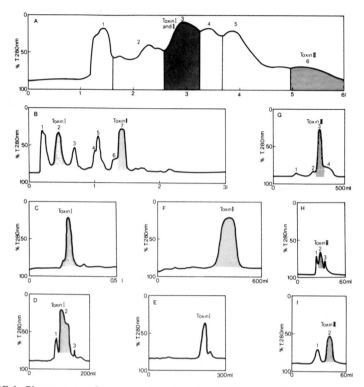

FIGURE 1. Chromatographic purification steps for ATX I, II and III
- A   Gelfiltration of the crude toxin concentrate (batch III proteins) on Sephadex G 50
- B   Chromatography of fraction A 3 on SP-Sephadex C 25
- C   Chromatography of fraction B 2 on QAE-Sephadex A 25
- D   Gelfiltration of the Toxin I fraction C 1 on Sephadex G 25
- E   Rechromatography of fraction D 2 on SP-Sephadex C 25
- F   Equilibrium rechromatcgraphy of fraction B 7 on SP-Sephadex C 25
- G   Gelfiltration of fraction A 6 on Sephadex G 25 superfine
- H   Gelfiltration of fraction G 3 on Sephadex G 10 fine
- I   Gelfiltration of fraction H 2 on Biogel P-2 minus 400 mesh

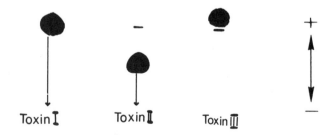

FIGURE 2. Polyacrylamide gel electrophoresis of ATX I, II and III Gel concentration: 13.5% Cyanogum ® Gel buffer: Trisborate-citrate (0.12 M) pH 8.6. Run: 2 hr., field strength 20V/cm, temperature 4° C. Electrode buffer: Na-borate 0.2 M pH 8.6

Table II

Purification Steps for CTX I, II, III and IV

Five kg *Condylactis aurantiaca* + 5 l EtOH homogenized, heated to 65°C, centrifuged; residue reextracted with 50% EtOH and centrifuged, then discarded. Combined alcoholic extracts dialyzed against 20 l demineralized water.

Alcoholic extracts (10^7 CU)
+ 150 g CM-Cellul. (dry) at pH 6.5, conductivity 4 mS x cm^{-1}

Batch I
eluted 2 l buffer at pH 8
(1 M NaCl/0.05 M Tris-HCl)

Elaute Batch I (1.6 x 10^5 CU)

Filtrate of Batch I
+ 150 g CM-Cellul. (dry) at pH 5.0, conductivity 2 mS x cm^{-1}

Batch II
eluted 2 l buffer at pH 8
(1 M NaCl/0.05 M Tris-HCl)

Elaute Batch II (1.6 x 10^5 CU)

Filtrate of Batch II
+ 500 g SP-Seph (wet) at pH 2.5, conductivity 2 mS x cm^{-1}

Batch III
eluted 2 l buffer at pH 8
(1 M NaCl/0.05 M Tris-HCl)

Elaute Batch III (1 x 10^7 CU)

Elauate of Batch III concentrated and chromat. on Seph. G 50; toxic fraction 5 concentrated, desalted on Seph. G 25 and lyophilized (1.2 g crude toxin, total toxicity 9 x 10^{6}CU): crude toxin is chromat. on SP-Seph. C 25 (Na-acetate buffer pH 4.0).

SP fraction 5 = Toxin I	SP fraction 7 = Toxin II	SP fraction 8 = Toxin III	SP fraction 10 = Toxin IV
chromat. on QAE-Seph. A 25 toxic fract. 2 desalted on Seph. G 25 superfine	chromat. on QAE-Seph. A 25 toxic fract. 2 desalted on Seph. G 25 superfine	chromat. on QAE-Seph. A 25 toxic fract. 2 desalted on Seph. G 25 superfine	chromat. on QAE-Seph. A 25 toxic fract. 2 desalted on Seph. G 25 superfine
8.2 mg Toxin I (15,000 CU/mg)	*33 mg Toxin II (50,000 CU/mg)*	*6 mg Toxin III (15,000 CU/mg)*	*10.5 mg Toxin IV (20,000 CU/mg)*

Table III

Amino Acid Compositions of the Toxins of *Condylactis aurantiaca* and *Anemonia sulcata*

A ACID	*Condylactis aurantiaca*				*Anemonia sulcata*		
	TOXIN I	TOXIN II	TOXIN III	TOXIN IV	TOXIN I	TOXIN II	TOXIN III
Asx	6.02 (6)	7.00 (7)	4.00 (4)	2.10 (2)	5	4	1
Thr	2.80 (3)	3.10 (3)	2.72 (3)	3.98 (4)	2	2	0
Ser	5.60 (6)	7.00 (7)	3.28 (1)	3.70 (4)	4	4	2
Glx	6.06 (6)	4.80 (5)	6.08 (6)	3.93 (4)	2	1	2
Pro	1.16 (1)	0.94 (1)	2.09 (2)	3.08 (3)	2	4	4
Gly	5.00 (5)	6.05 (6)	5.30 (5)	8.00 (8)	8	8	4
Ala	0.87 (1)	0	1.95 (2)	0.53 (0–1)	3	1	0
Cys[1]	4.99 (6)	5.90 (6)	4.11 (6)	6.20 (6)	6	6	4
Val	2.07 (2)	1.94 (2)	1.15 (1)	1.07 (1)	1	1.5[2]	1
Met[1]	0.81 (1)	0.85 (1)	0.59 (1)	0.75 (1)	1	0	0
Ile	0.99 (1)	1.00 (1)	1.20 (1)	0.96 (1)	2	3.5[2]	0
Leu	2.96 (3)	3.20 (3)	2.08 (2)	1.95 (2)	1	3	2
Tyr	0.95 (1)	1.03 (1)	2.35 (3)	4.07 (4)	1	0	0
Phe	0.97 (1)	1.08 (1)	1.20 (1)	1.86 (2)	1	0	2
Trp[3]	1.95 (2)	1.93 (2)	0.55 (0–1)	0.89 (1)	2	3	0
His	1.50 (1–2)	1.89 (2)	1.20 (1)	0.86 (1)	0	2	0
Lys	1.98 (2)	2.12 (2)	4.95 (5)	4.00 (4)	2	3	1
Arg	1.22 (1)	1.16 (1)	2.00 (2)	1.07 (1)	2	1	1
Total	49–50	51	49–50	49–50	45	47	24
Mol. wt.	5400–5537	5599	5444–5630	5397–5468	4702	4770	2678
N-terminal	Gly	Gly	Gly	Gly	Gly	Gly	Arg

[1] Determinded as cysteic acid and methionine sulfone. respectively after performic acid oxidation.
[2] Microheterogeneity Ile/Val in position 2 of the sequence (24).
[3] Determined spectrophotometrically.

The sequence of ATX$_{II}$ (Fig. 3) from *A. sulcata* has recently been determined (17,18). It represents the first sequence of a coelenterate toxin. This toxin was found to consist of 47 amino acid residues which are interconnected by three disulfide bridges. The sequence of ATX$_{III}$ from *A. sulcata* is also established (19). Further structural studies on ATX$_{II}$ were carried out by means of Laser Raman spectroscopy (20). Neither the sequence nor the spectroscopical studies revealed any structural homology between ATX$_{II}$ and other neuro- and cardiotoxins isolated from snake, bee or scorpion venoms (20, 21). Pure sea anemone toxins can now be prepared on a mg scale (15). This made possible extensive studies on the structure and function of these potent toxins.

1	2	3	4	5	6	7	8	9	10
Gly	Ile	Pro	Cys	Leu	Cys	Asp	Ser	Asp	Gly
	Val								
11	12	13	14	15	16	17	18	19	20
Pro	Ser	Val	Arg	Gly	Asn	Thr	Leu	Ser	Gly
21	22	23	24	25	26	27	28	29	30
Ile	Ile	Trp	Leu	Ala	Gly	Cys	Pro	Ser	Gly
31	32	33	34	35	36	37	38	39	40
Trp	His	Asn	Cys	Lys	Lys	His	Gly	Pro	Thr
41	42	43	44	45	46	47			
Ile	Gly	Trp	Cys	Cys	Lys	Gln			

FIGURE 3. The sequence of ATX II

Pharmacology—The pharmacological studies on the sea anemone toxins (ATX$_I$ and ATX$_{II}$) have been devoted to the investigation of the mode of their action on the mammalian heart muscle (22-24). The toxin, ATX$_{II}$, evokes a dose dependent positive inotropic effect in the nanomolar (2-100 nM) range (23). However, in contrast with cardiac glycosides, ATX$_{II}$ does not inhibit the action of the enzyme Na/K-ATP-ase (25).

The positive inotropic effect of ATX$_I$ on the isolated guinea pig auricles was found to be 100 times weaker than the effect of ATX$_{II}$ (22). Electromechanical studies with ATX $_{II}$ on mammalian cardiac muscle revealed that the positive inotropic effect was accompanied by a prolonged duration of the action potential (26).

Physiology—The effects of the three toxins from *A. sulcata* on the neuromuscular transmission and nerve action potential have been investigated on the exposed open muscle of the isolated first or second

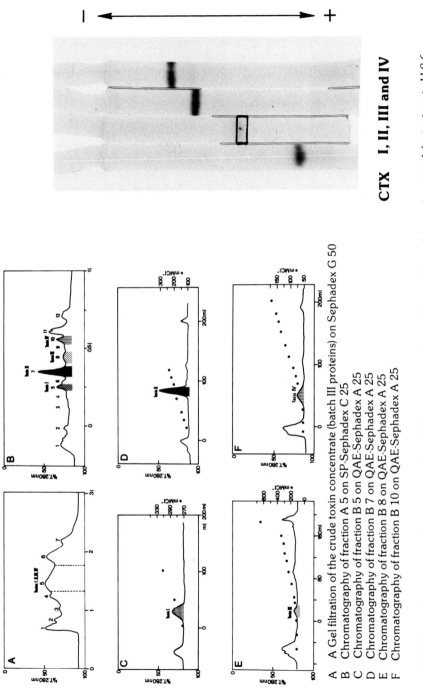

CTX I, II, III and IV

A Gel filtration of the crude toxin concentrate (batch III proteins) on Sephadex G 50
B Chromatography of fraction A 5 on SP-Sephadex C 25
C Chromatography of fraction B 5 on QAE-Sephadex A 25
D Chromatography of fraction B 7 on QAE-Sephadex A 25
E Chromatography of fraction B 8 on QAE-Sephadex A 25
F Chromatography of fraction B 10 on QAE-Sephadex A 25

FIGURE 4. Chromatographic purification for CTX I, II, III and IV and PAA-gel disc elec- trophoresis of the toxins at pH 8.6

walking leg of the crayfish *Astacus leptodactilus* (27,28). The toxins show presynaptic effects. The effects of ATX_I and ATX_{II} as well as CTX_{IV} are irreversible in contrast to ATX_{III} (28). A comparative study on the mechanism of action of ATX_I and ATX_{II} and CTX_{IV} indicates that the differences between the sea anemone toxins of different origin are very small indeed (27). The ATX_{II} acts on the sodium channel by selectively slowing down the sodium inactivation (29-33).

The small size of ATX_{II} (MW = 4770), its potent action on both the mammalian heart muscle and the neuromuscular transmission even in nanomolar concentrations, and its high affinity to the sodium system renders it as one of the most interesting substances for the study of the excitation phenomena of the heart muscle and nerve membranes and for the characterisation of the sodium channel.

Proteinase Inhibitors

Several species of sea anemones contain polyvalent proteinase inhibitors in relatively high concentrations. They were first detected in *A. sulcata* and later also in other sea anemones (13,34). The sea anemone proteinase inhibitors are polypeptides with molecular weights of about 6,500 Daltons (35-37). Five isoinhibitors from *A. sulcata* were isolated and characterised (35). In a later work the isolation of five additional isoinhibitors were described (37). The amino acid composition, molecular weight and inhibition spectrum of the isoinhibitors of *A. sulcata* and the Kunitz Inhibitor (BPTI) are strikingly similar. Therefore it was suspected that these inhibitors have also similar structures (35). Elucidation of the partial sequence of Isoinhibitor 5 II from *A. sulcata* showed that the structural similarity between the inhibitors of different origin does in fact exist (36), table IV.

The sea anemone proteinase inhibitors are the first homologs to the Kunitz Inhibitor (BPTI) found in nature. From the amino acid composition it can be concluded that the *A. sulcata* proteinase inhibitor is less basic than the Kunitz Inhibitor. This is also evident from the electrophoretic mobility of these two proteinase inhibitors (Fig. 6).

Sea anemone toxins and proteinase inhibitors can be obtained by the same procedures (Table I and Fig. 5).

Acknowledgments

The author wishes to thank Prof. Dr. Hans Fritz, Institut fur Klinische Chemie und Klinische Biochemie der Universitat Munchen for his generous support, Mrs. Maria Meier, Mrs. Edith Mempel and Mr. Joachim

Table IV

Partial Sequence of the Sea Anemone Proteinase Inhibitor (36) (SAI, fraction 5 II) in Comparison to the Sequence of the Kunitz Inhibitor (BPTI).

SAI	Ile	Asn	Gly	Asp	Cys	Glu	Leu	Pro	Lys	Val	Val	Gly	Pro	Cys	Arg	15
BPTI	Arg	Pro	Asp	Phe	Cys	Leu	Glu	Pro	Pro	Tyr	Thr	Gly	Pro	Cys	Lys	
SAI	Ala	Arg	Phe	Pro	Arg	Tyr	Tyr	Tyr	Asn	Ser	Ser	Ser	Lys	Arg	Cys	30
BPTI	Ala	Arg	Ile	Ile	Arg	Tyr	Phe	Tyr	Asn	Ala	Lys	Ala	Gly	Leu	Cys	
SAI	Glu	Lys	Phe	Ile	Tyr	Gly	Gly	Cys	Arg	Ala	· Lys	Arg	Asn	Asn	Asn	45
BPTI	Gln	Thr	Phe	Val	Tyr	Gly	Gly	Cys	Arg	Ala	Lys	Arg	Asn	Asn	Phe	
SAI	Lys	Ser	Glu	Asp	Cys	Met										60
BPTI	Arg	Ala	Glu	Asp	Cys	Met										

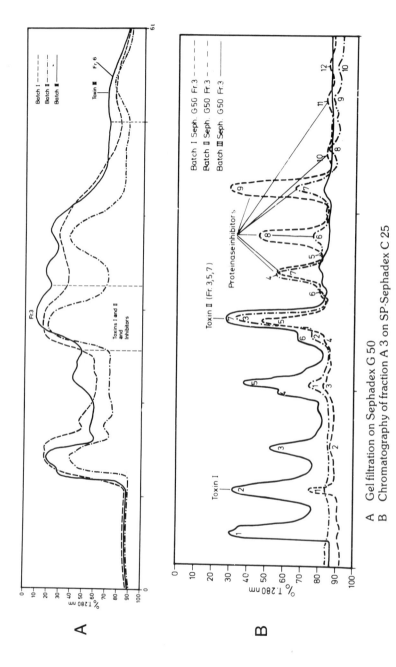

A   Gel filtration on Sephadex G 50
B   Chromatography of fraction A 3 on SP-Sephadex C 25

FIGURE 5. Simultanous purification of toxins and proteinase inhibitors from extracts of *Anemonia sulcata.*

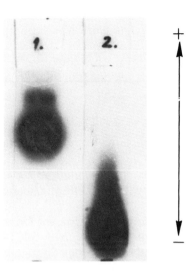

1. A.S. Trypsin inhibitor (SAI).

2. Bovine Pancr. Trypsin inhibitor (BPTI).

FIGURE 6. A comparative electrophoresis of the sea anemone proteinase inhibitor (SAI) and the Kunitz Inhibitor (BPTI) in polyacrylamide gel at pH 8.6. Conditions same as in figure 2.

FIGURE 7. *Anemonia sulcata* (photo Edith Mempel, Kiel Aquarium).

Zwick for excellent technical assistance. The work was supported by the Deutsche Forschungsgemeinschaft.

References

1. Halstead, B. W. (1965). *Poisonous and Venomous Marine Animals of the World.* United States Government Printing Office, Washington, D. C. **Vol. 1**, 297.
2. Mariscal, R. N. (1974). Nematocysts. In *Coelenterate Biology III,* Eds. Leonard Muscatine and Howard M. Lenhoff. Academic Press. p. 129.
3. Richet, C. (1902). Du Poison Pruritogene et Urticant Contenu dans les Tentacules des Actinies. *Compt. rend. soc. biol.* **54**, 1438.
4. Richet, C. (1903). Des Poisons Contenus dans les Tentacules des Actinies (congestine et thalassine). *Compt. rend. soc. biol.* **55**, 246.
5. Sonderhoff, R. (1936). IU ber das Gift der Seeanemonen. Ein Beitrag zur Kenntnis der Nesselgifte. *Ann. Chem.* **525**, 138.
6. Ackermann, D. (1953). Uber das Vorkommen von Homarin, Trigonellin und einer neuen Base Anemonin in der Anthozoe Anemonia sulcata. *Z. physiol. Chem.* **295**, 1.
7. Mathias, A. P., Ross, D. M. and Schachter, M. (1960). The Distribution of 5-hydroxytryptamin, Tetramethylammonium, Homarine and Other Substances in Sea Anemones. *J. Physiol.* **151**, 296.
8. Shapiro, B. I. (1968). Purification of a Toxin from Tentacles of the Anemone *Condylactis gigantea. Toxicon* **5**, 253.
9. *ibid.* (1968). A Site of Action of Toxin from the Anemone *Condylactis gigantea. Comp. Biochem. Physiol.* **27**, 519.
10. Shapiro, B. I., and Lilleheil, G. (1969). The Action of Anemone Toxin on Crustacean Neurons. *ibid.* **28**, 1225.
11. Lilleheil, G. and Shapiro, B. I. (1969). The Mechanism of Plateau Formation by Anemone Toxin. *ibid.* **30**, 281.
12. Narahashi, T., Moore, J. W. and Shapiro, B. I. (1969). Condylactis Toxin: Interaction with nerve membrane ionic conductances. *Science* **163**, 680.
13. Beress, L. and Beress R. (1971). Reinigung zweier krabbenlahmender Toxine aus der Seeanemone Anemonia sulcata. *Kieler Meeresforsch.* **27**, 117.
14. Beress, L., Beress, R. and Wunderer, G. (1975). Isolation and Characterisation of Three Polypeptides with Neurotoxic Activity from *Anemonia sulcata. FEBS-Letters* **50**, 311.
15. *ibid.* Purification of Three Polypeptides with Neuro– and Cardiotoxic Activity from the Sea Anemone *Anemonia sulcata. Toxicon* **13**, 359.

16. *ibid.* (1976). Purification and Characterisation of Four Polypeptides with Nerotoxic Activity from *Condylactis aurantiaca. Hoppe-Seyler's Z. Physio. Chem.* **357**, 409.
17. Wunderer, G., Machleidt, W. and Wachter, E. (1976).Toxin II from *Anemonia sulcata*—the First Sequence of a Coelenterate Toxin. *Hoppe-Seyler's Z. Physiol. Chem.* **357**, 239.
18. Wunderer, G., *et al.* (1976). Amino Acid Sequence of a Coelenterate Toxin: Toxin II from *Anemonia sulcata. Eur. J. Biochem.* **68**, 193.
19. Beress, L. Wunderer, G. and Wachter,E.(In press).Amino Acid Sequence of Toxin III from *Anemonia sulcata. Hoppe-Seyler's Z. Physiol. Chem.*
20. Prescott, B., *et al.* (1976). Structural Properties of Toxin II of Sea Anemone (*Anemonia sulcata*) Determined by Laser Raman Spectroscopy. *FEBS-Letters* **64**, 144.
21. Wunderer, G. (1975). Biologisch aktive Polypeptide aus der Seeanemone Anemonia sulcata. Dissertation thesis. *Technische Universitat Munchen.*
22. Alsen, C. (1975). Cardiotoxic Effect of Two Toxins Isolated from the Sea Anemone. *Naunyn-Schmiedeberg's Arch. Pharmakol.* **287**, 105.
23. Alsen, C., *et al.* (1976). The Action of a Toxin from the Sea Anemone *Anemonia sulcata* upon Mammalian Heart Muscles. *Naunyn-Schmiedeberg's Arch. Pharmakol.* **295**, 55.
24. Alsen, C., Scheufler, E. and Tesseraux, I. (1977). Investigations about the Mode of Action of a Toxin (ATX$_{II}$) Isolated from the Sea Anemone *Anemonia sulcata. Deutsche Pharmakologische Gesellschaft.* Abstracts of the 18th Spring Meeting **16**.
25. Alsen, C., and Reinberg, T. (1976). Characterisation of the Pharmacological and Toxicological Actions of Two Toxins Isolated from the Sea Anemone *Anemonia sulcata. Bull. Inst. Pasteur* **74**, 117.
26. Ravens, U. (1976). Electromechanical Studies of an *Anemonia sulcata* Toxin in Mammalian Cardiac Muscle. *Naunyn-Schmiedeberg's Arch. Pharmacol.* **296**, 73.
27. Rathmayer, W., Jessen, B. and Beress, L. (1975). Effect of Toxins of Sea Anemones on Neuromuscular Transmission. *Naturwiss.* **62**, 538.
28. Rathmayer, W. and Beress, L. (1976). The Effect of Toxins from *Anemonia sulcata* (*Coelenterata*) on Neuromuscular Transmission and Nerve Action Potentials in the Crayfish (*Astacus leptodactilus*). *J. Comp. Physiol.* **109**, 373.
29. Romey, G., and Lazdunski, M. (1975). Scorpion and Sea Anemone Neurotoxin Actions on Axonal Membranes. *Proceedings 5th International Biophysics Congress Copenhagen* **503**, 138.

30. Romey, G. *et al.*, (1976). Anemone Toxin: A tool to study molecular mechanisms of nerve action and excitation-secretion coupling. *Proc. Natl. Acad. Sci.* **73**, 4055.

31. Bergmann, C. *et al.* (1976). Inhibition de l'inactivation Sodium de la Membrane Nodale par la Toxine II d'*Anemonia sulcata*. *C. R. Acad. Sc. Paris,* t. 282, Serie D-1881.

32. Bergmann, C., *et al.*, (1976). Decreased Rate of Sodium Conductance Inactivation in the Node of Ranvier Induced by a Polypeptide Toxin from Sea Anemone. *Biochim. Biophys. Acta* **455**, 173.

33. Conti, F., *et al.*, (1976). Conductance of the Sodium Channel in Myelinated Nerve Fibres with Modified Sodium Inactivation. *J. Physiol.* **262**, 729.

34. Beress, L., Kortmann, H. and Fritz, H. (1972). Uber das Vorkommen Polyvalenter Proteinaseninhibitoren in Seeanemonen (*Actinaria*) mit einem dem Trypsin-Kallikrein-Inhibitor aus Rinderorganen analogen Hemmspektrum. *Hoppe-Seyler's Z. Physiol. Chem.* **353**, 111.

35. Fritz, H., Brey, B. und Beress, L. (1972). Polyvalente Isoinhibitoren fur Trypsin, Chymotrypsin, Plasmin und Kallikreine aus Seeanemonen (*Anemonia sulcata*), Isolierung, Hemmverhalten und Aminosaurezusammensetzung. *Hoppe-Seyler's Z. Physiol. Chem.* **353**, 19.

36. Wunderer, G., *et al.* (1976). Broad Specifity Proteinase Inhibitors from Sea Anemones. In *Protides of the biological fluids 23rd colloquium.* Ed. M. Peters, Pergamon Press, Oxford and New York, pp. 285.

37. Wunderer, G., *et al.*, (1976). Broad Specifity Inhibitors from Sea Anemones. *Methods in Enzymol.* **45**, 881.

Mechanism Of Cardiovascular Effects Of Palytoxin

Shrinivas K. Kulkarni, Ward G. Kirlin and Pushkar N. Kaul

Marine Pharmacology Laboratory
University of Oklahoma Health Sciences Center, College of Pharmacy
Oklahoma City, Oklahoma

The toxic nature of zoanthids of *Palythoa* genus was discovered accidentally by Ciereszko and Attaway (1) in 1961. The component responsible for the toxicity, palytoxin (PTX), was isolated several years later independently both at the University of Oklahoma (2) and the University of Hawaii (3). More recently, Kimura and Hashimoto (4) have also reported the isolation of palythoatoxin from the stomach of filefish which had apparently ingested *Palythoa*.

Our earlier studies revealed that PTX is biologically the most potent toxin and also the most potent coronary vasoconstrictor known (5,6). It was also suggested that PTX, as a pharmacologic tool, may aid in the understanding of the physiology of coronary artery, since the electrocardiographic (EKG) changes produced by the toxin in anesthetized animals closely simulated similar changes seen in human variant angina (6) caused by a spontaneous ideopathic coronary spasm.

Reports of Deguchi *et al.* (7) have confirmed most of our findings. Also, in line with our observation that the electrocardiographic changes elicited by PTX were similar to those produced by high concentrations of potassium (6), Ito *et al.* (8) have shown that PTX simulates the action of high extracellular potassium concentration on the vascular smooth muscle.

It was suggested earlier that the mode of toxic action of PTX involved profound coronary arterial constriction (5,6). The present study was undertaken to further investigate the mechanism as well as the probable site of action of PTX in laboratory animals. The results appear to further substantiate our belief that the heart is the primary site of action of PTX.

Materials and Methods

Palytoxin isolated from *P. caribaeorum* (Jamaican coasts) and *P. mammilosa* (Bahamas) was used in the present study (2). Solutions of

PTX were prepared in saline at 0–5°C. The toxin was tested on the isolated perfusing guinea pig and rat hearts for its coronary vascular effects and in anesthetized dogs and rats for its effect on the cardiovascular system.

Isolated heart preparation — The Langendorff heart preparation was set up as described previously (5). Guinea pigs (600–900 g) and rats (250–300 g) were stunned with a blow on the head, followed by carotid bleeding. The heart was removed and the aorta was cannulated to allow the coronary perfusion. The force and rate of contractions and the rate of coronary flow were recorded with the help of an amplifier-recorder system. A minimum of 5–6 heart preparations were tested for each observation.

Tris buffered physiological solution (NaCl, 131 mM; KCl, 5.6 mM; $CaCl_2$, 2.16 mM; $MgCl_2$, 0.25 mM; Tris, 5 mM; Glucose, 11 mM: pH, 7.35 and saturated with oxygen) was used to perfuse the heart. The calcium channel blockers, i.e., lanthanum chloride ($10^{-5}M$), verapamil (0.2 mg/l) and Bayer 1040 (0.1 mg/l) were also dissolved in the Tris solution. The heart was perfused with the Tris solution of each blocker for at least 15 min before administration of PTX.

Blood pressure studies — The effect of PTX on the blood pressure was studied in anesthetized rats and dogs. Mongrel dogs of either sex weighing 8–12 kg and albino rats (Sprague Dawley) weighing 200–250 g were anesthetized with 45 mg/kg of pentobarbital or with 1 g/kg of urethane. The right saphenous or femoral vein was cannulated for PTX administration. The left carotid artery was exposed and cannulated with a polyethylene cannula connected to a pressure transducer for monitoring the blood pressure. Electrodes were pinned to appropriate limbs to provide Lead II of the EKG record. An additional pair of electrodes was attached to the skin in the thoracic region to monitor respiration through a pneumograph. In order to determine if a central component is involved in the cardiac action of PTX, rats were chronically implanted with intracerebroventricular (i.c.v.) cannulae. Using the technique of Noble *et al.* (9), the right lateral ventricle was cannulated with a size 10 polyethylene tubing which fitted over a standard 27 gauge hypodermic needle. All doses of PTX were administered in 10-mcl volume of saline and each dose level was tested on at least 3–5 rats.

Results and Discussion

Site of action — In the anesthetized rats, PTX produced typical cardiovascular changes both on i.c.v. and i.v. administration, the effects appearing much faster with the i.v. administration than with the i.c.v. injections (Table I, II). The blood pressure rose within seconds of PTX administration in some cases but in most cases within 2–5 min of both the routes of administration. The pressure response was accompanied by a concommittant increase in pulse wave amplitude. The cardiac changes, e.g., bradycardia, ectopic beats and ventricular arrhythmias were observed even at low doses of 10–100 ng/kg of PTX (Fig. 1). With the i.c.v. doses, there was a delay of up to 15 min in the onset of action. Also, relatively larger doses were required to produce the pressor response. These observations suggest that the main site of action of PTX may be peripheral rather than central.

Unlike the effects seen with other marine toxins, e.g., saxitoxin and tetrodotoxin (10), PTX by i.c.v. route failed to show any effect on the respiration, thereby ruling out its effects on the pneumotaxic sensitive areas within the paraventricular region.

The question, however, remains as to how i.c.v. given PTX produces pressor response within minutes of the injection which are not adequate for the toxin to reach the lower hypothalamic or medullary centers known to regulate blood pressure. It actually takes more than an hour, for example, for apomorphine to reach the fourth ventricle and thus to elicit

Table I

Effect of Intravenous PTX on Blood Pressure in Rats

DOSE	B.P. RISE	ONSET TIME	LETHAL TIME
1 ng/kg	60 mm	60 sec	92 min
100 ng/kg	57.5 mm	6 sec	15 min
1 mcg/kg	90 mm	6.5 sec	4 min

Table II

Effect of Intracerebroventricular PTX on Blood Pressure in Rats

DOSE	B.P. RISE	ONSET TIME	LETHAL TIME
1 ng	10 mm	1 min	Recovered
10 ng	7.5 mm	5.5 min	Recovered
50 ng	15 mm	2 min	Recovered
1 mcg	54 mm	11.3 sec	43 min

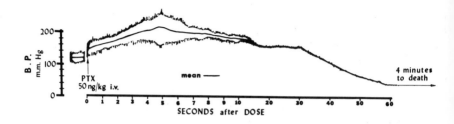

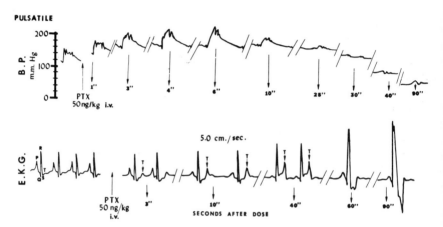

FIGURE 1. Effect of i.v. administered PTX on the blood pressure (B.P.) of an anesthetized dog (mean arterial pressure, top; pulsatile recording, middle) and the electrocardiogram (EKG, bottom).

emesis following i.c.v. administration (11). At least two possibilities seem plausible. One of these would suggest that perhaps there are blood pressure regulating sensors within the lateral ventricles, analogous to the suggested pneumotaxic sensitive areas (10), which might be affected by PTX when given by i.c.v. route. However, in that case the effect should have ensued relatively much more rapidly than it actually did in our experiments.

The second, and perhaps more plausible, explanation suggests that PTX is resorbed via the choroid plexus of the lateral ventricle and thus appears in the general blood circulation. This would start building PTX concentration in the circulating blood until it reaches a threshold level triggering a generalized peripheral vasoconstriction which results in the obvious rise of blood pressure. Supporting this contention is the fact that the perpheral blood samples, drawn following i.c.v. administration of PTX and tested on the isolated guinea pig heart coronary flow, showed effective concentrations of PTX within 15 min. This observation would further reinforce our belief that the site of action of PTX is peripheral and primarily cardiovascular in nature.

Mechanism of action — It is well known that both extra- and intracellular calcium play an important role in the smooth muscle contractility (12,13). With the availability of chemical agents such as lanthanum, verapamil and Bayer 1040, which specifically block calcium channels in the membrane, it has been possible to extensively investigate the role of calcium in the physiology of smooth muscle contraction (14). Using these calcium blockers, Ito *et al.* (8) have recently reported that PTX increases calcium influx into the smooth muscle cell while causing a contraction. Attempts in our laboratory to investigate a similar role of calcium in the action of PTX on the coronary arteries also indicated that the coronary vasoconstricting action of PTX was dramatically reduced in the absence of extracellular calcium (Fig. 2 and 3). However, in view of many limitations of such isolated preparations, it is difficult to interpret these findings. For example, it is well established that the isolated heart does not function in the absence of certain threshold level of extracellular calcium. Consequently, it could be argued that low calcium concentrations or calcium channel blockers create an abnormal and stressful environment for the muscle cells, and therefore any experiments carried out to varify the role

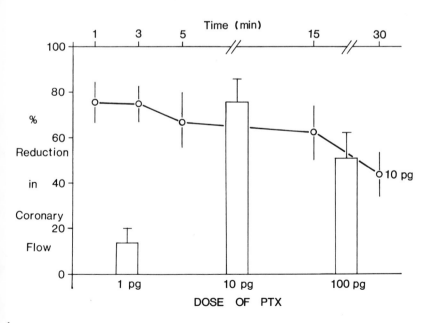

FIGURE 2. Effect of PTX on the coronary flow in an isolated perfusing guinea pig heart. The time course of action is shown for the 10 pg dose.

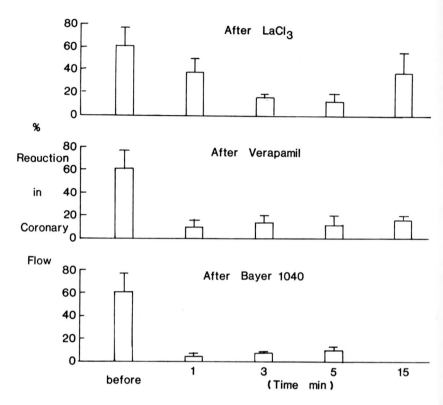

FIGURE 3. Reduction of coronary flow due to PTX in the absence and the presence of various calcium channel blockers. Partial blockade of the PTX action is apparent.

of calcium in such systems may be questionable. It is therefore relatively speculative to ascribe a definite role to calcium in mediating the coronary vasoconstrictor activity of PTX. Notwithstanding these reservations, the experimental evidence presented by Ito *et al.* (8) would suggest that calcium may be required for the action of PTX at least on the aortic strips.

Summary

Palytoxin, obtained from the coelenterate zoanthids of genus *Palythoa*, produces acute coronary constriction in the isolated perfusing guinea pig heart and EKG changes in anesthetized animals similar to those observed in human variant angina. The present study has revealed that the coronary vasculature is the primary site of cardiotoxic action of PTX. When PTX was administered in intracerebroventricular doses of 1–50 ng, the pressor response and the EKG changes occurred between 1 to 15 min of injection. These changes occurred much faster with the intravenous doses of the toxin. The contraction of aortic strip preparation produced by PTX could be counteracted by papaverine, and the coronary vasoconstriction in the isolated heart preparations was partially blocked by lanthanum, verapamil and Bayer 1040. The present evidence suggests that PTX has a direct effect on the coronary vasculature. Whether or not this effect requires extracellular calcium remains speculative at the present time.

Acknowledgments

The authors are grateful to Dr. M. K. Ticku for supplying the calcium channel blockers and to Suzanne Madden for technical assistance. This study was supported by the National Sea Grant Agency (NOAA), Grant 04-158-44062.

References

1. Attaway, D.H. (1968). Ph.D. Dissertation. The University of Oklahoma, Norman, Oklahoma.
2. Attaway, D.H. and Ciereszko, L.S. (1974). Isolation and Partial Characterization of Caribbean Palytoxin. *Proc. Sec. International Coral Reef Symp.* Brisbane, Australia, p. 497.
3. Moore, R.E. and Sheuer, P.J. (1971). Palytoxin: A new marine toxin from a coelenterate. *Science* **172**, 495.
4. Kimura, S. and Hashimoto, Y. (1973). Purification of the Toxin in a Zoanthid *Palythoa tuberculosa. Pub. Seto. Marine Biol. Lab.* **20**, 3.
5. Kaul, P.N., Farmer, M.R. and Ciereszko, L.S. (1974). Pharmacology of Palytoxin—The most potent marine toxin. *West. Pharmacol. Soc.* **17**, 294.
6. Kaul, P.N. (1976). Palytoxin—A new physiological tool. *Proc. Food-Drugs from the Sea*, Marine Technol. Soc. Washington, D.C., p. 311.
7. Deguchi, T., Urakawa, N. and Takamatsu, S. (1976). Some Pharmacological Properties of Palythoatoxin Isolated from the Zoanthid, *Palythoa tuberculosa.* In *Animal, Plant and Microbial Toxins.* Eds. Ohsaka, A., Hayashi, K. and Sawai, Y., Vol. 2, Plenum Publishing Corp. New York, p. 379.
8. Ito, K., Karaki, H. and Urakawa, N. (1977). The Mode of Action of Palytoxin on Vascular Smooth Muscle. *Eur. J. Pharmacol.* **46**, 9.
9. Noble, E.P., Wurtman, R.J. and Axelrod, J. (1967). A Simple and Rapid Method for Injecting H³-norepinephrine into the Lateral

Ventricle of the Rat Brain. *Life Sci.* **6**, 281.

10. Jaggard, P. and Evans, M.H. (1975). Administration of Tetrodotoxin and Saxitoxin into the Lateral Cerebral Ventricle of the Rabbit. *Neuropharmacology* **14**, 345.

11. Borison, H.L. *et al.* (1963). Vomiting, Hypothermia and Respiratory Paralysis due to Tetrodotoxin (Puffer Fish Poison) in the Cat. *Tox. Appl. Pharmac.* **5**, 350.

12. Breemen, C. van (1969). Blockade of Membrane Calcium Fluxes by Lanthanum in Relation to Vasculature Smooth Muscle Contractility. *Arch. Int. Physiol. Biochem.* **77**, 710.

13. Weiss, G.B. (1974). Cellular Pharmacology of Lanthanum. *An. Rev. Pharmacol.* **14**, 343.

14. Schumann, H.J., Gorlitz, B.D. and Wagner, J. (1975). Influence of Papaverine, D-600, and Nifedipine on the Effects of Noradrenaline and Calcium on the Isolated Aorta and Mesenteric Artery of the Rabbit. *Naunyn-Schm. Arch. Pharmacol.* **289**, 409.

A Dual Adrenergic Compound From The Sponge
Verongia fistularis

Keith H. Hollenbeak and Francis J. Schmitz
Department of Chemistry, University of Oklahoma, Norman, Oklahoma
and
Pushkar N. Kaul and Shrinivas K. Kulkarni
University of Oklahoma Health Sciences Center, College of Pharmacy, Oklahoma City, Oklahoma

As part of our ongoing search (1,2) for drugs from the sea we have been looking for cardioactive compounds. In an earlier paper (3) we described the identification of histamine and N-methylated histamines as the inotropic agents in the extracts of several sponges, including *Verongia fistularis*, the Langendorff preparation of an isolated perfusing guinea pig heart being used to guide the isolation. In the course of that work, fractions were also checked for their effect on blood pressure in anesthetized dogs. One of the fractions from *V. fistularis* caused a moderate but transient increase in blood pressure, followed immediately by a small, short-lived decrease. This biphasic response is characteristic of that produced by epinephrine. However, the active fraction failed to show the polarographic oxidation curve (4) typical of catecholamines. Therefore, we set out to isolate and identify the agent responsible for the biphasic response and to define its pharmacologic activities as well as mechanism of action.

Isolation of the Biphasic Agent.

Specimens of *V. fistularis* were collected at Summerland Key, Florida. The crude aqueous isopropyl alcohol extracts exhibited hypotensive activity in the anesthetized dog, 1 mg/kg causing a transient 70 mm drop in blood pressure. The concentrated aqueous alcohol extract was defatted by continuous extraction with methylene chloride and then extracted with 1-butanol (Fig. 1). The butanol fraction showed a biphasic activity; 1mg/kg inducing a 105 mm increase in blood pressure. In the presence

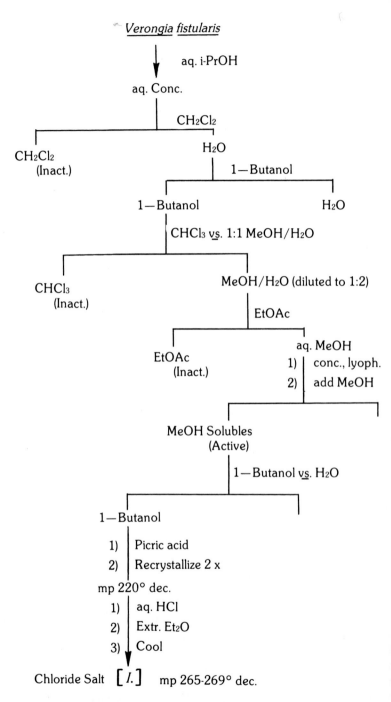

FIGURE 1. Flow chart for the isolation of *I*.

of tolazoline, a 45 mm decrease in the pressure was observed. The active fraction was dissolved in 50% aqueous methanol and the solution was washed with chloroform and ethyl acetate, consecutively. The aqueous phase was concentrated and lyophilized. The lyophilizate was triturated with methanol and the dissolved material was partitioned between 1-butanol and water. The butanol solubles exhibited the biphasic response, 100 mcg/kg causing an immediate transient 20 mm rise in blood pressure, followed by a 35 mm fall of short duration.

Final purification was effected through picrate formation and subsequent conversion to the chloride. Treatment of an aqueous solution of the active fraction with excess saturated picric acid solution yielded a precipitate which was recrystallized twice from acetone-methanol to give a pure picrate, mp 220°C dec. The homogeneity of the picrate was indicated by its nmr spectrum (acetone-d_6-DMSO-d_6). This showed singlets in a 1:1 ratio at §8.66 and §7.60 corresponding, respectively, to the two aromatic protons of picric acid and two aromatic protons in the natural product. The remaining signals occurred at §3.38 (s, 9H) and at §3.20 and 3.76 (A_2B_2 multiplet, 4H).

The picrate was cleaved by dissolving it in 1 N hydrochloric acid and extracting the solution thoroughly with ether to remove picric acid. Cooling of the aqueous solution induced crystallization of some pure chloride salt, and an additional product crystallized after the mother liquor was concentrated at reduced pressure and diluted with ethanol. The pure salt, I, mp 265-269°C dec. analyzed for $C_{11}H_{16}NOBr_2Cl$.

Identification and Synthesis of *I*.

The salt *I* was characterized as a phenol by OH absorption at 3450 cm^{-1} in the infrared spectrum and pH dependent absorptions in the ultraviolet spectrum: in acid, λ_{max} 281nm (ϵ 1000); in base, λ_{max} 305nm (ϵ 2,458). The change in the uv maxima as a function of pH is characteristic (5) of phenols, and the actual maximum in acid is the same as that reported for 4-hydroxy-3,5-dibromophenylacetic acid (6).

The phenol ring in *I* was further characterized as a symmetrically tetrasubstituted one by the nmr spectrum which showed a sharp two proton singlet at §7.64 (relative to HDO at §5.00) as the only low field absorption. That two of the ring substituents were bromine and located ortho to the hydroxyl group was indicated by the position of the uv maximum (6) and analogy with other dibromotyrosine-related sponge metabolites (7,8). Halogen substitution in the non-aromatic portion of the molecule was ruled out by the remainder of the nmr spectrum.

The structure of the aliphatic portion of *I* was ascertained from the upfield nmr signals. These consisted of an A_2B_2 pattern (9) centered at §3.26

and §3.76 ascribable to a -CH₂-CH₂- unit, and a nine-proton singlet at §3.00 attributable to the methyl groups of a trimethylalkylammonium unit. Combination of these partial structures with the phenol ring generates the structure *I* [2(3,5dibromo-4-hydroxyphenyl)-ethyltrimethylammonium chloride] for the active compound from *V. fistularis*.

Substantiating evidence for structure *I* was obtained from the mass spectrum. The base peak was observed at m/e 58 corresponding to [(CH₃)₂ N-CH₂]⁺. The highest mass peaks in the spectrum occur at m/e 276, 278, 280 (1:2:1 ratio), as expected for the styrene that would be formed from *I* by the thermal elimination of trimethylamine and hydrochloric acid.

Verification of structure *I* was sought by synthesis, especially to confirm the biosynthetically logical, but unproven, location of the bromines on the aromatic ring. A synthetic sample was also desired to verify the pharmacological activity, and thereby to exclude the possibility that the observed activity was due to a highly active, trace impurity. The synthetic route is outlined in figure 2. Dibromination of tyramine in acetic acid yielded 3,5 dibromotyramine hydrobromide, mp 265-267°C (lit. 270°C) (10). Dimethylation of this product with formic acid-formaldehyde (11) gave an N,N-dimethyl derivative which was quaternized by heating with methyl iodide in methanol containing sodium bicarbonate. Recrystallization of the resultant quaternary ammonium salt from dry methanolic hydrochloric acid solution gave a product with ir and nmr spectra identical to those of the natural product, *I*. Use of sodium carbonate in the final methylation step resulted in O- as well as N-methylation.

The quaternary salt *I* has not been reported previously, though other dibromotyrosine related metabolites have been isolated from sponges (7,8). In all but one of these, the methylene carbon corresponding to the one bearing nitrogen in *I* is part of an amide or nitrile group.

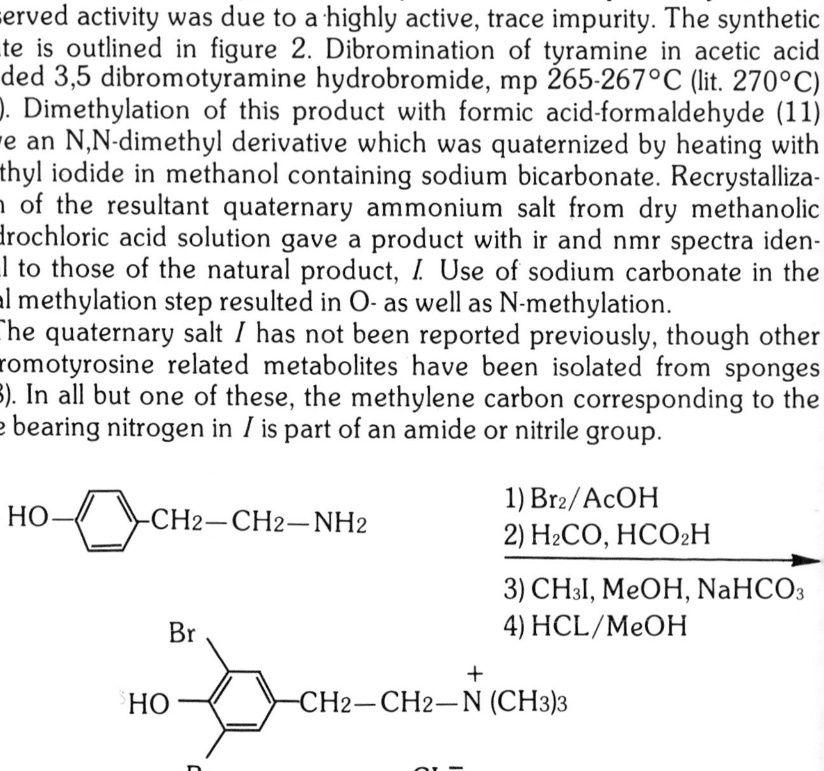

FIGURE 2. Synthesis of *I*

Pharmacology of *I*.

   Intravenous injection of 100 mcg/kg of *I* in an anesthesized dog caused a small, transient hypertensive response (20 mm, 25 sec), followed by
a similar short-lived hypotensive reaction (20 mm, 30 sec); see figure 3.
Larger doses of *I* (1 mg/kg) caused a marked and relatively sustained rise
in blood pressure (120 mm, 4.8 min), typical of that induced by 1 mcg/kg
of epinephrine. This pressor effect was blocked by an *alpha* adrenergic
antagonist, tolazoline (12 mg/kg), thus characterizing *I* as an *alpha*
adrenergic agent.
   When the pressor effect of *I* was blocked by tolazoline, a fall in blood
pressure was observed, a *beta*-adrenoreceptor mediated response. This
depressor effect was blocked by propranolol (2 mg/kg), a *beta*-adrenergic
blocker, thereby identifying a dual adrenergic effect of *I* on blood
pressure. Synthetic and natural *I* caused identical responses when ad-

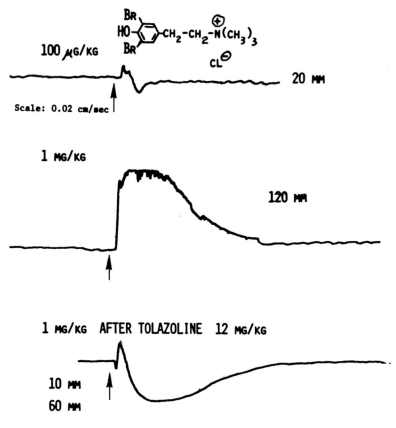

FIGURE 3. Effect of *I* on blood pressure.

ministered consecutively in identical doses to the same dog. Thus the possibility that the dual adrenergic activity might be due to a trace impurity seems ruled out.

Studies on the central nervous system showed that *I* had stimulant properties. Spontaneous motor activity in mice was increased 41% at a 1 mg/kg i.p. dose. A preliminary study on the smooth muscle preparations indicated that *I* had a non-specific spasmogenic response at 10 mcg/ml bath concentrations. Both atropine and antihistamine could partially antagonize this response. Although the mechanism of this action is difficult to explain at present, the quaternary structural features of *I* may possibly contribute to its spasmogenic activity in smooth muscles.

The salt *I* also exhibited cytotoxicity (ED$_{50}$ 20 mcg/ml) in the *in vitro* lymphocytic leukemia (P388) screen carried out by the National Cancer Institute testing laboratory (12).

Conclusion

A new beta-phenethylamine derivative *I* exhibiting dual adrenergic activity has been isolated from a marine sponge, *V. fistularis.* The overall skeleton and substitution pattern of epinephrine as well as the quaternary ammonium feature are evident in *I* if bromine is considered to be isosteric with a hydroxyl group. The compound thus appears to be a structural as well as pharmacologic hybrid of epinephrine and acetylcholine.

Acknowledgments

This work was supported by a Commerce Department NOAA Sea Grant 7-158-44067. We gratefully acknowledge grants from the Phillips Petroleum Company, Bartlesville, Oklahoma, and NSF (GP 38410) which aided in the purchase of nmr spectrometers. Some mass spectra were provided by Dr. K. Biemann's laboratory, MIT, and combustion analyses were carried out by Dr. E. Meier, Stanford University. We thank Suzanne Madden for her technical assistance in carrying out some of the pharmacologic experiments.

References

1. Schmitz, F.J. *et al.* (1977). Chemistry Related to the Search for Drugs from the Sea. In *Marine Natural Products Chemistry,* Eds. D.J. Faulkner and W. Fenical, Plenum Publishing Corp., N.Y., p. 293.

2. Kaul, P.N. *et al.* (1977). Pharmacologically Active Substances from the Sea, II: Various cardiovascular activities found in the extracts of marine organisms *Lloydia* **40**, 253.

3. Hollenbeak, K.H., Schmitz, F.J. and Kaul, P.N. (1976). Cardiotonic Agents from Marine Sponges: Isolation of histamine and N-methylated histamines. In *Proc. Food-Drugs from the Sea.* Marine Technol. Soc., Washington, D.C. p. 282.

4. We thank Dr. Leroy Blank, University of Oklahoma for performing this analysis.

5. Scott, A.I. (1964). *Interpretation of the Ultraviolet Spectra of Natural Products,* The MacMillan Co., N.Y. p. 91 ff.

6. Sharma, G.M., Vig, B. and Burkholder, P.R. (1970). Studies on Antimicrobial Substances of Sponges. IV. Structure of a bromine-containing compound from a marine sponge. *J. Org. Chem.* **35**, 2823.

7. Minale, L. *et al.* (1976). Natural Products from Porifera. In *"Progress in the Chemistry of Natural Products"* **33**, 1.

8. Minale, L. (1976). Natural Product Chemistry of the Sponge, *Pure and Applied Chemistry* **48**, 7.

9. At 100 MHz the A_2B_2 signals matched well the computed pattern for the case $J/AA' = 4$, $J/BB' = 4$, $J/AB = 1$ and $J/AB' = 2$. See K.B. Wiberg and B.J. Nist, *"The Interpretation of NMR Spectra",* W.A. Benjamin, Inc., N.Y., (1962) p. 433.

10. Zeynek, R. (1921). Preparation of Chloroand Bromotyrosine and the analogous Tyramines", *Z. Physiol Chem.* **114**, 275.

11. Moore, M.L. (1949), The Leuckart Reaction, *Org. Reactions* **5**, 301.

12. Gueran, R.I. *et al.* (1972). Protocols for Screening Chemical Agents and Natural Products Against Animal Tumors and Other Biological Systems. *Cancer Chemother. Rep.* Part 3, No. 2.

Adenosine As The Causative Asystolic Factor From A Marine Sponge

Clifford W.J. Chang*, Alfred J. Weinheimer**, James A. Matson**

*Department of Chemistry, University of West Florida, Pensacola, Florida
**Department of Medicinal Chemistry and Pharmacognosy, University of Houston, Houston, Texas

and

Pushkar N. Kaul

University of Oklahoma Health Sciences Center, College of Pharmacy, Oklahoma City, Oklahoma

The preliminary report by Zelenski *et al.* (1) concerning an asystolic (heart-blocking) factor in the extract of a sponge, *Dasychalina cyathina* has provided the foundation for this investigation. At that time the observations appeared to be unique, and in light of the dearth of reports in the chemical literature regarding sponge metabolites which possess asystolic activity, the isolation work was undertaken.

Recollection of the sponge, *D. cyathina*, was made in February 1975. The isopropanol–water (1:1, v/v) extract was lyophilyzed and tested in the isolated perfusing guinea pig heart. Contrary to the earlier observations that a 500 mcg sample of the extract had produced a transient asystole followed by a 150% increase in the inotropic response (1), an extract of the recollected sample was found relatively inactive in terms of asystolic activity. Up to a 5-mg dose, the extract failed to produce reversible cessation of the heart beat. With a dose of 5 mg, the heart failed. However, the cardioactive component was detected after fractionation of the crude extract. Figures 1 and 2 illustrate the modified procedure of the previously reported scheme (1).

Isolation

In the modified procedure designed to eliminate the problems of emulsion, the concentrated extract was further lyophilyzed. The resultant solid,

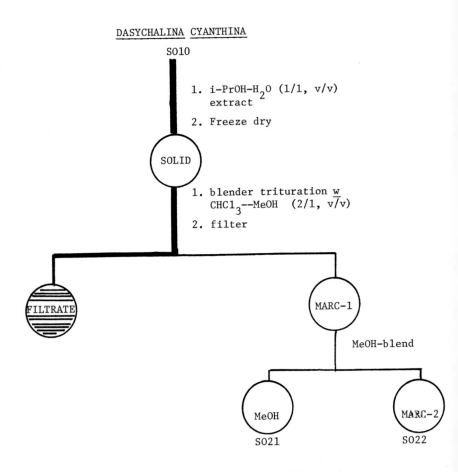

FIGURE 1. Preliminary fractionation of *D. cyanthina.*

treated with a 2:1 mixture of chloroform-methanol, provided an active filtrate and an inactive marc (Fig. 1) when tested on the isolated perfusing heart preparation. Fractionation of the filtrate (Fig. 2) by partitioning with water reoriented the cardioactive compound into the aqueous methanol layer (S020). Finally, continued partitioning of this fraction with *n*-butanol concentrated the activity into the *n*-butanol layer (S023). In the fractionation scheme, the presence of some sixteen amino acids was confirmed in the methanol blend (S021) of the original marc, the remaining marc (S022), the methanol-water extract (S020), the aqueous layer (S024) of the *n*-butanol partition, and the *n*-butanol layer (S023) itself (2).

Chromatography of the methanol triturate of the *n*-butanol fraction (S023), using a column of Sephadex LH-20 and methanol as the eluent, provided a convenient separation of most of the inactive organic

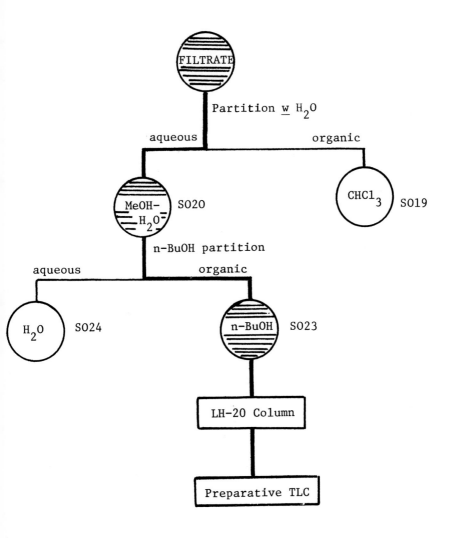

FIGURE 2. Further fractionation of *D. cyanthina.*

biopolymers and amino acids from the cardioactive fractions. Guided by bioassay, the active fractions were found to consist chiefly of salts and the amino acids were present as inactive contaminants. The preparative thick-layer chromatograms (TLC) of the acetone-triturate from the active LH-20 column fractions were again monitored by bioassay. Silica gel $P_{254-366}$ was the adsorbent and 10% methanol in acetone constituted the solvent system. After development, the major fluorescent band with R_f 0.31–0.11 was separated and worked up to give a ninhydrin-inactive fraction.

Structure Elucidation

Coupled with the information gained from the elution characteristics of the LH-20 column and from the TLC conditions, a polar compound of small molecular weight could be predicted. Supportive evidence was deduced from the broad infrared bands at *ca.* 3320–2400 and 1700 cm^{-1} and single-proton resonances at §8.60 and 8.40.

When other TLC solvent systems were examined, however, to ascertain the homogeneity of the sample, it was found that a mixture of 2-propanol–ammonia–water (9:0.5:0.5, v/v) had resolved the "active band" into two components. These were subsequently identified as 2′-deoxyadenosine *I* and adenosine *II* on the basis of their optical rotations and spectroscopic evidence (3). A higher ultraviolet-sensitive TLC band yielded thymidine which was inactive in the heart bioassay. The one-proton quartet at §7.65 and a three-proton doublet at §1.91 clearly demonstrated the presence of the thymine nucleus. Together with the one-proton triplet at §6.28 (J = 8 Hz) of the ribose residue, the structure *III* was assigned and confirmed later by its optical rotation and melting point.

I   *II*   *III*

It now became clear that the ninhydrin-inactive compounds were nucleosides in small concentrations. Furthermore, the asystolic factor may be attributed to either adenosine or 2′-deoxyadenosine, or to both compounds. Table I includes data on the asystolic responses of various nucleosides. Screening of the common nucleosides available to us indicated that adenosine was indeed the prime causative asystolic factor in the extract of *D. cyathina*, since adenosine at a dose of 100 mcg caused the cessation of heart beat, while both 2′-deoxyadenosine and 2′-deoxyguanosine were inactive at the same dose level. The latter two compounds, however, were active at a dose level of 1 mg (Table 1, Fig. 3).

Table I
Dose Response of Some Common
Nucleosides Causing Asystole

COMPOUND	DOSE	RESPONSES
adenosine	100 mcg	active
	1 mg	active
2′-deoxyadenosine	100 mcg	inactive
	1 mg	active
guanosine	1 mg	inactive
2′-deoxyguanosine	100 mcg	inactive
	1 mg	active
cytidine	1 mg	inactive
thymidine	1 mg	inactive
uridine	1 mg	inactive

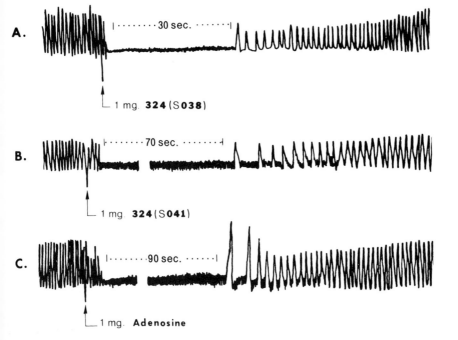

FIGURE 3. Cardiac asystolic activity of the fractions from the marine sponge *D. cyathina* and authentic sample of adenosine. A, an earlier fraction; B, the fraction from which adenosine was isolated; C, authentic adenosine.

Discussion

The presence of nucleosides in a sponge was demonstrated by Bergman some twenty-five years ago (4). Of some sixteen different species examined, only *Cryptothia crypta* elaborated the free but uncommon nucleosides, spongothymidine *IV* (5) spongouridine *V* (5) and spongosine *VI* (6). The isolation of the common ribonucleosides and deoxyribonucleosides were obtained only after degradation of the ribonucleic acids and deoxyribonucleic acids (4).

It is interesting that early research on natural products of sponges, specifically the nucleosides, had catalyzed the synthesis and pharmacological evaluation of adenine arabinoside *VII*. This compound has

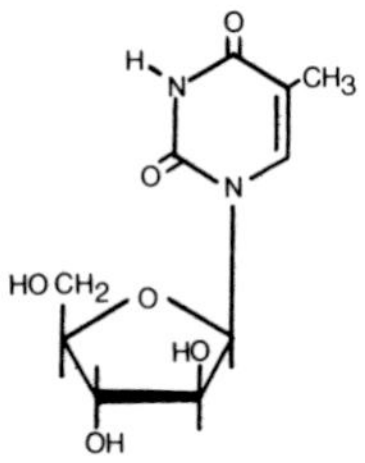

IV

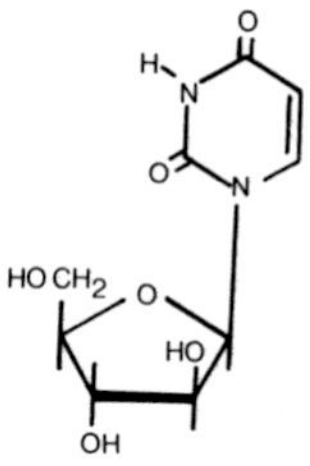

V

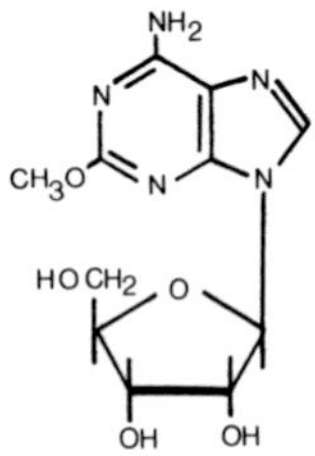

VI

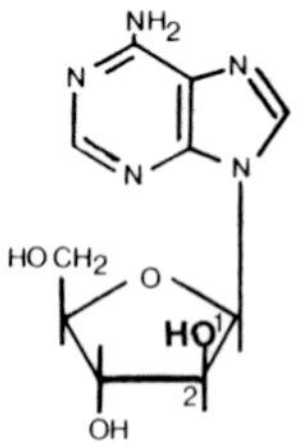

VII

been used successfully in therapy of cancer patients and more recently in patients suffering from *Herpes encephalitis*. The present finding further adds to the evidence that marine organisms contain biologically active substances which may be useful as drugs either as such or after their chemical modifications.

Acknowledgments

C.W.J.C. acknowledges the University of West Florida for a Faculty Service and Development Award. The authors also appreciate the technical assistance of Ms. Suzanne Madden and Mr. Ward Kirlin. This work was supported in part by the National Institute of General Medical Sciences grant GM20250 and the U.S. Commerce Department (NOAA) Sea Grant No. 7-158-44067.

References

1. Zelenski, S.G., Weinheimer, A.J. and Kaul, P.N.(1976). A Cardioactive Compound Isolated from the Sponge, *Dasychalina cyathina*. In *Proc. Food-Drugs from the Sea*. Marine Technol. Soc., Washington, D.C., p. 288.
2. Chang, C.W.J. and Weinheimer, A.J. Unpublished data.
3. Weinheimer, A.J., *et al.* (in press) Lloydia.
4. Bergman, W., Watkins, J.C. and Stempien, M.F. Jr. (1957). Contributions to Study of Marine Products. XLV. Sponge nucleic acids. *J. Organic Chem.* **22**, 1308.
5. Bergman, W. and Burke, D.C. (1955). Contributions to the Study of Marine Products. XXXIX. The nucleosides of sponges. III. Spongothymidine and Spongouridine. *J. Organic Chem.* **20**, 1501.
6. Bergman, W. and Burke, D.C. (1956). Contributions to the Study of Marine Products. XL. The nucleosides of sponges. IV. Spongosine. *J. Org. Chem.* **21**, 226.

SECTION III

Other Pharmacologic Substances
from the Sea

Pharmacologically Active Substances From The Sea, III:A Marine Derived Inhibitor Of Drug Metabolism

Pushkar N. Kaul and Shrinivas K. Kulkarni,
University of Oklahoma, Health Sciences Center
College of Pharmacy, Oklahoma City, Oklahoma
and
Francis J. Schmitz and Keith H. Hollenbeak
Department of Chemistry, University of Oklahoma
Norman, Oklahoma

Most drugs useful to man have had their origin in nature. Despite the extensive synthetic and engineering abilities of medicinal chemists, it has not been possible to surpass the quality and intensity of pharmacologic activity of many naturally occurring drugs, e.g., digitalis glycosides, morphine, atropine, reserpine etc. Until recently, the primary source of these potent drugs has been terrestrial plants. Although nearly 70 percent of the earth is covered with water, the marine life forms remain largely unexplored as a source of useful pharmacologic agents. However, interest in exploring the oceans for new drugs has been increasing. Recently, a few reviews and compendia have summarized the scanty and scattered research activities of the last two decades relative to marine natural products (1-8).

Our program on drugs from the sea has directed efforts toward detecting various pharmacological activities in the extracts of marine invertebrates, and toward isolating and characterizing those active substances which show promise as potential therapeutic agents. Primary attention has been focussed on the cardiovascular, anticancer and central nervous system (CNS) active substances (9-16).

This paper concerns itself primarily with the extracts of marine animals exhibiting pharmacologic activity on the CNS of mammalian species. The fractionation of the extracts of one of these marine animals, *Aplysia dactylomela* (sea hare), has led to the isolation of a novel dibromochloro acetylenic cyclic ether, dactylyne, which turned out to be a potent inhibitor of drug metabolizing enzyme systems.

Methods

Marine animal collection and extraction—The animals, collected from various sites (15), were cut in small pieces and freshly immersed in 95 percent isopropyl alcohol or methanol in sealed containers in which they were transported to our laboratories. After variable maceration time periods at room temperature, the solvent was filtered to obtain an aqueous alcoholic extract. The extract was evaporated under reduced pressure below 40°C and finally freeze dried to provide the crude extract for pharmacologic studies.

Isolation of dactylyne—Although dactylyne had been isolated and structurally characterized earlier (17), its potential as a pharmacologic agent was discovered in the course of following a bioassay-guided fractionation of the aqueous alcoholic extracts of the bodies of sea hares (*A. dactylomela*) from which the digestive glands had been excised at the time of collection (May, 1975, Bimini, Bahamas). The alcohol (2-propanol) was separated from the preserved animals and concentrated under reduced pressure at less than 40°C and the residue was freeze-dried to yield fraction A. This fraction was diluted with distilled water and the mixture was continuously extracted with methylene chloride to yield fraction B. Partition of B, according to the procedure of Kupchan (18), afforded a hexane soluble fraction (Fraction C) and a carbon tetrachloride extract (Fraction D). Both these fractions exhibited a significant potentiation of pentobarbital hypnosis.

Subsequent chromatography of fraction D over Sephadex LH-20 with chloroform–methanol (1:1) as solvent yielded a fraction (E) which prolonged the pentobarbital sleep time in mice by more than 300 percent. This fraction was recognized by its nmr spectrum to consist primarily of dactylyne (17).

Dactylyne

Quantities of pure, crystalline dactylyne for pharmacologic testing were isolated from extracts of the digestive glands of *A. dactylomela* using the procedure outlined earlier (17), but with the following modifications. Sephadex LH-20 gel filtration using chloroform-methanol (1:1) was employed for the initial chromatographic step, instead of Florisil chromatography. The second improvement in the isolation process was the use of high pressure liquid chromatography with microparticle silica gel and hexane–tetrahydrofuran (4:1) for the final purification. Pure dactylyne at a dose level of 5 mg/kg increased the sleep time by more than 600 percent.

Pharmacologic studies—Sprague-Dawley rats (150-200 g) and Swiss-Webster mice (25-30 g) were used for pharmacologic studies. All extracts were administered intraperitoneally (i.p.) at various dose levels. A 50 mg/kg dose, selected on the basis of preliminary dose-response studies, was used to generate pharmacologic data presented in these studies. Chlorpromazine hydrochloride (3 mg/kg, i.p.) was used as a reference drug. In all experiments, 3-10 animals were used per treatment group. Positive activity was confirmed by repeat experiments.

Experiments relative to effects on the CNS included determination of pentobarbital hypnosis, spontaneous and locomotor activities, and gross behavior, all carried out in mice by the methodology described earlier (19).

Dactylyne, besides being subjected to the CNS tests, was also tested for its cardiovascular effects by the method described elsewhere (20). Acute toxicity was studied in mice to obtain data relative to its LD_{50}. Subacute toxicity was studied in mice given daily intraperitoneal doses of 120 mg/kg for 15 days, following which the animals were sacrificed to remove various vital organs for gross morphological and histological examinations.

In experiments relative to pharmacokinetic studies on pentobarbital in the control and dactylyne pretreated mice, the blood levels of the barbiturate were determined by using the fluorometric method of Hollister *et al.* (20). The blood samples were collected by sacrificing mice at various time intervals.

Results and Discussion

The pharmacological profiles of the extracts of marine organisms which exhibited the CNS activity are shown in table I. A majority of these extracts had either zero or insignificant effect on the cardiovascular system. Those of *A. dactylomela* and *Spheciospongia vesparia* showed potent CNS depressant activity, as evidenced by the potentiation of pentobarbital hypnosis and decrease in both spontaneous and locomotor activities of mice (Table I). Also, unlike other extracts tested, these two extracts had a consistent effect on all of the parameters investigated and the activity was comparable to that of chlorpromazine (3 mg/kg, i.p.).

The extract of *A. dactylomela* when fractionated as described yielded crystalline dactylyne. Although dactylyne was isolated in this laboratory previously (17) by chromatography of hexane extract over Florisil and then silicic acid, gel filtration using Sephadex LH-20 in chloroform-methanol (1:1) has proven superior to Florisil for the preliminary fractionation. This procedure minimizes the loss or alteration of labile, halogenated compounds.

Table I

Pharmacological Activity of Extracts of Various Marine Animals on the Central Nervous System (CNS)[1]

ORGANISM	PHYLUM	PB[2] HYPNOSIS IN MICE	SMA[2] IN MICE	LA[2] IN MICE	RECTAL TEMP IN RATS
Actinopyga agassizi	Echinodermata	Increased[3]	Increased	Decreased[3]	Decreased
Aplysia dactylomela	Mollusca	Increased	Decreased	Decreased	Decreased
Briareum abestinum	Coelenterata	Decreased	Inactive	Increased	Inactive
Caranz ruber	Chordata	Increased	Inactive	Inactive	Inactive
Chaetodon striatus	Chordata	Increased	Decreased	Decreased	Inactive
Chrondrosia collectrix	Porifera	Inactive	Inactive	Decreased	Inactive
Culcita novae guinae	Echinodermata	Decreased	Increased	Decreased	Increased
Donax denticulatus	Mollusca	Increased	Decreased	Decreased	Inactive
Morula granulata	Mollusca	Increased	Decreased	Inactive	Inactive
Spheciospongia vesparia	Porifera	Increased	Decreased	Decreased	Inactive
Stypodium zonale	Phaeophyta	Increased	Decreased	Decreased	Decreased

[1] A dose of 50 mg/kg of the extracts dissolved in saline was used in groups of 3-10 animals per treatment.

[2] PB, pentobarbital; SMA, spontaneous motor activity; LA, Locomotor activity.

[3] Increase (20-60%) and decrease (20-80%) refer to values with respect to saline treated control animals. A CNS depressant of major tranquilizer type increases PB hypnosis and decreases other three activities listed.

Table II

Pharmacological Profile of Dactylyne

TREATMENT[1]	PB[2] HYPNOSIS hr. ± S.D.	SMA[2]	LA[2] Scores ± S.D.	RECTAL TEMP. °C	TOXICITY
Saline	1.0 ± 0.16	82 ± 22	303 ± 45	36 ± 0.2	—
Dactylyne (25 mg/kg)	>10	88 ± 22	274 ± 18 P > 0.05	36 ± 0.2	non-lethal up to 200 mg/kg i.v.
Chlorpromazine (3 mg/kg)	4 ± 0.82	40 ± 5	141 ± 38 P < 0.01	33 ± 0.4	—

[1] Each treatment group consisted of 6-8 animals.
[2] PB, pentobarbital (60 mg/kg i.p.); SMA, spontaneous motor activity as movements per hour per group of 3 mice; LA, locomotor activity as mean scores/mouse/10 min.

Dactylyne, stable on long storage only when crystalline, cannot be induced to crystallize unless it is quite pure. In order to effect final purification efficiently, high pressure liquid chromatography using microparticle silica gel and hexane–tetrahydrofuran (4:1) was employed.

Dactylyne exhibited no effect on cardiovascular, respiratory and central nervous systems. However, at 25 mg/kg dose, it significantly potentiated the pentobarbital induced hypnosis in mice (Table II). That the earlier fractions from the extract of *A. dactylomela* had exhibited CNS depressant activity, e.g., decrease in motor activity and body temperature, which was found absent in dactylyne poses a paradox. It is conceivable that those fractions may have contained other component(s) possessing the CNS activity.

Dactylyne had no effect on the CNS responses elicited by stimulants such as amphetamine, quipazine, and apomorphine. Nor did it protect animals against pentylenetetrazol-induced convulsions, as is done by barbiturates. However, as low as 1 mg/kg of dactylyne significantly ($P<.001$) potentiated the pentobarbital hypnosis in mice. This potentiation was subsequently found to be due to an inhibiton by dactylyne of the enzyme system(s) involved in metabolizing pentobarbital. The blood level and pharmacokinetic studies confirmed this. Thus, the elimination half-life of pentobarbital was increased from 0.66 hour in control (saline treated mice) to over 9 hours in the dactylyne (10 mg/kg) pretreated mice (Table III). This type of effect is well known with another inhibitor, SKF-525A of a totally different chemical structure. As has been observed with this inhibitor (21), dactylyne does not alter the blood levels of pentobarbital at the time of sleep onset or at the time of awakening (Table III).

Table III

The Blood Levels, Sleep-time and Half-life of 60 mg/kg Pentobarbital (PB) in 10 mg/kg Dactylyne Pretreated Mice

TREATMENT —	PB (mcg/ml)		SLEEP TIME (hr)	PB $t\frac{1}{2}$ (hr)
	at onset	on awakening		
Control $n = 8$	41. $\pm$ 1 7.43	15.9 $\pm$ 3.37	1.1 $\pm$ 0.16	0.66
Dactylyne $n = 8$	48.1 $\pm$ 3.47	16.8 $\pm$ 3.99	7.8 $\pm$ 0.53	9.25

An interesting observation is that dactylyne, though in activity similar to SKF-525A, appeared to be relatively less toxic and somewhat more potent. For example, the prolongation of pentobarbital hypnosis was far greater with dactylyne on a mg/kg dose basis. Also, the intravenous LD_{50} of SKF-525A is 60 mg/kg (22), whereas doses of up to 200 mg/kg of dactylyne by the same route were nonlethal. Furthermore, preliminary subacute organ toxicity studies on dactylyne in mice revealed no apparent gross morphological or histological lesions.

Conclusion

These and our previously reported studies relative to marine derived biologically active substances further substantiate our belief that the sea offers a great resource for potential drugs. If dactylyne survives further preclinical chronic toxicity tests, we may have perhaps the first clinically useful drug metabolism inhibitor at hand.

Acknowledgments

The authors appreciate the technical assistance of Ms. Charlene Burns and pilot histopathological observations of Dr. S.D. Kosanke.

These studies were supported by Office of Sea Grant, NOAA, Grant 04-158-44062 and by N.I.H. Grant QM 20250.

References

1. Baslow, M.H. (1969). Marine Pharmacology. The Williams and Wilkins Co. Baltimore.
2. Marderosian, A.D. (1969). Marine Pharmaceuticals. *J. Pharm. Sci.* **58**, 1.
3. Baslow, M.H. (1971). Marine Toxins. *An. Rev. Pharmacol.* **11**, 447.
4. Ruggieri, G.D. (1976). Drugs from the Sea. *Science* **194**, 491.
5. Worthen, L.R., Ed. (1973). Proc. Food-Drugs from the Sea, Marine Technol. Soc., Washington, D.C.
6. Webber, H.H. and Ruggieri, G.D., Ed. (1976). Proc. Food-Drugs from the Sea. Marine Technol. Soc., Washington D.C.
7. Faulkner, D.J. and Fenical, W.H. (1977). Marine Natural Products Chemistry. Plenum Press, New York.
8. Baker, J.T. and Murphy, V. (1976). *Handbook of Marine Science*, Vol. 2, CRC Press, Cleveland.
9. Kaul, P.N. (1973). Pharmacologically Active Substances of Marine

Origin. In *Proc. Food-Drugs from the Sea*, Marine Technol. Soc. Washington, D.C. p. 200.

10. Kaul, P.N., Farmer, M.R. and Ciereszko, L.S. (1974). Pharmacology of Palytoxin: The most potent marine toxin known. *Proc. West. Pharmacol. Soc.* **17**, 294.

11. Weinheimer, A.J. and Karns, T.K.B. (1976). A Search for Anticancer and Cardiovascular Agents in Marine Organisms. In *Proc. Food-Drugs from the Sea* Marine Technol. Soc. Washington, D.C. p. 491.

12. Hollenbeak, K.H., Schmitz, F.J. and Kaul, P.N. (1976). Cardiotonic Agents from Marine Sponges: Isolation of histamine and n-methylated histamines. In *Proc. Food-Drugs from the Sea*, Marine Technol. Soc., Washington, D.C. p. 282.

13. Zelenski, S.G., Weinheimer, A.J. and Kaul, P.N. (1976). A Cardioactive Compound Isolated from the Sponge, *Dasychalina cyathina*. In *Proc. Food-Drugs from the Sea*, Marine Technol. Soc., Washington, D.C. p. 288.

14. Kaul, P.N. (1976). Palytoxin, A New Physiological Tool. In *Proc. Food-Drugs from the Sea* ., Marine Technol. Soc., Washington, D.C. p. 311.

15. Kaul, P.N. *et al.* (1977). Pharmacologically Active Substances from the Sea II. *Lloydia* **40**, 253.

16. Schmitz, F.J. *et al.* (1977). Chemistry Related to the Search for Drugs from the Sea. In *Marine Natural Products Chemistry*, Eds. Faulkner, D.J. and Fenical, W.H., Plenum Press, N.Y., p. 293.

17. McDonald, F.J. *et al.* (1975). Marine Natural Products. Dactylyne, an acetylenic dibromochloro–ether from the sea hare *Aplysia dactylomela*. *J. Org. Chem.* **40**, 665.

18. Kupchan, S.M. *et al.* (1973). Bruceantin, a new antileukemic Simaroubolide from *brucea antidysenterica*. *J. Org. Chem.* **38**, 178.

19. Kulkarni, S.K., Magarian, R.A. and Kaul, P.N. (1977). Pharmacological Activity of Some 1-Adamantanamine Derivatives. *Ind. J. Pharmac.*, **9**, 129.

20. Hollister, L.E., Kanter, S.L. and Clyde, D.J. (1963). Studies of Prolonged Action Medication III. Pentobarbital sodium in prolonged-action form compared with conventional capsules: Serum levels of drug and clinical effects following acute doses. *Clin. Pharmacol. Therap.* **4**, 612.

21. Axelrod, J., Reichenthal, J. and Brodie, B.B. (1954). Mechanism of the Potentiating Action of beta-diethylaminoethyl Diphenyl-propylacetate. *J. Pharm. Exp. Therap.* **112**, 49.

22. Usdin, E. and Amasi, R.L.S. (1963). Psychotropic and Related Compounds. *Psychopharm. Service Center Bull.* **2**, 17.

Structure And Bioactivities Of
Verongia aurea Components

Yang M. Goo and Kenneth L. Rinehart, Jr.
Department of Chemistry
University of Illinois
Urbana, Illinois

Following our initial reports on the identification of 3,5-dibromohomogentisamide *I* from *Verongia aurea* (1,2), we have continued our studies of the compounds responsible for the antimicrobial activities of this interesting sponge employing two quite different approaches.

The most extensive procedure employs the classical methodology of column chromatography with examination of individual chromatographic fractions for inhibition of gram-positive or gram-negative bacteria, fungi or yeasts. The primary guide to correlation of bioactivity with structure in these chromatographic studies, which will be described elsewhere, has been field desorption mass spectrometry, a technique noted in an earlier report (3).

In the present report we wish to describe a simpler approach, which involves detailed examination of crude bioactive extracts by gas chromatography-mass spectrometry (GC-MS), followed by synthesis of compounds, whose structures have been assigned, in order to test their bioactivities. Obviously, this approach is limited to relatively simple compounds sufficiently volatile for gas chromatography.

Antimicrobial activity of *V. aurea* is largely centered in the hexane-insoluble portion of the ether extract (Fig. 1) of *V. aurea* sample #852 (AHBE 16-III-74-1-6). The gas chromatographic trace of this extract, shown in figure 2, is quite different from the gas chromatogram of the cor-

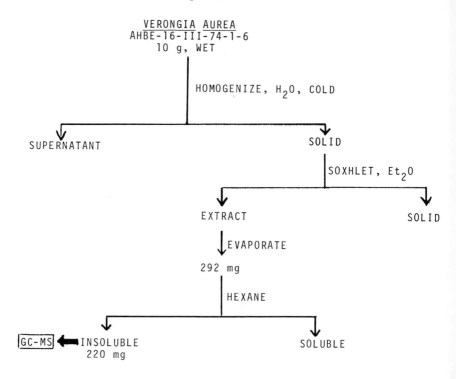

FIGURE 1. Extraction and fractionation of *Verongia aurea* #852 (AHBE-16-III-74-1-6).

responding extract of another sample of *V. aurea* (#947, AHBE 19-III-74-1-1) (3). The GC trace of #947 is dominated by the peak due to 3,5-dibromohomogentisic acid lactone *II*, a compound arising on the GC column by loss of ammonia from *I*, but the peak due to *II* in figure 2 is the very small Peak H.

The GC peaks in figure 2 were examined by field ionization mass spectrometry (GC-FIMS, e.g., Fig. 3, top) to confirm molecular ions as well as by electron impact mass spectrometry (GC-EIMS, e.g., Fig. 3, bottom) to assign structures from fragmentation patterns, and these were supplemented by high resolution data (GC-HREIMS). Peaks A, E and D are closely related by their fragmentation patterns (Fig. 4) and are assigned as 2,6-dibromobenzoquinone, the corresponding hydroquinone, and a mono-O-methyl ether of the hydroquinone, respectively. Synthesis of these compounds by known (4,5) procedures (Fig. 5) and coinjection with *V. aurea* extract #852 confirmed their identities and served to locate the O-methyl group on the phenolic hydroxyl *meta* to the bromine atoms (4-O-methyl).

The mass spectra of peaks B, C, F and G indicate a close relationship of these compounds (Fig. 6), whose structures were assigned as mono-

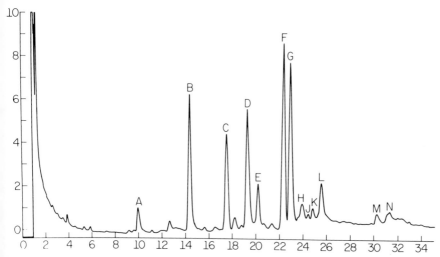

FIGURE 2. Gas chromatographic trace of hexane-insoluble portion of the ether extract of *V. aurea* # 852. Conditions: 12' x 1/8" glass column packed with 3% OV-17 on GC-Q; programming from 160°C to 270°C at 4°C per min; helium flow rate 17.1 ml per min; attenuation 1×10^{-10} amps per mv.

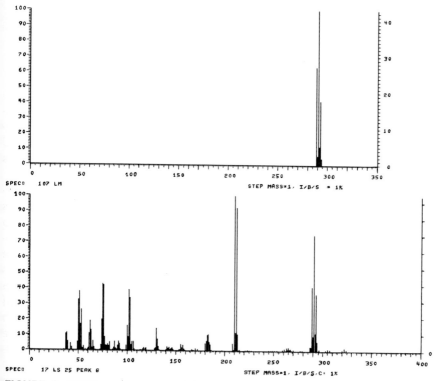

FIGURE 3. GC-FI mass spectrum (above) and corresponding GC-EI mass spectrum (below) of peak G from gas chromatogram in figure 2.

109

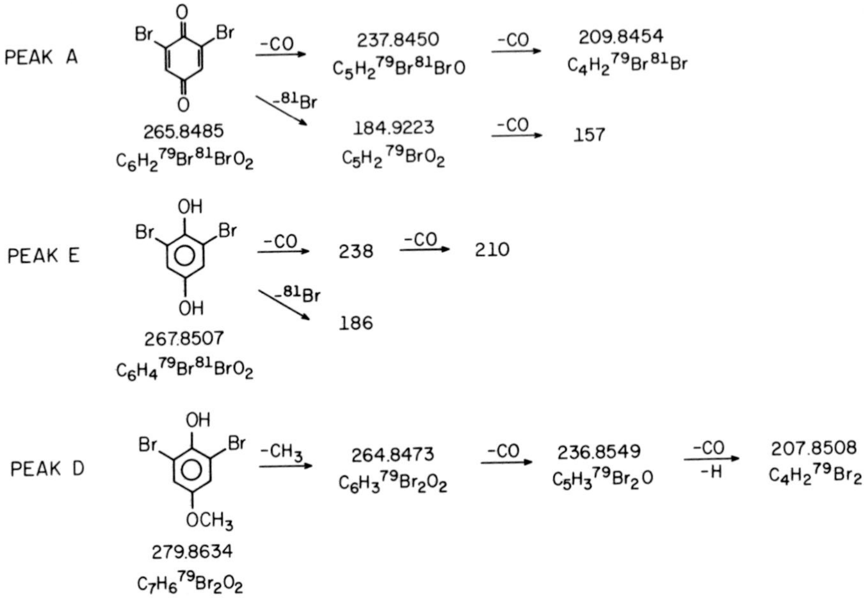

FIGURE 4. Mass spectral fragmentation pattern of compounds in peaks A, E and D of gas chromatogram in figure 2.

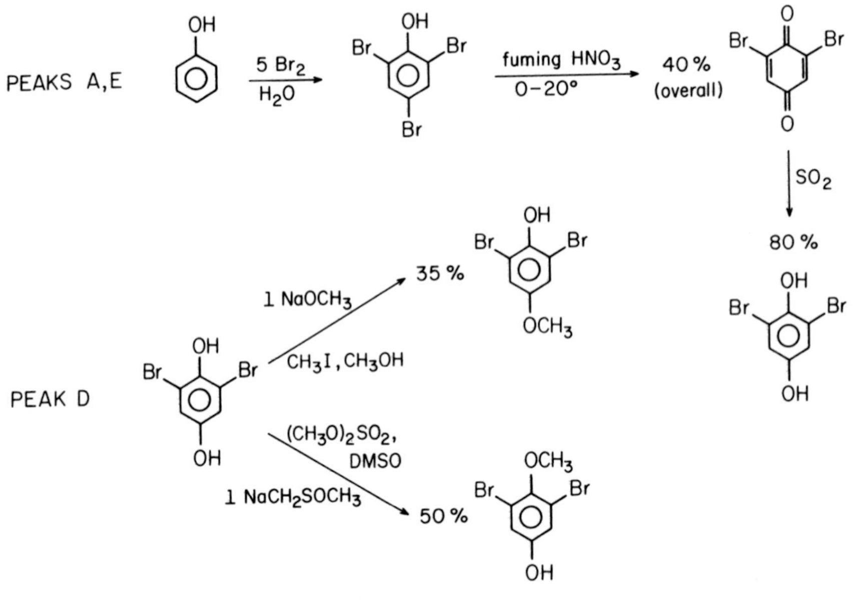

FIGURE 5. Synthesis of compounds giving peaks A, E and D (2, 6-dibromo-4-methoxyphenol) in gas chromatogram of figure 2.

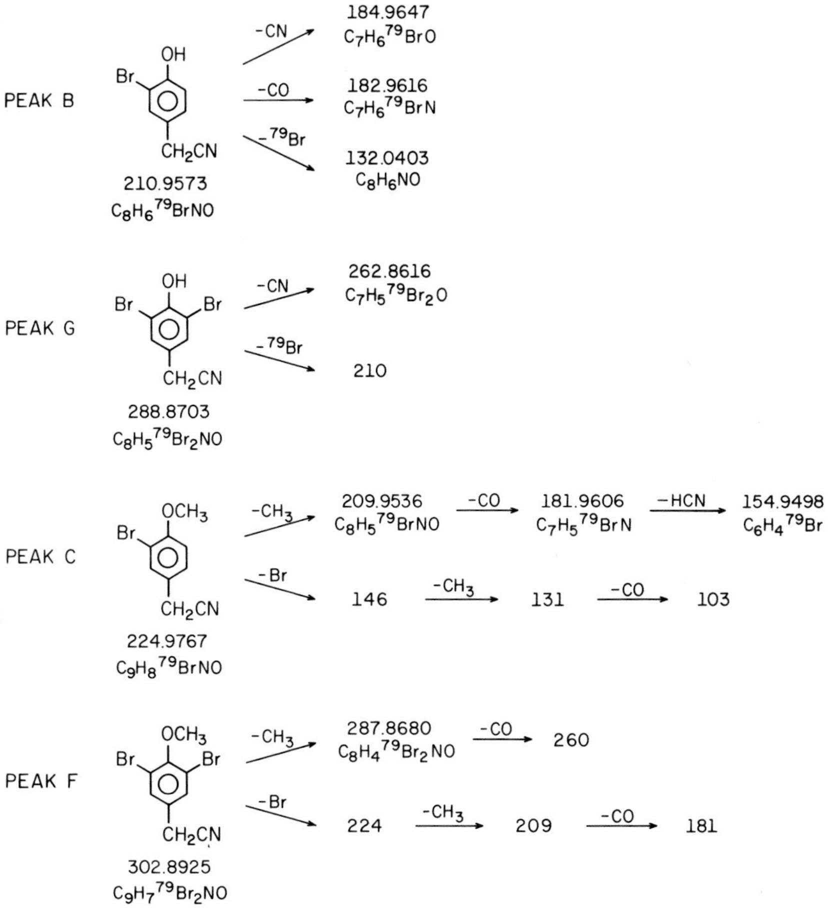

PEAK B

$C_8H_6{}^{79}BrNO$
210.9573

$\xrightarrow{-CN}$ 184.9647 $C_7H_6{}^{79}BrO$

$\xrightarrow{-CO}$ 182.9616 $C_7H_6{}^{79}BrN$

$\xrightarrow{-{}^{79}Br}$ 132.0403 C_8H_6NO

(structure: OH, Br, CH_2CN)

PEAK G

$C_8H_5{}^{79}Br_2NO$
288.8703

$\xrightarrow{-CN}$ 262.8616 $C_7H_5{}^{79}Br_2O$

$\xrightarrow{-{}^{79}Br}$ 210

(structure: OH, Br, Br, CH_2CN)

PEAK C

$C_9H_8{}^{79}BrNO$
224.9767

$\xrightarrow{-CH_3}$ 209.9536 $C_8H_5{}^{79}BrNO$ $\xrightarrow{-CO}$ 181.9606 $C_7H_5{}^{79}BrN$ $\xrightarrow{-HCN}$ 154.9498 $C_6H_4{}^{79}Br$

$\xrightarrow{-Br}$ 146 $\xrightarrow{-CH_3}$ 131 $\xrightarrow{-CO}$ 103

(structure: OCH_3, Br, CH_2CN)

PEAK F

$C_9H_7{}^{79}Br_2NO$
302.8925

$\xrightarrow{-CH_3}$ 287.8680 $C_8H_4{}^{79}Br_2NO$ $\xrightarrow{-CO}$ 260

$\xrightarrow{-Br}$ 224 $\xrightarrow{-CH_3}$ 209 $\xrightarrow{-CO}$ 181

(structure: OCH_3, Br, Br, CH_2CN)

FIGURE 6. Mass spectral fragmentation pattern of compounds in peaks B, G, C and F of gas chromatogram in figure 2.

and dibromo-*p*-hydroxyphenylacetonitriles and their corresponding methyl ethers. Of these four compounds, 3-bromo-4-methoxyphenyl-acetonitrile has been previously described (6) and the other three were prepared by standard procedures (Fig. 7). Again, the synthetic compounds co-chromatographed with the appropriate peaks in the extract.

Two additional peaks in the chromatogram, M and N, were assigned, from their fragmentation patterns shown in figure 8, as 3,5-dibromo-4-hydroxyphenylacetamide (7) and its methyl ether. Synthesis of these compounds by the procedure of Yamada *et al.* (8) from *p*-hydroxyphenylacetic acid (Fig. 9), and coinjection with the extract con-

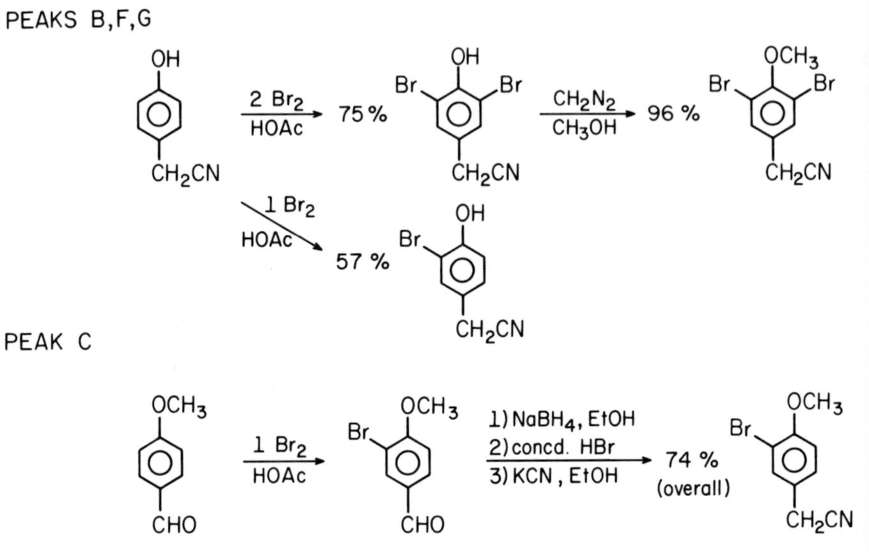

PEAKS B,F,G

PEAK C

FIGURE 7. Synthesis of compounds giving peaks B, F, G and C in gas chromatogram of figure 2.

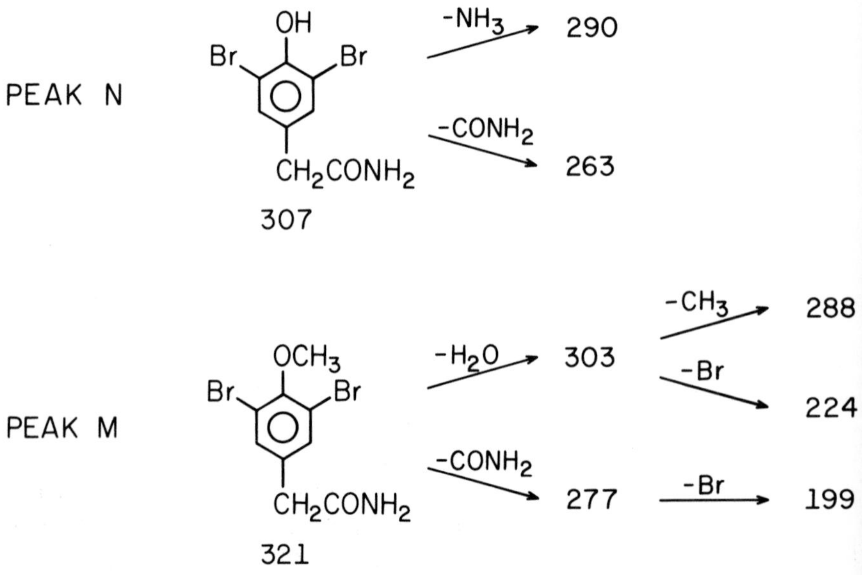

PEAK N

PEAK M

FIGURE 8. Mass spectral fragmentation pattern of compounds in peaks N and M of gas chromatogram in figure 2.

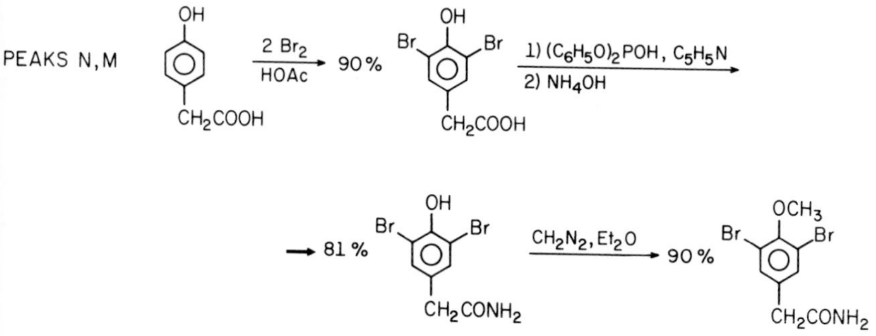

FIGURE 9. Synthesis of compounds giving peaks N and M in gas chromatogram of figure 2.

Table I

Antimicrobial Activities of 2,6-Dibromoquinone (1), 2,6-Dibromohydroquinone (2), 2,6-Dibromo-4-methoxyphenol (3), 3,5-Dibromo-4-methoxyphenol (4), 3,5-Dibromo-4-hydroxyphenylacetonitrile (5), 3,5-Dibromo-4-methoxyphenylacetonitrile (6) and 3-Bromo-4-hydroxyphenylacetonitrile (7).

Bacteria		1	2	3	4	5	6	7
		MIC/µg/ml[a,b]						
Staphylococcus aureus	UC 76	250	62.5	125	125	>1000	>1000	>1000
	UC 570	N.T.	125	N.T.	N.T.	>1000	N.T.	>1000
	UC 746	N.T.	125	N.T.	N.T.	>1000	N.T.	>1000
Streptococcus pyogenes	UC 152	500	62.5	125	125	1000	>1000	500
Streptococcus faecalis	UC 694	1000	500	250	250	>1000	>1000	>1000
Escherichia coli	UC 45	1000	500	N.T.	N.T.	1000	>1000	>1000
Escherichia coli	UC 311	N.T.	N.T.	250	250	N.T.	N.T.	N.T.
Klebsiella pneumoniae	UC 58	1000	250	125	125	500	>1000	1000
Salmonella schottmuelleri	UC 126	1000	500	250	250	1000	>1000	>1000
Pseudomonas aeruginosa	UC 95	500	250	N.T.	N.T.	>1000	>1000	>1000
Pseudomonas aeruginosa	UC 231	N.T.	N.T.	>500	>500	N.T.	N.T.	N.T.
Diplococcus pneumoniae	UC 41	500	62.5	125	125	500	>1000	1000
Proteus vulgaris	UC 232	N.T.	N.T.	250	250	N.T.	N.T.	N.T.
Fungi		Zone of inhibition, mm[c]						
Saccharomyces pastorianus	UC 1342	N.T.	0	N.T.	N.T.	0	N.T.	0
Candida albicans	UC 1392	trace	~15	N.T.	N.T.	0	~25	~14
Graphium fructicolum	UC	N.T.	trace	N.T.	N.T.	~23	N.T.	~18
Penicillium oxalicum	UC 1268	trace	0	N.T.	N.T.	18	~25	~18

[a]Agar dilution assay; [b]N.T. = not tested; [c]Dip-disk assay.

113

firmed the identity of peaks M and N. Field desorption spectra of the crude extract confirmed that the compounds giving rise to the peaks above were, in fact, present in the extract, except for *II* which arises from *I.*

The ether extract of *V. aurea* (AHBE 16-III-74-1-6) inhibited gram-positive and gram-negative bacteria as well as fungi and yeasts. As table I shows, the principal source of antibacterial activity lies with the hydroquinone-related compounds (2 and 3 in Table I), while the nitriles (5, 6, and 7 in Table I) are the main antifungal compounds.

Acknowledgments

This study was supported in part by grant AI 04769 from the National Institute of Allergy and Infectious Diseases. High resolution mass spectra were obtained on a mass spectrometer provided by grants from the National Cancer Institute (CA 11388) and the National Institute of General Medical Sciences (GM 16864). We thank Messrs. G. E. Zurenko and C. Lewis, The Upjohn Company, for antimicrobial analyses.

References

1. Rinehart, K. L., Jr., *et al.* (1976). Identification of Compounds in Selected Marine Organisms by Gas Chromatography Mass Spectrometry, Field Desorption Mass Spectrometry, and Other Physical Methods. In *Proc. Food-Drugs from the Sea*, Marine Technol. Soc. Washington D.C. p. 434.
2. Krejcarek, G. E., *et al.* (1975). A Rearranged Dibromotyrosine Metabolite from *Verongia aurea. Tetrahedron Lett.* 507.
3. Rinehart, K. L., Jr., *et al.* (1975). Structures of Halogenated and Antimicrobial Organic Compounds from Marine Sources. In *The Nature of Seawater.* Ed. E. D. Goldberg , Physical and Chemical Sciences Research Report 1, Abakon Verlagsgesellschaft, Berlin, p. 651.
4. Ungnade, H. E., and Zilch, K. T. (1951). Phenoxyquinones. II. The diphenoxyquinones. *J. Org. Chem.* **16**, 64.
5. Dorman, L. C., (1966). Selective Mono-O-alkylation of 2,6-dibromohydroquinone. *J. Org. Chem.* **31**, 3666.
6. Naik, R. G., and Wheeler, T. S. (1938). Reactivity of the *omega*-Halogen Atom in *p*-Alkoxybenzyl Halides: preparation of phenylacetic acids. *J. Chem. Soc.* 1780.
7. Stempien, M. F., *et al.*, (1973). Physiologically Active Substances from Marine Sponges. II. Antimicrobial substances present in ex-

tracts of the sponge *Verongia archeri* and other species of the genus *Verongia.* In *Food-Drugs from the Sea Proc. 1972,* Ed. L. R. Worthen, Marine Technol. Soc. Washington D. C. p. 105.

8. Yamada, Y., *et al.* (1974). An Effective Synthesis of a Bromine-containing Antibacterial Compound from Marine Sponges. *Chem. Lett.* 1399.

Some New Marine Anticancer Agents

*Alfred J. Weinheimer, *James A. Matson, Tom K.B.
Karns, M. Bilayet Hossain, and D. van der Helm
University of Oklahoma, Department of Chemistry
Norman, Oklahoma
*Department of Medicinal Chemistry and Pharmacognosy, University of
Houston, Houston, Texas*

At a previous meeting, we reported (1) some preliminary results of a survey of marine organisms for the presence of potential anticancer agents. In the present report, we wish to briefly summarize the complete results of that survey, which has now been concluded. We also wish to report on the identity of the cytotoxic principles present in one of the active species discovered in the survey.

A total of 2252 individual species were evaluated in the study. Most of the specimens used for the study were collected by Dr. Robert E. Schroeder (2) in the sub-tropical and tropical waters of the Caribbean region and several locales in the South Pacific. Small quantities (3 lb.) of each of the species were preserved in isopropyl alcohol and forwarded to our laboratories where standard 50% aqueous isopropyl alcohol extracts were prepared from each specimen. Each of these extracts has been examined by the National Cancer Institute's (NCI) preliminary *in vivo* screening test against P-388 leukemia in mice. Many of the extracts have also been examined for cytotoxic activity in the *in vitro* KB test.

Table I summarizes the results of this survey by phylum, showing the number of species surveyed within each of the major phyla, the number within each phylum showing confirmed activity in the NCI tests, and the corresponding percentage yield of active species within each phylum. Table II presents a similar analysis of the survey data from the standpoint of locale of collection. The comparison of yields of active species by phylum demonstrates that natural products possessing anticancer properties are widely distributed throughout the major marine phyla, and occur with significant frequency in each of the phyla except algae. Comparison of yields by locale shows some striking variations for which no ready rationalizations are apparent.

Table I

Yield of Active Species by Phylum

PHYLUM	Number of SPECIES	Number of ACTIVES	YIELD (%)
Coelenterata	737	75	10.2
Porifera	450	64	14.2
Mollusca	215	27	12.6
Echinodermata	187	18	9.6
Arthropoda/Crustacea	81	6	7.4
Chordata/Tunicata	30	4	13.3
Chordata/Pisces	348	46	13.2
Algae	204	5	2.5
Total	2252	245	10.9

Table II

Yield of Active Species by Region

REGION	No. SPECIES	No. ACTIVES	YIELD (%)
Florida Keys	190	18	9.5
Grand Cayman	207	44	21.2
Puerto Rico	73	11	15.1
Rest of Caribbean (Virgin Islands, Texas Gulf, Mexico, Bahamas, Florida Gulf)	708	24	3.4
Eniwetok	63	4	6.3
New Zealand	130	14	10.8
Australia	496	82	16.5
Fiji	290	47	16.2
Washington (Puget Sound)	57	1	1.7
Mexico (Lower California)	38	0	0.0
Total	2252	245	10.9

The overall yield of 10.9% of confirmed active species discovered in this survey is impressively high. It contrasts very favorably with the approximately 3% yield observed in the long-standing NCI program with terrestrial plants. However, it is closely comparable with the 9% yield observed by Sigel *et al.* (3) in their early study of a smaller sample of Caribbean species.

In following up the leads provided by the survey, we have previously isolated (4) the cytotoxic agent, asperdiol, an epoxy cembranediol present in two active species of Caribbean gorgonians of the *Eunicea* genus. We now wish to report the results of our studies of another active species, the soft coral *Sinularia flexibilis*, which was collected at Hayman Island on the Great Barrier Reef of Australia.

The crude aqueous alcohol extract of this species had shown confirmed activity in the *in vivo* PS test. Fractionation of this extract was conducted with the guidance of bioassays in the *in vitro* version of the PS test, and also the *in vitro* KB test. In the initial solvent partition between water and chloroform, the bioactivity was localized in the chloroform phase. Partitioning of the contents of this phase using hexane, carbon tetrachloride and chloroform *vs.* 10, 25 and 35% water in methanol, respectively, localized the activity in the carbon tetrachloride and chloroform phases. These fractions were further refined by chromatography on Sephadex LH-20 in methanol, and then by chromatography on silica gel using mixtures of acetone and hexane. The latter chromatography afforded three crystalline active principles, two of which, sinularin (m.p. 150-152°C, $C_{20}H_{30}O_4$) and dihydrosinularin (m.p. 110-112°C, $C_{20}H_{32}O_4$), were recognized as new compounds. Using the single crystal X-ray diffraction method, sinularin and dihydrosinularin were shown to have the structures and absolute configurations depicted in *I* and *II*, respectively. The third active principle was found to be the known cembranolide, sinulariolide *III*, which Tursch *et al.* (5) had isolated previously from *S. flexibilis* from Indonesian waters.

I	*II*	*III*

The effective doses for 50% inhibition (ED_{50}) of the *in vitro* KB and PS cell lines by sinularin (NSC 285706), dihydrosinularin (NSC 285707) and sinulariolide (NSC 285705) are 0.3 and 0.3, 16 and 1.1, and 20 and 7.(mcg/ml, respectively.

The ring sizes of the lactones in these three cembranolides are uncom mon. Although numerous examples of cembranolides possessinç *gamma*-lactones have been reported, sinulariolide is the only known cem branolide having the seven-membered *epsilon*-lactone ring. The six membered *delta*-lactone ring in *I* and *II* has a known counterpart only ir the cembranolide crassin acetate *IV* which occurs in several species oï Caribbean gorgonians of the *Pseudoplexaura* genus.

IV

The two *delta*-lactones, *I* and *IV*, provide an interesting contrast in ab solute configurations. The two compounds are closely similar in manç structural details, including the *delta*-lactone function bridging ring members 1 and 3, the tertiary methyl carbinol function at position 4, and the *trans* double bond at position 7. Despite the difference in functionali ty, each also has *trans* skeletal geometry about ring members 11 and 12. However, the two compounds are fundamentally enantiomeric with eacн other. In terms of the recently proposed (6) configuration convention for cembranes, they may be classified as members of the *alpha*-series (sinularin) and the *beta*-series (crassin acetate).

The same enantiomeric configurational relationship appears to hold true for other cembranoids derived from the soft corals or the gorgonians These two groups of invertebrates, alcyonaceans and alcyonarians, respectively, are the sources of all marine cembranoids isolated to date Of the limited number of individual cembranoids from each taxonomic group for which absolute configurations have been established, all oï those derived from the alcyonaceans possess the *alpha*-configuration, and all those from the alcyonarians possess the *beta*-configuration.

Acknowledgments

This investigation was supported by Grant Nos. CA 17562 and CA 11055, and Contract No. CM-67108, awarded by the National Cancer In- stitute, DHEW, and by Grant No. 04-158-44062 awarded by the Office of Sea Grant, NOAA. We thank Dr. Robert E. Schroeder for collecting the specimens and Dr. J. Verseveldt for their identification.

References

1. Weinheimer, A.J. and Karns, T.K.B. (1976). A Search for Anticancer and Cardiovascular Agents in Marine Organisms. In *Proc. Food-Drugs from the Sea.* Marine Technol. Soc. Washington, D.C.,p.491.
2. Present address: Route 2, Box 69 D, Summerland Key, Florida 33042.
3. Sigel, M.M. *et al.* (1970). Anticellular and Antitumor Activity of Extracts from Tropical Marine Invertebrates. In *Proc. Food-Drugs from the Sea.* Marine Technol. Soc. Washington, D.C. p. 281
4. Weinheimer, A.J. *et al.* (1977). Marine Anticancer Agents: Asperdiol, a cembranoid from the gorgonians, *Eunicea asperula* and *E. tourneforti. Tetrahedron Letters,* 1295.
5. Tursch, B. *et al.* (1975). Chemical Studies of Marine Invertebrates-XI. Sinulariolide, a cembranolide diterpene from the soft coral *Sinularia flexibilis. Tetrahedron,* **31**, 129.
6. Weinheimer, A.J. *et al.* (1977). Marine Anticancer Agents: sinularin and dihydrosinularin, new cembranolides from the soft coral, *Sinularia flexibilis. Tetrahedron Letters,* 2923.

The Occurrence Of Cytotoxic Compounds In Marine Organisms

J. W. Nemanich, Richard F. Theiler and Lowell P. Hager
Department of Biochemistry
University of Illinois
Urbana, Illinois

Marine research at the University of Illinois has been divided between a number of independent research groups (Biochemistry, L. P. Hager; Chemistry, K. L. Rinehart and Plant Pathology, P. D. Shaw) that have been interested in the content and distribution of organic halogens in marine organisms, the occurrence of antimicrobial activity in extracts of marine organisms, the elucidation of structures, the biogenesis of halometabolites and the isolation and purification of potentially new antibiotics. During the Alpha Helix Baja California expedition of February and March, 1974, some 900 species of marine plants and animals were surveyed for organic halogen content (1) and antimicrobial activity (2). That work demonstrated the widespread occurrence of both halogen containing compounds and antimicrobial activity within marine organisms. About 25% of the organisms collected yielded lipid extracts which contained in excess of 10 mcg of organic halogen per gram wet weight of tissue. Furthermore, 18% of the organisms possessed significant levels of antimicrobial activity and a correlation between high levels of organic halogen and antimicrobial activity was noted.

Recently, we have been encouraged by reports of anticancer and cytotoxic activities exhibited by marine organisms (3-5). These reports suggest that marine organisms will prove an especially promising area for further investigation. In the report by Weinheimer and Karns (5), isopropyl alcohol extracts of 1664 diverse tropical marine organisms were evaluated for anticancer activity. The preliminary screen indicated that 8.9% of the animal species, and 1.6% of the algal species examined exhibited significant levels of anticancer activity. In addition, Sigel *et al.* (3) conducted a similar survey of tropical marine organisms. Their results were consistent with the findings of Weinheimer and Karns and indicated that 9% of the marine animals tested possessed anticancer activity.

In addition to the Weinheimer and Karns study, a number of investigators have reported the purification and characterization of a number of marine anticancer agents (6,7). Cytosine arabinoside is currently the only clinically useful anticancer agent developed as a result of research in marine biochemistry. Its synthesis was based upon the structures of unusual arabinosylnucleosides isolated from the Caribbean sponge, *Cryptothia crypta* (8) and it is one of the primary agents employed today in cancer chemotherapy.

In the present study we have examined extracts obtained during the Alpha Helix Baja expedition for cytotoxic activity against a human nasopharyngeal carcinoma (KB cells) cultured *in vitro*. A total of 675 different species of marine plants and animals were included in the survey. Marine organisms collected from the Western coasts of Mexico including the Gulf of California exhibited a phylogenetic distribution of cytotoxic activity similar to that reported for tropical marine organisms (5), results which further substantiate the occurrence in marine species of a wide variety of potential anticancer compounds. In addition, one interesting correlation between cytotoxicity and antimicrobial activity was observed.

Materials and Methods

Collection and preparation of organisms—Approximately 900 species of marine plants and animals were collected by Hager *et al.* (1) during the Alpha Helix Baja expedition of 1974. Following classification, 2 gm samples of each species were homogenized in a blender with 20 ml of toluene:methanol (1:3). Solids were removed by centrifugation, and the supernatants were assayed for organic halogen content as well as for antimicrobial activity. Toluene:methanol fractions were subsequently stored at -20°C until examined for cytotoxic activity.

KB cells and the cytotoxicity assay—KB cells were purchased frozen from American Type Culture Collection (Rockville, Maryland) and were cultured as monolayers on 12 ml of growth medium in 100x15 mm tissue culture plates at 37°C in a humidity controlled CO_2 incubator. The growth medium was Dulbecco's Modified Eagle's Medium (Flow Laboratories) prepared with a final concentration of 5% fetal calf serum (v/v) (Grand Island Biol. Co.), and 1% mixture of the antibiotics penicillin, streptomycin, and amphotericin B (Fungizone, ISI Biological). The cytotoxicity assay employing KB cells, initially developed by Oyama and Eagle (9), was revised by Smith *et al.* (10) and the procedure has been recently summarized in a NCI Protocol (11). Several modifications of this procedure were employed in order to include microscopic observations of morphological changes in the cells and to simplify the assay procedure.

Cytotoxicity assays were performed in 35x10 mm four-well tissue culture plates (Falcon, type 3004). Growth inhibition was quantitated by cell counting. Extracts from 675 species of marine organisms prepared during the Alpha Helix Baja expedition were assayed for cytotoxicity. Aliquots of these extracts (150-300 mcl) were added to 13x10 mm sterile screw-top test tubes, and were dried for 30 min under a stream of nitrogen. Residue weights (approx. 1 mg) were accurately determined using a microbalance. An appropriate volume of growth medium was added to yield a final residue concentration of 200 mcg/ml.

Growth medium, 2 ml, containing $4-6 \times 10^4$ cells/ml was added to each 35 x 10 mm sample well and cells were grown for 24 hours after which the medium was removed and 2 ml of the medium containing the test material was added to the cells. The number of control plates which received 2 ml of medium without the test material was determined by the following recommended relationship (11): number of controls = twice the square root of *n*, the number of test materials being assayed. In addition, a known cytotoxic compound, colchicine or vinblastine, was included in every series of assays to serve as a positive control. Assays were terminated 3 days after the addition of test material and the cells remaining were determined by cell counting. The effect of the test material on cell growth was measured as % cells surviving, which equal the ratio of number of cells in test plates to the average number of cells in the control plates multiplied by 100.

The concentration of an extract in mcg/ml required to inhibit cell growth to 50% of control values was referred to as the ED_{50}. Extracts from organisms exhibiting significant levels of cytotoxicity ($ED_{50} \leq 200$ mcg/ml) were retested at concentrations of 100, 50 and 10 mcg/ml in order to more accurately determine an organism's level of cytotoxicity.

Results

Cytotoxicity of marine oganisms—Extracts from 675 species of marine organisms were tested for cytotoxicity toward KB cells in tissue culture. The results from the screening procedure indicated that 60 species of marine animals and 5 marine algae possessed significant levels of cytotoxicity (defined as an $ED_{50} \leq 200$ mcg/ml) (Table I). A total of 9.6% of the species tested exhibited significant activity (Table II). Cytotoxic activity was by no means evenly distributed among all the marine phyla. Only 2.9% of the marine algae surveyed displayed cytotoxic activity whereas 11.8% of the marine animals displayed significant levels of cytotoxicity. In addition, no significant activity was observed for any species of red algae which represented over 55% of the marine plants collected. The animal phyla, *Porifera, Cnidaria* and *Echinodermata* were

Table I. Cytotoxicity of Organic Extracts from Marine Animals

Phylum Genus	Species	ED$_{50}$ in mcg/ml [1]	LTH [2]	LBR [3]	Antimicrobial Activity E. coli	B. subt.	S. cerev.	P. atro.
Porifera								
Verongia	aurea	< 100	132	x	+	+	-	-
Plocamia	karykina	< 50	5	1	+	+	-	+
Haliclona	sp. 1	< 200	8	0	-	+	-	-
Halichondria	sp. 1	< 200	6	x	-	-	-	-
Geodia	mesotriana	< 200	0	0	-	-	-	-
Dysidea	sp. 1	< 50	110	x	-	+	-	-
Litaspongia	sp. 1	< 200	8	0	-	-	-	-
Litaspongia	sp. 2	< 50	6	0	-	+	-	-
Tedania	nigrescens	< 100	3	0	-	+	+	+
Tedania	sp. 1	< 10	28	33	+	+	+	+
Iloterectya	cerebella	< 50	128	140	+	+	-	+
Plocamionida	(igzo?)	< 50	3	0	+	+	+	+
Terpios	zeteki	< 200	10	5	-	-	+	-
Acarnus	erithicus	< 10	9	0	+	+	+	+
Laxasoberites	sp. 1	< 100	124	280	+	+	-	-
	(odiferous yellow)	< 200	4	0	-	-	+	-
Cnidaria								
Aglaophenia	propingua	< 50	4	0	-	+	-	-
Aglaophenia	sp. 1	< 200	6	x	+	+	-	-
Palythoa	sp. 1	< 50	7	0	-	+	-	-
Epizoanthus	gabrieli	< 50	9	x	-	-	-	-
Astrangia	lajollaensis	< 200	40	0	-	-	-	-
Tubastraea	tenuilamellosa	< 100	22	30	+	+	+	+

Phylum / Genus	Species	ED$_{50}$[1] in mcg/ml	LTH[2]	LBR[3]	Antimicrobial Activity E. coli	B. subt.	S. cerev.	P. atro.
Gorgonia	adamsi	< 10	17	0	–	+	–	–
Gorgonia	sp. 2	< 100	44	0	–	+	–	–
Gorgonia	sp. 6	< 200	3	0	–	–	–	–
Gorgonia	sp. 11	< 200	27	0	–	+	–	–
Cnidaria								
Gorgonia	sp. ?	< 200	5	0	–	+	–	–
Gorgonia	sp. 12	< 200	6	0	–	–	+	–
Gorgonia	sp. 14	< 50	45	x	–	+	–	+
Mollusca								
Cheilea	cepacea	< 100	5	0	–	–	–	–
Hexaplex	regius	< 100	12	x	–	–	–	–
Neorapana	tuberculata	< 100	78	80	–	+	–	+
Oliva	kaleontina	< 200	1	0	–	–	–	–
Berthellina	illisima	< 50	12	0	+	+	–	+
Nembrotha	eliora	< 100	45	33	+	+	+	+
Hermissenda	crassicornis	< 200	30	0	–	+	–	–
Spondylus	princeps	< 100	12	0	–	–	–	–
Ectoprocta								
Pedicellina	sp. 3	< 100	13	x	+	+	–	–
Arthropoda								
Petrochirus	californiensis	< 200	8	0	–	–	–	–
Coenobita	compressus	< 200	4	0	–	–	–	
Echinodermata								
Picnopodia	helianthoides	< 100	8	x	–	–	–	–

Table I. (cont'd).

Table I. (cont'd).

Phylum Genus	Species	ED$_{50}$[1] in mcg/ml	LTH[2]	LBR[3]	E. coli	Antimicrobial Activity B. subt.	S. cerev.	P. atro.
Heliaster	kubinijii	< 200	8	0	-	-	+	-
Pharia	pyramidata	< 200	30	0	-	-	-	-
Linckia	columbiae	< 100	11	0	-	+	-	-
Leptychaster	sp. 1	< 100	10	0	-	-	-	-
Mediaster	aequalis	< 10	6	x	-	-	-	-
Luidia	superba	< 100	9	0	-	-	+	+
Patiria	miniata	< 200	20	x	-	+	-	-
Henricia	leviuscula	< 100	9.5	x	-	-	-	-
Mitrodia	bradlegi	< 200	24	0	-	-	-	-
Echinodermata								
Seleakothoria	lubrica	< 100	5	0	-	-	+	+
Brandtothuria	arincola	< 100	4	0	-	-	+	+
Labidodemas	americanum	< 200	3	0	-	-	+	-
Psolidium	dorsipes	< 100	6	x	-	-	+	+
Pentamera	chierchia	< 100	9.5	0	-	-	+	+
Neothyone	gibbosa	< 100	5	0	-	-	+	-
Cucumeria	sp. 1	< 100	9.5	x	-	-	+	+
Ophioderma	variegatum	< 200	18	54	-	+	-	-
Toxoneustes	reseus	< 50	9	x	-	-	-	-
Chordata								
Aplidium	sp. 3	< 50	3	0	-	+	+	+

Cytotoxicity of Organic Extracts from Marine Algae

Chlorophyta							
Entomorpha	acanthophora	< 100	x	0	–	–	–
Cladophora	delicatula	< 200	3	0	–	–	–
Caulerpa	peltata	< 200	8	x	–	–	–
Phaetophyta							
Dictyota	johnstonii (?)	< 50	15	x	+	+	+
Zonaria	farlowa	< 200	5	x	–	–	–

[1] Amount of sample required to inhibit KB cell growth to the percent indicated.

[2] Level of total organohalogen present in one gram of tissue (**mcg/g**).

[3] Level of total organobromine present in one gram of tissue (**mcg/g**).

Table II

Distribution of Marine Organisms
Showing Cytotoxicity Toward KB Cells in Tissue Culture

Animals	# Species Tested	# Species Active[1]	%[2]
Porifera	52	16	31.0
Demospongia (class)	49	16	32.7
Cnidaria	47	13	27.7
Gorgonia (genus)	9	7	77.8
Ctenophora	3	0	0
Platyhelminthes	5	0	0
Nemertina	3	0	0
Annelida	31	0	0
Mollusca	163	8	4.9
Arthropoda	68	2	2.9
Sipunculida	4	0	0
Entoprocta	2	0	0
Ectoprocta	10	1	10.0
Chaetognatha	1	0	0
Echinodermata	71	19	26.8
Asteroida (class)	25	10	40.0
Holothuroidea (class)	20	7	35.0
Chordata	47	1	2.1
TOTAL (Animals)	507	60	11.8

Plants	# Species Tested	# Species Active	%
Chlorophyta	26	3	11.5
Phaetophyta	43	2	4.6
Rhodophyta	93	0	0
"Miscellaneous"	6	0	0
TOTAL (Plants)	168	5	2.9

[1] $ED_{50} \leq 200$ mcg/ml

[2] Percent of total species tested that were active.

the most active comprising 80% of the species displaying cytotoxic activity. Among the sponges collected, 32.7% of the species within the class *Demospongia* were active. Cytotoxic activity exhibited within the *Cnideria* were primarily restricted to the genus *Gorgonia* where 7 of the 9 species tested showed significant levels of activity.

Morphological changes associated with cytotoxicity—Utilizing light microscopic examinations, changes in the morphological appearance of KB cells were routinely monitored following the addition of test materials. These changes were typified by alterations in the cell membrane, cytoplasm and nucleus. Morphological changes among cultured cells were directly related to the presence of cytotoxic activity. Furthermore, the 65 species of marine organisms that exhibited cytotoxic activity could be classified according to the unique morphological changes they induced when placed in contact with growing cells. In general, active organisms within the same Order induced similar morphological changes suggesting that the active compounds exhibited nearly identical modes of action. Observations of this nature may prove useful to investigators interested in purifying cytotoxic compounds which, on the basis of morphological observations, display distinctly different modes of action.

Comparisons between cytotoxicity, antimicrobial activity and levels of organic halogen—The cytotoxicity data for the 675 organisms surveyed was compared to information on antimicrobial activity (2) as well as organic halogen content (1). We failed to observe any meaningful correlation between organic halogen content and cytotoxic potency based upon an organisms's known ED_{50}, although a positive correlation between increased organic halogen content and antimicrobial activity has previously been documented (2).

The cytotoxic activity of all the extracts were compared to their antimicrobial activity against the following microbes: *Escherichia coli, Bacillus subtilis, Saccharomyces cerevisiae,* and *Penicillium atrovenetum.* A comparison of the level of cytotoxicity versus the percent of organisms eliciting antimicrobial activity is shown in figure 1. In this comparison antimicrobial activity for a species was considered positive only if it demonstrated activity against one or more of the microbes listed above. The results demonstrate that antimicrobial activity is related to increased cytotoxicity in the KB assay in a nearly linear fashion. In fact, 72% of the marine animals which exhibited significant cytotoxic activity also displayed antimicrobial activity. Furthermore, only 12% of the organisms surveyed exhibited antimicrobial activity without eliciting cytotoxic activity ($ED_{50} \leq 200$ mcg/ml). An additional comparison between an organisms's spectrum of antimicrobial and cytotoxic activity was also conducted (Fig. 2). In this comparison the "spectrum of activity" refers to the

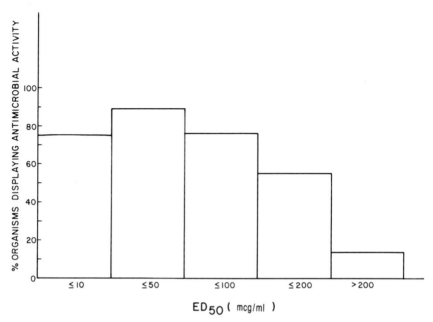

FIGURE 1. The percent of marine organisms which display antimicrobial activity versus the percent of extracts showing cytotoxicity in the KB assay. An organism was considered to possess antimicrobial activity if it was lethal to any of the microbes; *E. coli, B. subt., S. cerev.* and *P. atro.* As the level of cytotoxicity to KB cells increases so does the percentage of organisms that display antimicrobial activity.

number of different microbes an organism is active against. For example, an organism which is active against all 4 microbes would have a value of +4 (Fig. 2). These results demonstrated that, in general, as marine organisms become increasingly lethal in the KB assay, they also exhibit a wider spectrum of antimicrobial activity.

Discussion

The KB cell cytotoxicity assay provided a reproducible technique for detecting cytotoxic agents present in extracts of marine organisms. Extracts which exhibited growth inhibition were quantitated by cell counting as this technique was found to be as sensitive as other methods which have relied on Lowry positive protein determinations (9). In addition to being less time consuming, quantitation by cell counting was preferred because it enabled a continuous microscopic observation of cellular changes following exposure of the cells to cytotoxic agents.

In our survey of marine organisms for cytotoxins, we have chosen to

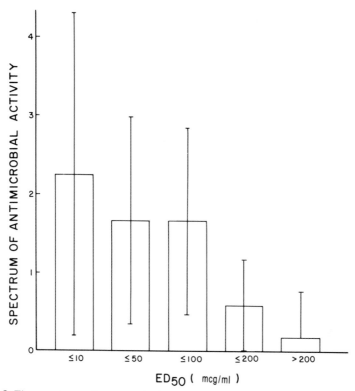

FIGURE 2. The spectrum of antimicrobial activity as a function of cytotoxicity toward KB cells. The spectrum of activity refers to the total number of microbes a marineorganism was active against. An organism possessing activity against all 4 of the microbes; *E. coli, B. subt., S. cerev.,* and *P. atro* was recorded as a value of +4. In general, increases in cytotoxicity toward KB cells indicated an increase in the spectrum of that organism's antimicrobial activity.

recognize as "significant", those extracts which possess an $ED_{50} \leq 200$ mcg/ml. In contrast, the current NCI standards consider an $ED_{50} \leq 20$ mcg/ml to be significant. We chose the different level for several reasons. First, the organisms collected on the Baja expedition were extracted with toluene:methanol (1:3) to simplify the survey of each species for organic halogen content. These same organic extracts often contained large quantities of organic materials that were insoluble in growth medium. Previous reports indicate that in general, an extraction with 50% ethanol or isopropyl alcohol is an optimal system for solubilizing cytotoxic compounds (5). On the basis of these results it is doubtful that the toluene:methanol extraction procedure would approach the ethanol or isopropyl alcohol extraction in effectiveness. Second, correlations relating cytotoxicity to antimicrobial activity or organic halogen content were desired and these correlations would not have been possible had only extracts with an $ED_{50} \leq 20$ mcg/ml been considered.

Out of a total of 675 species of marine organisms, 11.8% of the animals and 2.9% of the plants exhibited significant cytotoxic activity. Our results closely paralleled the work of others (3-5) and again illustrated the relative absence of active cytotoxic compounds among marine algae. It should be noted that in the Weinheimer and Karns survey both an *in vitro* KB test and an *in vivo* PS test were employed to evaluate anticancer activity. Of the 138 species they confirmed as containing potential anticancer compounds, only 32 gave positive tests in the KB system (ED_{50} ≤ 10 mcg/ml), whereas the remaining 106 were found to be active in the PS system. The KB test results were not presented for the 106 species active in the PS assay and it would be interesting to determine what percentage of these species would have been active in the KB assay had the level of "significant" activity been raised from 10 mcg/ml to 100 or 200 mcg/ml. In contrast to the results of Weinheimer and Karns, reports as early as 1959 have indicated that KB cell cytotoxicity closely parallels *in vivo* antineoplastic activity, and that by increasing the minimum accepted level of KB activity would select virtually all known anticancer compounds (12,13).

An excellent correlation was observed between cytotoxic activity and antimicrobial activity. It was observed that as cytotoxic potency increased so did the percentage of species displaying antimicrobial activity. Similarly, as cytotoxic potency increased so did the spectrum of microbes against which the extracts were active. This relationship suggests that most cytotoxic compounds possess a nonspecific toxicity with respect to both prokaryotic and eukaryotic cells and indicates that the active agents are interfering with cellular processes common to both cell types. In light of these results it is interesting to note that many clinically useful anticancer compounds were initially developed as antibiotics, actinomycin D, mitomycin C, mithramycin and dannorubicin from *Streptomyces* etc. (14).

The complexity and length of time (4 days) required to perform the KB assay often restricts its application as a screening procedure at collection sites whereas antimicrobial assays can be easily applied and are capable of predicting potential cytotoxic activity in greater than 70% of all species surveyed. Since it is difficult to collect large quantities (over 5 kg) of all specimens desired for primary cytotoxic screening and for purification purposes, initial application of antimicrobial assays could reduce the number of species of interest thus enabling collectors to concentrate their efforts on a smaller group of potentially active species.

The absence of any correlation between the organic halogen content and the cytotoxic activity of the marine extracts was surprising, especially since our previous work had demonstrated a correlation between halometabolite levels and antimicrobial activity. We had attempted to explain the correlation between halometabolite levels and antimicrobial activity on the basis of a general toxicity of high levels of halogenated organic molecules such as brominated or chlorinated phenols. However, this argument does not appear to be applicable because of the lack of correlation between halometabolite levels and toxicity in the KB cell assay.

In conclusion, we feel that surveys for cytotoxic activity coupled with antimicrobial assays may offer fundamental information with regard to the nature of the effective compounds. For example, an investigator interested in the isolation of potentially useful antibiotics may be primarily interested in compounds which affect bacterial or fungal growth without eliciting cytotoxic effects in mammalian cells. Our data with regard to cytotoxicity and antimicrobial activity effectively demonstrates which species of marine organisms most likely contain such compounds. Similarly, on the basis of our data, investigators can select cytotoxic organisms which do not elicit secondary antimicrobial effects or they may select for cytotoxic organisms which have a broad spectrum of activity against both prokaryotic and eukaryotic cells. Thus comparisons of this nature may prove useful in the selection of marine organisms that elicit an activity especially suited to the interests of the investigator prior to extensive purification and structural identification of the active compound(s).

Acknowledgments

The authors wish to thank Ms. N. J. Theiler for technical assistance in performing KB assays during her interim leave from Luther College, Decorah, Iowa. Financial support was provided by a grant from the National Science Foundation (NSF PCM 76-12547).

References

1. Hager, L.P. *et al.* (1976). A Survey of Organic Halogens in Marine Organisms. In *Proc. Food-Drugs from the Sea*. Marine Technol. Soc. Washington, D.C. p. 421.
2. Shaw, P.D. *et al.* (1976). Antimicrobial Activities from Marine Organisms. *ibid.* 429.
3. Sigel, M.M. *et al.* (1970). Anticellular and Antitumor Activity of Extracts from Tropical Marine Invertebrates. *ibid.*
4. Pettit, G.R. *et al.* (1970). Antineoplastic Components of Marine Animals. *Nature* **227**, 962.
5. Weinheimer, A.J., and Karns, K.B. (1976). A Search for Anticancer

and Cardiovascular Agents in Marine Organisms. In *Proc. Food-Drugs from the Sea*. Marine Technol. Soc. Washington, D.C. p. 491.

6. Li, C.P., Goldin, A. and Hartwell, J.L. (1974). Antineoplastic Substances from the Seas: A review. *Cancer Chemotherapy Reports* **4**, 97.

7. Weinheimer, A.J., and Matson, J.A. (1975). Crassin Acetate, the Principle Antineoplastic Agent in Four Gorgonians of the *Pseudoplexaura* Genus. *Lloydia* **38**, 378

8. Bergmann, W. and Burke, D.C. (1955). Contributions to the Study of Marine Products. XXXIX. The Nucleosides of sponges. III. Spongothymidine and spongouridine. *J. Org. Chem.* **20**, 1501.

9. Oyoma, U.I., and Eagle, H. (1956). Measurement of Cell Growth in Tissue Culture with a Phenol Reagent (Folin-Ciocalteau). *Proc. Soc. Exp. Biol. Med.* **91**, 305.

10. Smith, C.G., Lummis, W.L. and Grady, J.E. (1959). An Improved Tissue Culture Assay. I. Methodology and cytotoxicity of antitumor agents. *Canc. Res.* **19**, 843.

11. National Cancer Institute, Protocol. (1972). Cell Culture Screen, KB. *Cancer Chemotherapy Reports* **3**, 17.

12. Eagle, H. and Foley, G.E. (1959). Susceptibility of Cultured Human Cells to Antitumor Agents. *Ann. New York Acad. Sci.* **76**, 534.

13. Hartwell, J.L. (1976). Types of Anticancer Agents Isolated from Plants. *Cancer Treatment Reports* **60**, 1031.

14. Brule, G. *et al.* (1973). *Drug Therapy of Cancer.* World Health Organization, Geneva, p. 48.

Immunomodulation By Extract Of
Ecteinascidia turbinata

Wolf Lichter, Abdul Ghaffar, Larry L. Wellham
and M. Michael Sigel
Laboratory of Virology
Department of Microbiology
University of Miami
School of Medicine
Biscayne Annex
Miami, Florida

We have previously reported that *Ecteinascidia turbinata* (Ete) can exert a number of profound immunosuppressive effects (1-3). Thus the extract inhibited antibody production *in vivo*; prolonged skin graft survival of allogeneic skin transplants in mice: diminished graft versus host (GVH) reaction; suppressed antibody production and ablated the mitogenic response of lymphocytes to lectins. In the last mentioned activity Ete was able to inhibit ^{3}H-thymidine uptake, not only when incorporated at the time of mitogen stimulation but also when added as late as 24 hours (and partly as late as 48 hours) after stimulation.

Recently we extended these studies to include additional immunological parameters such as formation of anti-SRBC plaque forming cells (PFC), antibody dependent cellular cytotoxicity (ADCC) and a quantitative and qualitative characterization of spleens from Ete treated animals. Some of these parameters appear to be diminished following administration of Ete, but what was an unexpected finding is that certain cellular components and/or reactions appear to be amplified rather than decreased by treatment with Ete. Some of these observations are summarized in this paper.

Materials and Methods

Male 6-8 weeks old DBA/2 x C57B1 F_1 (BDF$_1$) and female Balb/c and DBA/2 mice were used in all studies.

Ecteinascidia turbinata extracts—*Ecteinascidia turbinata* (Ete) were collected in aqueous ethanol at a concentration of approximately 50% achieved by dilution with sea water and the animal's body fluid. The total material, solid and liquid, was homogenized in the cold by grinding in a Waring blender followed by Sorvall high speed blender. The extracted materials referred to as Ete, were lyophilized and stored at 4°C. Some specimens were separated into a liquid and solid part at the time of collection. This separation was achieved by expressing the liquid through a cotton cloth.

Preparation of spleen cells—Spleens were removed aseptically and forced through a stainless steel screen (30 mesh) or gently disrupted in a glass tissue homogenizer (Bellco Glass Co.) to obtain a cell suspension. The cell suspension was washed in Hanks' balanced salt solution (HBSS) with antibiotics and exposed to a momentary hypotonic shock to lyse the red blood cells. After an additional wash the cells were resuspended in Eagle's Hanks medium supplemented with amino acids (EHAA), antibiotics and 2% heat inactivated fetal bovine serum (FBS). The viability of cells was assessed by trypan blue exclusion procedure and the concentration of these cells was adjusted according to the requirement. The same scheme of cell preparation but different medium (RPMI-1640) was used for cytotoxicity and cell fractionation studies.

Blastogenic transformation—Suspensions containing $0.5 - 1$ x 10^6 cells/ml were cultured with concanavalin A (Con A) at a final concentration of 1 mcg/ml. The cultures were incubated for 72 hr at 37°C in humidified air with 5% CO_2. Sixteen hr before the end of the incubation period 2 mCi of ^{3}H-thymidine was added to each culture. The cells were washed twice with cold saline and resuspended in 1 ml of cold 5% trichloroacetic acid (TCA). The acid insoluble precipitate was washed with cold absolute ethanol and solubilized by overnight incubation at 37°C in Hyamine (Packard). The content of each tube was then mixed with 10 ml of scintillation fluid (Amersham/ Searle Corp.) and transferred to scintillation vials. Radioactivity was counted in a Tricarb Liquid Scintillation Spectrometer (Packard Instr.). The results are expressed as the ratio of mitogenic response of Ete treated mice over control mice.

Antibody dependent cellular cytotoxicity ADCC—The splenocytes were assayed for cytotoxic activity by the method of Perlmann (4). Chicken red blood cells (CRBC) were labeled with ^{51}Cr and incubated at 37°C for 18 hr with rabbit anti-chick serum and mouse splenocytes in RPMI-1640 with 5% heat inactivated FBS. The ratio of splenocytes (effector cells) to labeled CRBC (target cells) was 25:1. After incubation the cultures were centrifuged and the radioactivity in the supernatant and pellet determined in a gamma counter. The radioactivity count of the supernatant was divided by the total count of the culture (supernatant + pellet) to determine the percentage release. The cytotoxicity was calculated by subtracting percentage release in cultures without antibody from percentage release from cultures with antibody and corrected for percentage total release from the labelled CRBC.

Plaque assay—Control and Ete treated mice were injected with 2 x 10^8 washed sheep red blood cells (SRBC) in 0.2 ml. The number of plaque forming cells (PFC) was assessed by the method of Cunningham (5) 4 days after antigenic challenge for IgM PFC and 6 days after antigenic challenge of IgG. The IgG PFC were detected using rabbit anti-mouse IgG serum (Miles Laboratories) as described by Dresser and Greaves (6).

Cells with receptor for the Fc region (FcR)—Washed SRBC were sensitized with rabbit anti-SRBC IgG (Cordis Labs, Miami, Fla.). Tenth of an ml of lymphocytes (2 x 10^6) in HBSS was mixed with 0.1 ml of 1% SRBC sensitized with rabbit anti-SRBC IgG, centrifuged at 200 x g and incubated for 30 min at 37°C. After the 30 min incubation, the cell pellet was gently resuspended with a pasteur pipette, mounted on a slide and examined under oil immersion in a phase contrast microscope. Lymphocytes with at least three adhering SRBC were considered positive for the FcR.

Results

Results of mitogenic response to Con A by control and Ete-treated mice summarized in figure 1 clearly indicate that treatment with Ete caused a profound depression in the capacity of lymphocytes to respond to this mitogen (open symbols). The ability of Ete-treated spleens to respond fell sharply 2 days after treatment, and recovered to normal by day 12 in Balb/c and by day 21 in DBA/2 mice. It is interesting to note that there was an inverse relationship between the splenic size and the responsiveness to Con A (Fig. 1; closed symbols).

The increase in the splenic weight of Ete-treated mice corresponded with an increase in the number of nucleated cells recovered from these spleens (Fig. 2). The increase in the cellular content of the spleen was maximal 6 days after treatment and it returned to normal by day 21 (Fig. 2).

The increase in the cellularity of spleens from Ete treated animals also paralleled the incidence of FcR positive cells in these organs. Thus results given in table I indicate that treatment with Ete causes over 50% rise in the frequency of FcR positive cells in the spleens.

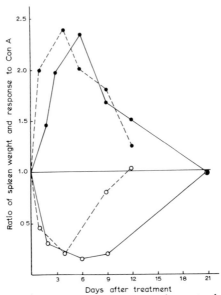

FIGURE 1.Suppression of blastogenic responses in splenocytes from Balb/c (broken lines) and DBA/2 (solid lines) mice treated with Ete. 250 mg/kg Ete injected i.p. Note the inverse relationship between blastogenic response (open symbols) and spleen weight (closed symbols).

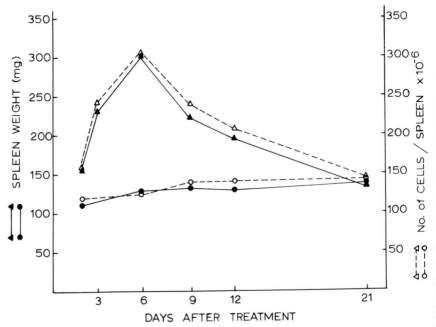

FIGURE 2.Increase in the weight (closed symbols) and cellularity (open symbols) of spleens from Ete treated mice. Circles: controls; triangles: 250 mg/kg Ete injected i.p.

In parallel with the increase in cellularity and the frequency of FcR positive cells was the ability of splenocytes from Ete-treated animals to cause cytolysis of antibody coated target cells. As indicated by data in table II, Ete treatment caused 84% increase in the ability of splenocytes to cause ADCC. It is interesting that the bulk of the ADCC activity is not associated with either 'T' or 'B' cell enriched populations.

We have previously shown that Ete can inhibit antibody production when injected into mice (1). This effect was confirmed in these studies using PFC assay for the measurement of anti-SRBC responses. The suppression was however limited to groups in which Ete was given i.p. prior to the i.p. immunization. When the agent was injected by the i.v. route, it failed to produce a suppressive effect: instead it augmented the anti-SRBC responses (Fig. 3).

Table I
Increased FcR positive cells
in spleens of Ete treated BDF₁ mice

Days after treatment	% of cells with FcR Control	Ete
+2	37	54 (57%)
+4	40	64 (60%)
+5	35	52 (49%)

Treatment with Ete at 250 mg/kg i.p.
Numbers in parenthesis indicate the percentage increase over controls

Table II
Increased ADCC caused by Splenocytes
from Ete Treated Balb/c Mice

Cell Description	Percent Lysis Splenocyte Source: Control	Ete treated
Unseparated	40.0	73.75 (84%)
Nylon non-retained[a]	15.0	27.5 (80%)
Nylon eluted[b]	20.0	22.5 (12%)

Treatment with Ete at 250 mg/kg i.p. and tested 4 days later.
[a]T-cell enriched.
[b]B-cell enriched.
Numbers in parenthesis indicate the percentage increase over controls.

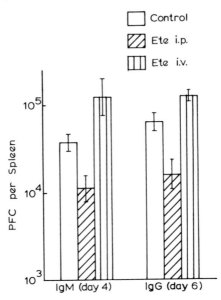

FIGURE 3.Route dependent suppression or enhancement of anti-SRBC responses by Ete (250 mg/kg, i.p.).

Discussion

The results reported here confirm previous findings that Ete can suppress the immune response of SRBC and blastogenic response to mitogens. What is unexpected is that Ete given by the i.v. route failed to suppress anti-SRBC responses. Route dependent suppression and augmentation of anti-SRBC responses has also been observed with *Corynebacterium parvum* which suppresses the PFC responses to i.p. injected antigen when given i. p. but not when injected i.v. (7). This parallel between Ete and *C. parvum* coupled with the enlargement in the splenic weight and cellularity opens a strong possibility that Ete may also have properties of an immunopotentiating agent. Some of the properties common to *C. parvum* and Ete have been listed in table III.

The increase in the number of cells in the spleen of Ete treated animals coincides with an increase in the frequency of FcR positive cells and their ability to induce ADCC. It is likely that the increase in FcR positive cells is representative of an increase in the proportion of macrophages and activated T cells which possess FcR receptors (8-10). Macrophages/monocyte type cells with Fc receptors have been claimed to be the main effector cells in the lysis of antibody-coated erythroid cells (11). It is apparent that the increase in the cytotoxic capacity of splenocytes from Ete treated animals is not in the 'B' cell population. It seems to be

Table III
Comparison of Biological Activities of *C. parvum* and Ete

Assay	*C. parvum*	Ete
GVH	suppressed	suppressed
Skin graft	no change	suppressed
PHA	suppressed	suppressed
Antitumor	positive	positive
Splenomegaly	positive	positive
Hepatomegaly	positive	positive
RE stimulation	positive	positive
Cytotoxic macrophages	positive	positive
ADCC	enhanced	enhanced
Anti-SRBC response	(i.v.) enhanced	(i.v.) enhanced
Anti-SRBC response	(i.p.)suppressed	(i.P)suppressed
Anti-SIII	suppressed	suppressed

associated in bulk in the macrophage/monocyte population, and partly in the 'T' cell enriched fraction.

These and other findings (unpublished data) indicate that Ete can serve as a stimulator of the reticuloendothelial system. Whether or not the RES stimulation is also responsible for its immunosuppressive properties is yet to be established. It has been previously shown that RE stimulation can cause the suppression of GVH, blastogenic response to mitogens (12) and anti-SRBC response (7). The role of cellular and humoral mediators of suppression by Ete is under current investigation.

Acknowledgments

Authors wish to thank Miss Sheila Long for technical assistance. This work was supported by the Sea Grant and USPHS Contract No. NO1-CM-57041 from the NCI.

References

1. Lichter, et al. (1973). Biological Activities Exerted by Extracts of *Ecteinascidia turbinata.* In *Proc.Food-Drug from the Sea,* Marine Technol. Soc. Washington, D.C., p. 117.
2. Lichter, W., et al. (1975). *Ecteinascidia turbinata* Extracts Inhibit DNA Synthesis in Lymphocytes After Mitogenic Stimulation by

Lectins. *Proc. Soc. Exp. Biol. Med.*, **150**, 475.

3. Lichter, et al. (1976). Inhibition of DNA systhesis by *Ecteinascidia turbinata* extracts (Ete). In *Proc. Food-Drug from the Sea*, Marine Technol. Soc. Washington, D.C., p.395.

4. Perlmann, P. and Perlmann, H. (1971). ^{51}Cr-release from Chicken Erythrocytes: An Assay System for Measuring Cytotoxic Activity of 'Nonspecifically' Activated Lymphocytes *in vitro* . In *In Vitro Methods in Cell Mediated Immunity*. Eds. B. Bloom and P. R. Glade Academic Press, N.Y. p. 361.

5. Cunningham, A. J. and Szenberg, A. (1968). Further Improvements on the Plaque Technique for Detecting Single Antibody-forming Cells. *Immunology*. **14**, 599.

6. Dresser, D. W. and Greaves, M. F. (1973). Assay for Antibody Producing Cells. In "Handbook of Experimental Immunology." 2nd ed. Ed. D.M. Weir. Blackwell Scientific, Oxford. Chapter 27.

7. Ghaffar, A. and Sigel, M. M. (1977). Immunomodulation by *Corynebacterium parvum*. I. Variable Effects on Anti-sheep Erythrocyte Antibody Response. Submitted for publication.

8. Lay, W. H. and Nussensweig, V. (1968). Receptors for Complement on Leukocytes. *J. Exp. Med.*, **128**, 991.

9. Anderson, C. L. and Grey, H. M. (1974). Receptors for Aggregated IgG on Mouse Lymphocytes. Their Presence on Thymocytes, Thymus Derived and Bone Marrow Derived Lymphocytes. *J. Exp. Med.*, **139**, 1175.

10. Epstein, R. S., et al. (1976). Emergence of a Subpopulation of Lymphocytes Bearing ∅ Antigen and Complement Receptor During Tumor Growth. *Int. J. Cancer.*, **18**, 458.

11. Greenberg, A. S. Shen, L. and Medley, G. (1975). Characteristics of the Effector Cells Mediating Cytotoxicity Against Antibody Coated Target Cells. I. Phagocytic and Nonphagocytic Effector Cell Activity Against Erythrocytes and Tumor Target Cells in a [51]Cr Release Cytotoxicity Assay and [125I] IUDR Growth Inhibition Assay. *Immunology*, **29**, 719.

12. Scott, M. T. (1972). Biological Effects of the Adjuvant *Corynebacterium parvum*. I. Inhibition of PHA, Mixed Lymphocyte and GVH Reactivity. *Cell. Immunol.*, **5**, 459.

Action Of Cembranolides Derived From Octocorals On Larvae Of The Nudibranch
Phestilla sibogae

Michael G. Hadfield* and Leon S. Ciereszko*

*Kewalo Marine Laboratory, Pacific Biomedical Research Center
University of Hawaii, Honolulu, Hawaii
**The University of Oklahoma Department of Chemistry
Norman, Oklahoma*

The octocorals called gorgonians, or horny corals, are coelenterates of the Class *Anthozoa*, Subclass *Octocorallia* or *Alcyonaria*, Order *Gorgonacea*. They are prominent members of the sessile shallow water coral reef community in the Caribbean area. They have few predators and are successful in the severe competition for "space" on solid substrate in coral reef areas.

We feel that the success of gorgonians against predation and against overgrowth by competing organisms is in part due to the secretion of defense substances. Some of these appear to be the slimy secretions of polysaccharide sulfate as in the case of *Pseudopterogorgia americana* [1]. Others are derivatives of cembrene, a diterpene containing a 14-membered ring. Derivatives of cembrene, including lactones, the cembranolides, occur in many of the shallow water octocorals which have been examined [1–4] and are toxic to a variety of organisms [5]. Some of these inhibit ciliary movement [6,7].

In this paper we report the effects of some cembranolides on the larvae of the nudibranch, *P. sibogae*, a gastropod easily cultured in laboratory aquaria throughout the year [8]. The larvae are equipped with prominent velar cilia which have a regular beat that is easily observed. A possible chemical defense against settlement by larvae on gorgonians would be interference with their ciliary activity and thus their mobility.

Material and Methods

Larvae used in these experiments were obtained from egg masses laid by laboratory-reared adult *P. sibogae*. Freshly laid egg masses were removed from aquaria and placed in plastic screen baskets suspended in flowing seawater. After 7–8 days, the egg masses were placed in bowls of Millipore-filtered seawater (MPF-SW) and opened with fine tipped forceps. This procedure frees the larvae which are subsequently free swimming. These larvae were maintained in the dark, in bowls of MPF-SW until they were to be used in experiments. In the present experimental series, larvae were 12 days old (= days past egg laying).

The cembranolides tested were crassin acetate isolated from *Pseudoplexaura porosa* (Houttuyn), eunicin from *Eunicea mammosa* (Lamouroux), eupalmerin acetate from *E. succinea* (Pallas) from Puerto Rico, jeunicin from *E. mammosa* obtained from Jamaica, and peunicin (9) from *E. succinea*, var. *plantiginea* collected off Panama. The cembranolides were obtained by extracting the dried cortex of the gorgonians in a continuous extractor with *n*-hexane. The extracts were concentrated to obtain crude crystalline material. This was washed with *n*-hexane. The crude cembranolides were dissolved in benzene and decolorized by passing the benzene solution through a column of Florisil. The crystalline material obtained on concentration and the addition of hexane was recrystallized from a mixture of benzene and hexane.

A solution of 10 mg of each cembranolide dissolved in 10 ml acetone was diluted with seawater to the desired concentrations in parts per million. Acetone was driven off by heating the solution in an oven at 60°C for one-half hour. Tests were made with larvae at 10, 5 and 1 ppm.

Larvae of *P. sibogae* were put into test solutions at 20 larvae per 20 ml. Each test situation was replicated. Controls consisted of larvae in seawater or seawater which had added acetone and had been heated. A number of other organic compounds obtained from gorgonians, such as ancepsenolide and briarein A were tested and did not affect the larvae, possibly because of their very low solubility in sea water.

Results

Crassin acetate—Larvae exposed to crassin acetate at 5 or 10 ppm were inactive within 1 hour; 100% mortality in 24 hours. At 1 ppm, the larvae were immobile and partially deciliate in 17 hours; 100% mortality in 48 hours.

Eunicin—Within 10 minutes of exposure to eunicin in seawater at 10 ppm, velar cilia began to disappear. Within 24 hours, all larvae were dead. A pulse exposure as brief as 15 minutes produced anti-ciliary effects; 25% of exposed larvae died within 48 hours while the remainder lost their cilia. Larvae exposed to eunicin at 5 ppm showed 100% mortality in 24 hours. At 1 ppm, the larvae exhibited excessive mucus secretion and "paralysis" within 12 hours.

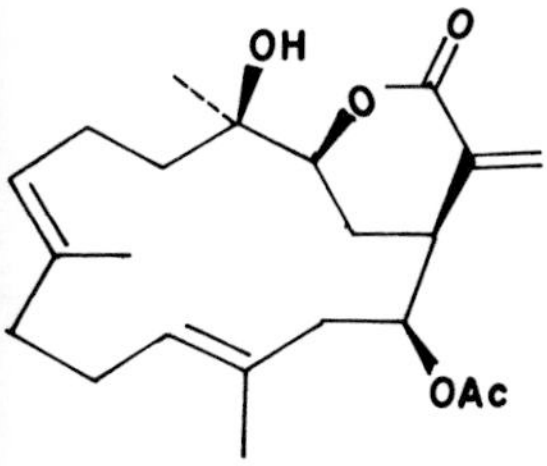

CRASSIN ACETATE

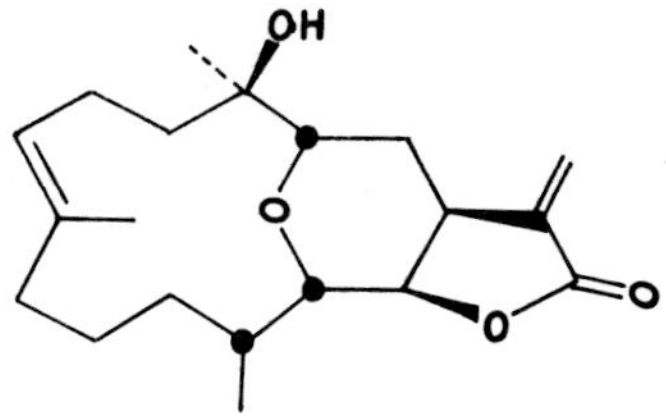

EUNICIN

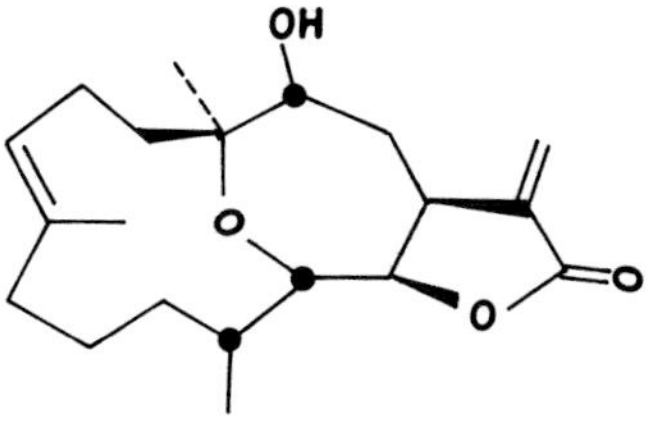

JEUNICIN

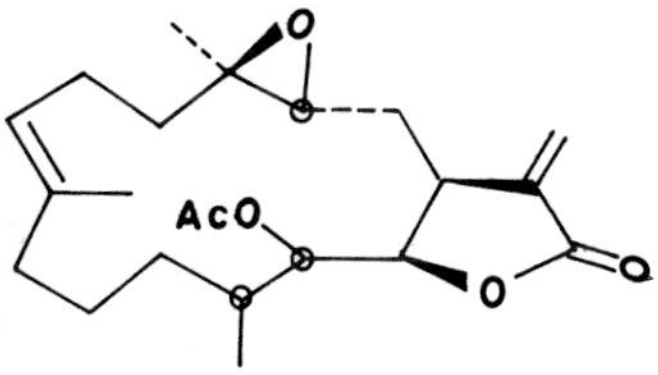

EUPALMERIN ACETATE

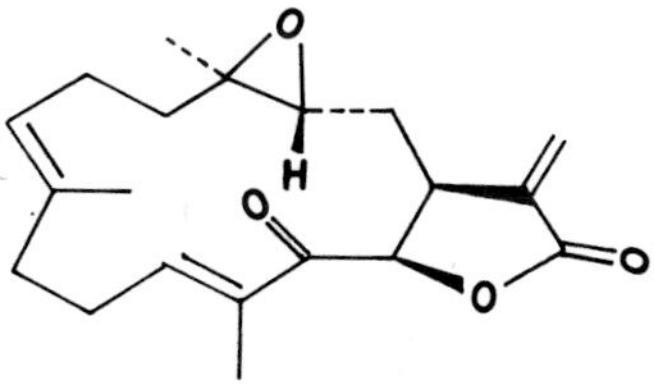

PEUNICIN

When larvae were exposed to eunicin solutions in seawater, the cilia did not simply "fall off", nor did the ciliated cells come free, as they do in normal metamorphosis. The cilia disappeared as though dissolved or resorbed.

Jeunicin—Larvae exposed to jeunicin at 5 or 10 ppm showed declining activity within 2 hours, with 100% mortality in 24 hours. At 1 ppm, the larvae were stressed within 24 hours. They were not swimming but still alive by day 3.

Eupalmerin acetate—At 5 and 10 ppm, larvae became inactive within 1 hour; all were dead in 24 hours. At 1 ppm, larvae were still swimming after 17 hours of exposure; most were dead in 48 hours.

Peunicin—At 5 ppm, larvae were paralyzed within 10 minutes. After 16 hours, most larvae lost their velar cilia; in 48 hours all were dead.

Discussion

Larvae of *Phestilla* normally undergo metamorphosis in response to a product released by their prey, the scleractinian coral *Porites compressa*

147

(10,11). A major feature of metamorphosis is loss of velar cilia. Since the cilia are the organelles which provide the swimming force in the larvae, the pelagic life is ended when larvae lose their cilia (8). The gorgonian cembranolides, in that they also induce ciliary loss, might act thus as artificial or incomplete metamorphic inducers for *Phestilla* larvae, a possibility that will be further clarified when the structure of the true inducer is elucidated (11).

More likely than the above suggestion is one that the gorgonian products display more general toxicity; one symptom of this toxicity is ciliary destruction. This notion is supported by the fact that we could not, by serial dilution of the cembranolides, separate the anti-ciliary activity from lethal doses.

One of the few, and perhaps the most prominent of the feeders on Caribbean gorgonians, is the flamingo tongue snail, *Cyphoma gibbosum* (12). This gastropod is exposed to large doses of cembranolides while it browses on gorgonians, apparently without ill effect. It may be interesting to expose larval forms of *Cyphoma* to cembranolides to determine what the effects may be. It is possible that the cembranolides, or related compounds, trigger metamorphosis and consequently selective settling of *Cyphoma* on gorgonians while acting as chemical defenses against other organisms. This would be another example of a selective adaptation to noxious substances.

Other gastropods of the Family *Ovulidae* (13) are associated with octocorals. The egg cowry, *Ovula ovum*, is usually found on soft corals on which it feeds (14), as is the umbilicate false cowry, *Calpurnus verrucosus* (12). It is possible that the otherwise noxious cembrene derivatives secreted by the octocorals serve as"homing" signals to the larval forms of their gastropod associates by immobilizing the larvae without killing them. This would require selective action on the cilia involved in swimming. If all of the cilia, internally in the gut, sensory and excretory organs, as well as externally in the velar swimming ridges, were lost, the larva could not survive for long. It is possible that there may be selective absorption of the cembranolides. We have made chance observations that some ciliates are not affected.

Acknowledgments

We thank William F. Van Heukelem for his able technical assistance. This work was supported in part by NIH Grant No. 1 RO 1 RR01057, and in part by U.S. Department of Commerce Sea Grant Project 3-158-56.

References

1. Ciereszko, L.S. and Karns, T.K.B. (1973). Comparative Biochemistry of Coral Reef Coelenterates. In *Biology and Geology of Coral Reefs*, Eds. O.A. Jones and R. Endean., Vol. II, Biology 1, Academic Press, Inc., New York, p. 183.
2. Tursch, B. (1976). Some Recent Developments in the Chemistry of Alcyonaceans. *Pure and Applied Chemistry* **48**, 1.
3. Braekman, J.C. (1977). Recent Developments in Terpenoid and Steroid Chemistry of Alcyonacea. In *Marine Natural Products Chemistry*, Eds. D.J. Faulkner and W. H. Fenical, Plenum Press, New York, p. 5.
4. Kashman, Y. (1977). Cembrane Derivatives from *Sarcophytum glaucum. ibid.* p. 17.
5. Ciereszko, L.S. (1962). Chemistry of Coelenterates. III. Occurrence of antimicrobial terpenoid compounds in zooxanthellae of alcyonarians. *Trans. N. Y. Acad. Sci.* Ser. II **24**, 502.
6. Perkins, D.L. and Ciereszko, L.S. (1973). The Environmental Toxicity of Crassin Acetate Using *Tetrahymena pyriformis* as a Model. *Hydrobiologia* **42**, 77.
7. Perkins, D.L. and Ciereszko, L.S. (1974). Effect of a Macrocyclic Diterpene from Tobacco on *Tetrahymena pyriformis* (GL). *Proc. Okla. Acad. Sci.* **54**, 34.
8. Bonar, D.B. and Hadfield, M.G. (1974). Metamorphosis of the Marine Gastropod *P. sibogae* Bergh (Nudibranchia: Aeolidacea). Light and electron microscopic analysis of larval and metamorphic stages. *J. Exp. Mar. Biol. Ecol.* **16**, 227.
9. Chang, C.Y. (1977). I. Purification and Characterization of Briarein A, a Chlorine Containing Diterpenoid from Gorgonian *Briareum asbestinum* (Pallas). II. Isolation and Characterization of Two New Cembranolides from the Gorgonian *Eunicea succinea* (Pallas); Peunicin and Isopeunicin. III. Location of Methyl Group in Methylgorgostanol. Ph.D. Dissertation, The University of Oklahoma, Norman.
10. Hadfield, M.G. and Karlson, R.H. (1969). Externally Induced Metamorphosis in a Marine Gastropod. *Amer. Zoologist* **9**, 317.
11. Hadfield, M.G. (1977). Chemical Interactions in Larval Settling of a Marine Gastropod. In *Marine Natural Products Chemistry.* Eds. D. J. Faulkner and W. H. Fenical. Plenum Press, New York, p. 403
12. Abbott, R. T. (1972). *Kingdom of the Seashell.* Crown Publishers, Inc., New York, pp. 98, 153.
13. Emerson, W.K. and Jacobson, M.K. (1976). *American Museum of Natural History Guide to Shells,* Alfred A. Knopf, p. 109.

14. Bennett, I. (1971). *The Great Barrier Reef.* Lansdowne Press Pty., Ltd., Melbourne, p. 130.

SECTION IV

**Biochemical and Chemical
Studies on Marine Animals
and Plants**

Bromoperoxidase From The Red Algae
Bonnemasisonia hamifera

Richard F. Theiler, J. S. Siuda and Lowell P. Hager
Department of Biochemistry
University of Illinois
Urbana, Illinois

During the Alpha Helix Baja California Expedition of 1974, over 1,000 samples of marine organisms were collected and surveyed for halometabolites (1). This work demonstrated the widespread occurrence of both organic bromine and chlorine containing compounds and indicated that expanded studies on the chemistry of marine natural products would lead to the discovery and characterization of many new halometabolites. About 25% of the organisms collected on the Baja Expedition yielded lipid extracts which contained in excess of 10 mcg of organic halogen per gram wet weight of tissue. Within this survey, the red algae (Rhodophyta) were found to be a rich source of halogen containing organic compounds (Table I). This finding was not unexpected, as red algae have been recognized as halogen rich since the late 1800's (2). Five orders of red algae (Nemaliales, Cryptonemiales, Grigartinales, Rhodymeniales, and Ceramiales) are known to contain a diverse array of halogenated terpenes, hydrocarbons and phenols (3). More recently, members of the family Bonnemaisoniaceae (Nemaliales) have been shown to produce quite a different class of polyhalogenated organic molecules (4-6). These compounds include 1,1,3,3-tetrabromo-2-heptanones, dibromo-, tribromo-, and bromoiodo-2-heptanones, as well as halogenated acetones, butenones, and haloforms.

Our first objective in the study of marine halometabolites has been the elucidation of the structures of halogen containing natural products in organisms known to contain large amounts of organo-bromine and chlorine. Secondly, we are interested in examining the biosynthesis and metabolism of these compounds. We have assumed that the biogensis of marine halometabolites must encompass halogenation reactions similar to those of chloroperoxidase. Chloroperoxidase, which has been purified from the fungus, Caldariomyces fumago, is capable of introducing iodine, bromine, and chlorine atoms into organic molecules via an electrophilic substitution mechanism (7). More recently, peroxidase activity has been

Table I

The Halogen Content of Various Rhodophyta Species

Rhodophyta Scientific Name	mcg Organo-Halogen/100 mg Dry Weight		Organo-Bromine as % Total Halogen	Total Halogen as % Dry Weight
	Organo-Bromine	Total Halogen		
Asparagopsis taxiformis	122	222	55	0.22
Bonnemaisonia hamifera	105	120	88	0.12
Laurencia pacifica	189	291	65	0.29
Plocamium pacificum	199	638	31	0.64

demonstrated in extracts from red (8), brown (9) and green (10) algae. Crude extracts from the brown algae *(Laminaria digitata)* and green algae *(Enteromorpha linza)* have been shown to incorporate iodide into tyrosine whereas the red algae *(Cystoclonium purpureum)* has reportedly been shown to incorporate bromide, but not iodide, into halogenated phenols. However, additional information and especially pure enzyme preparations must be obtained if we are to understand biological halogenation reactions involving polyhalogenated ketones, terpenes and haloforms.

In this study we have examined biological halogenation reactions in the odorous algae, *Bonnemaisonia hamifera.* A powerful brominating activity has been detected in crude extracts of the algae. Extracts of *B. hamifera* have been previously shown to contain major quantities of brominated and minor quantities of iodinated derivatives of 2-heptanone (4). The *B. hamifera* bromoperoxidase has been partially purified and differs from chloroperoxidase in two important aspects.

Methods

B. hamifera was collected in the vicinity of Punta Mejia off the Northernmost point of Isla Angel De La Guarda in the Gulf of California in March of 1974. The algae were collected by scuba divers at depths of 15–40 feet, after which algal samples were stored frozen at–20° C.

Enzyme Assays

As shown in figure 1, the rate of formation of 2-bromo-2chloro-5, 5-dimethyl-1, 3-cyclohexanedione (bromochlorodimedon) from 2-chloro-

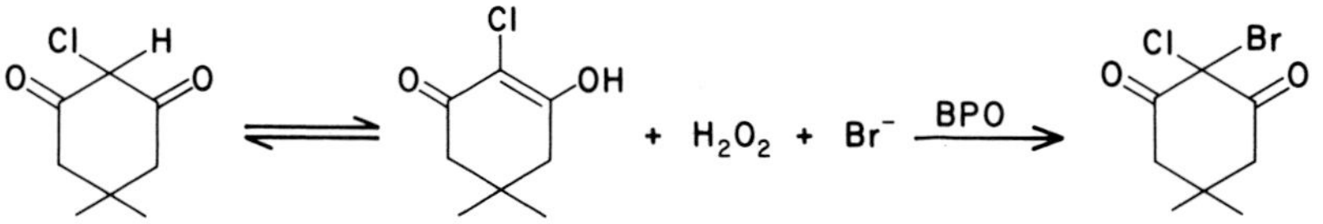

AS MEASURED BY DECREASE IN ABSORBANCE

At 292 mμ (pH 5.4, $\epsilon = 20,000 M^{-1} cm^{-1}$)

FIGURE 1. The standard assay employed for detection of biological halogenation. For bromoperoxidase the standard assay was based upon the rate of formation of bromochlorodimedon from monochlorodimedon.

155

5,5-dimethyl-1,3-cyclohexanedione (monochlorodimedon) formed the basis of the standard assay for bromoperoxidase activity (11). The reac tion mixture contained 100 mcmoles of potassium phosphate-citrate buf fer pH 5.4, 1 mcmole of hydrogen peroxide, 0.2 mcmoles of monochlorodimedon (MCD), 100 mcmoles of halogen anion and a suitable quantity of enzyme in a total volume of 2 ml. Reactions were in itiated by the addition of enzyme and assays were monitored by the decrease in absorbance at 292 nm, $\epsilon = 20,000$. In this communication specific activities reported for enzyme preparations were based upon the standard assay for bromoperoxidase activity.

The enzymatic formation of iodine was measured by the increase in ab sorbance at 350 nm due to the formation of I_3^-. The triiodide reaction mixtures contained 100 mcmoles of phosphate-citrate buffer pH 5.4, bromoperoxidase, 1 mcmole of hydrogen peroxide and variable concen trations of iodide in a total volume of 2 ml.

Fluorescence measurements of the rate of tyrosine halogenation were monitored by the decrease in tyrosine fluorescence at excitation and emission wavelengths of 275 nm and 303 nm, respectively (11). Reaction mixtures contained 100 mcmoles of phosphate-citrate buffer pH 5.4, 1 mcmole of hydrogen peroxide, and 10 mcmoles of iodide or bromide ion and a suitable quantity of bromoperoxidase in a total volume of 2 ml.

Radiobromination Assays With $^{77}Br^-$

Incubation mixtures contained 150 mcmoles of phosphate-citrate buf fer pH 5.4, 150 mcmoles of radioactive $^{77}Br^-$ at a specific activity of 20,000 cpm per mcmole, 300 microlitres of partially purified bromoperoxidase, 1.5 mcmoles of hydrogen peroxide plus 10 mcmoles of a suitable acceptor molecule in a total volume of 3.0 ml. Reaction mix tures were incubated at room temperature over a period of 30 min during which time an additional 1.5 mcmoles of hydrogen peroxide was added to the reaction mixture every 3 min. The enzyme assays were terminated by the addition of 1.8 ml of 7 N sulfuric acid. The reaction mixtures were extracted twice with two volumes of diethyl ether. The ether extracts were dried over $MgSO_4$, concentrated to a small volume, and radioactivi ty was determined utilizing a gamma counter.

Radiobromination of Bovine Serum Albumin

Bovine serum albumin (10 mg) was radiolabeled with $^{77}Br^-$ at a specific activity of 200,000 cpm per mcmole. Incubation mixtures contained BSA, 150 mcmoles of phosphate-citrate buffer, 15 mcmoles of $^{77}Br^-$,

).15 mcmoles of hydrogen peroxide and 300 microlitres of partially purified bromoperoxidase in a total volume of 3.0 ml. The enzyme radiobromination reactions were carried out at the pH optimum of bromoperoxidase (pH 5.4) as well as at pH values of 6.0 and 7.0. Reaction mixtures were incubated at room temperature over a period of 30 min. during which time an additional 0.15 mcmoles of hydrogen peroxide was added to the reaction mixture every 3 min. The radiobromination reactions were terminated by the addition of an equal volume of ice cold 10% trichloroacetic acid. Protein precipitates were isolated by centrifugation at 15,000 x g for 10 min. The supernatants were discarded and residue fractions were resuspended, washed, and centrifuged two additional times with 10% TCA to remove non-covalently bound $^{77}Br^-$. Radioactivity due to covalently bound ^{77}Br labeled protein was determined utilizing a gamma counter.

Materials

Buffers used in these experiments were made with glass-distilled water and reagent grade chemicals. Phosphate-citrate buffers were made by titrating a known concentration of dibasic potassium phosphate with a concentrated citric acid solution to the desired pH. The substrates *beta*-ketoadipic acid, acetoacetic acid, and bovine serum albumin were purchased from Sigma Chemical Co., St. Louis, Mo. 3-Ketooctanoic acid was synthesized by a modification of the method of Ställberg-Stenhagen (12).

Results

Preparation of bromoperoxidase—Crude homogenates of bromoperoxidase were routinely prepared by homogenizing 50 gm of frozen algae with 100 ml of 0.05 M phosphate-citrate buffer pH 6.0. Samples were homogenized at 3° C for 10 min utilizing an Omnimixer (Ivan Sorvall, Inc.) after which the mixture was subjected to sonic oscillation (Branson) for 3 min in 15-sec bursts. The supernatant fraction containing solubilized bromoperoxidase was isolated by centrifugation at 15,000 x g for 20 min. The red viscous supernatant fraction containing the enzyme could be stored at 4° C for periods up to several months without significant losses of brominating activity.

Partial purification—Utilizing a series of repetitive extractions and two buffer systems, the enzyme could be routinely purified 5–10 fold when compared to the activity of crude homogenates. Frozen algae (50 gm) was homogenized, sonicated and centrifugated as described above with 100 ml of 0.1 M Tris-HCl buffer pH 8.0 containing 0.1 M NaCl and 1 mM EDTA. The supernatant (S1) was removed and the residue was again extracted with 100 ml of the same buffer. The resulting supernatant (S2) was removed and the residue was further extracted two additional times with 100 ml of 0.05 M phosphate-citrate buffer pH 6.0. Repetitive extractions gave rise to four supernatant fractions (S1–S4) the latter of which yielded an enzyme fraction purified some 8-fold over the crude homogenate (Table II).

Fractionation on DEAE-cellulose—The supernatant fraction S4 (Table II) was subsequently subjected to ion-exchange chromatography on DEAE-cellulose. The enzyme was applied to a column in 0.05 M phosphate-citrate buffer pH 6.0 and was eluted with a gradient from 0 to 2.0 M in NaCl (Fig. 2). Peak fractions of bromoperoxidase activity were subsequently pooled, dialyzed, lyophilized, and resuspended in a suitable volume of 0.05 M phosphate-citrate buffer, pH 6.0. Lyophilization of bromoperoxidase resulted in about a 50% loss of activity, however, the resuspended enzyme when stored at 4° C was stable with little or no loss of activity for periods of up to six weeks. To date, bromoperoxidase has been routinely purified some 25-fold, with a 25–30% overall recovery of enzymatic activity (Table II).

Bromoperoxidase assays—In this study, the standard assay for detection of biological halogenation contained the acceptor molecule, monochlorodimedon (MCD), hydrogen peroxide and bromide ion as

Table II
A Summary of the Partial Purification of Bromoperoxidase

Sample	Specific Activity[*]	Fold Purification	% Yield
Crude Homogenate	5	1	100
Sequential			
Extraction S1	0.1	–	1
S2	0.3	–	1
S3	4	–	5
S4	41	8	93
Concentrated sample from DEAE-cellulose	120	24	25

[*]mcmoles of MCD brominated/minute/mg protein

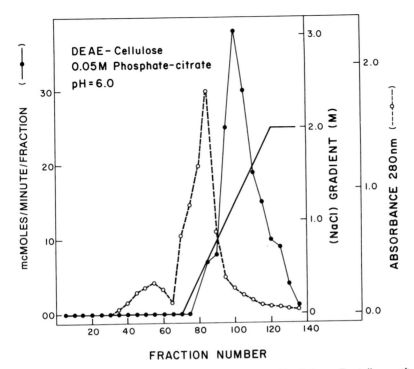

FIGURE 2. Fractionation of bromoperoxidase on DEAE-cellulose. Partially purified samples containing the enzyme were chromatographed by ion exchange chromatography in 0.05 M phosphate-citrate buffer pH 6.0. Protein was monitored by absorbance at 280 nm and enzyme activity was measured by the bromination of monochlorodimedon. Protein which bound to the resin was eluted with a linear gradient of 0-2.0 M NaCl. The peak fraction of bromoperoxidase activity eluted between 1.1 and 1.2 M NaCl. Ion exchange columns were poured in glass columns (2.5 x 20 cm) and contained a bed volume of about 100 ml. The recovery of enzymatic activity ranged from 50-60%.

outlined under Methods. Utilizing this assay, extracts of the algae were found to actively brominate MCD. The formation of bromo-chlorodimedon was linear with respect to increased enzyme concentration (Fig. 3). Furthermore, the rate of bromination was critically dependent upon the molar concentrations of hydrogen peroxide and bromide in the reaction medium (Fig. 4). The effect of bromide ion concentration on the rate of bromination of MCD obeys typical first order reaction kinetics at low substrate concentrations shifting to zero order at high concentrations. The enzyme exhibited maximal velocity at 0.05 M bromide ion concentration. Similarly, hydrogen peroxide showed maximal velocity at 1 mM, while both substrates served as effective inhibitors of the enzyme at high concentrations (Fig. 4).

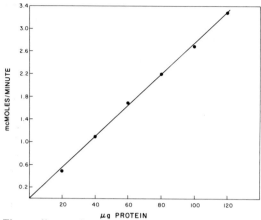

FIGURE 3. The effect of enzyme concentration on the bromination of monochlorodimedon. Reactions were performed under the standard assay conditions described in Materials and Methods.

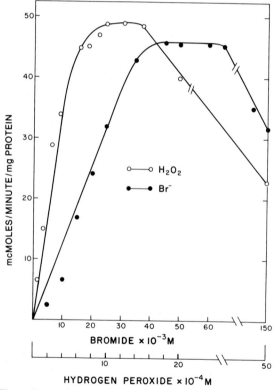

FIGURE 4. The effect of substrate concentration on the rate of bromination of monochlorodimedon. Assay conditions are the same as those described in Materials and Methods with the corresponding variation in bromide concentration and hydrogen peroxide as indicated.

pH optimum —The pH optimum for enzymatic halogenation is an important aspect of the reaction catalyzed by bromoperoxidase. Utilizing MCD as a substrate, the enzyme elicited activity at a rather broad pH-range (Fig. 5). The pH optimum for bromination of MCD was found to be 5.4, although this optimum may vary somewhat depending upon the nature of the acceptor molecule. A pH optimum of 5.4 has also been reported for peroxidases from a number of different species of marine algae (8–10). It is important to note that unlike chloroperoxidase, bromoperoxidase is capable of performing halogenation reactions in the physiological pH range.

Halogen ion oxidation other than bromide ion —The ability of bromoperoxidase to catalyze the oxidation of iodide was measured by spectrophotometrically monitoring the formation of I_3^- (Fig. 6). The rate of

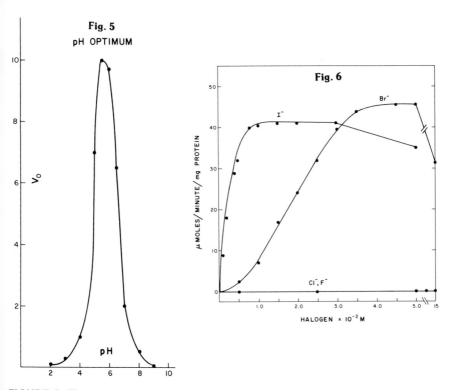

FIGURE 5. The pH optimum for bromination of monochlorodimedon. Enzyme assays were performed as described in Materials and Methods. All data points represent the pH prior to incubation in the presence of the enzyme.

FIGURE 6. The ability of bromoperoxidase to oxidize halide ions. Enzyme assays were performed as described in Materials and Methods except for variations in the concentration of halide ion as indicated. Reaction rates were measured as follows: For I^-, the rate of formation of I_3^-; for Br^-, Cl^- and F^-, the rate of halogenation of monochlorodimedon.

oxidation was first order at low I^- concentrations becoming zero order at higher concentrations. As its names implies, bromoperoxidase was unable to oxidize either Cl^- or F^- but can effectively oxidize I^- or Br^-.

Bromoperoxidase as a hemoprotein — The purest samples of bromoperoxidase obtained did not exhibit a distinct Soret Band and had a high background absorbance in the 350–400 nm range. In order to overcome this problem, difference spectra between the oxidized and dithionite reduced forms of the enzyme were recorded (Fig. 7). The difference spectra showed absorbance maxima at 419, 512 and 553 nm in-

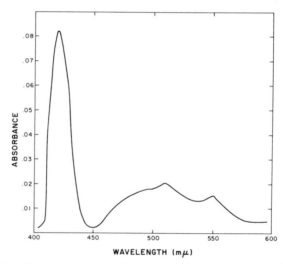

WAVELENGTH (mμ)

FIGURE 7. The difference spectrum between oxidized and reduced bromoperoxidase. The difference spectrum was measured on preparations of the enzyme that were purified some 30 -fold. Hemeprotein was reduced by adding a small amount of sodium dithionite to a cuvette containing the sample.

dicating that bromoperoxidase is a typical hemeprotein. Comparison of these spectra to the difference spectra for crystalline cytochrome b_5 (13) yielded nearly identical absorbance maxima and minimum, suggesting the presence of a low spin heme environment in the partially purified preparations. In addition, the enzyme was tested against a number of known inhibitors of both hemeproteins and flavoproteins (Table III). Acriflavin and 8-hydroxyquinoline, known inhibitors of flavoproteins, failed to inhibit the enzyme at concentrations as high as $10^{-3}M$. These findings tend to rule out a flavin prosthetic group in the bromoperoxidase reaction.

From the spectral data and sensitivity of the enzyme to cyanide (50% inhibition at $10^{-5}M$) and azide (50% inhibition at less than $10^{-5}M$), we

Table III
Effect of Various Inhibitors on Bromoperoxidase

Assays were performed according to the standard assay procedure outlined in Materials and Methods with the inhibitor included at the concentration indicated. All incubations were performed at the pH optimum for enzymatic bromination.

Inhibitor	Concentration mcM	Inhibition %
Sodium Azide	10	83
	100	100
Potassium Cyanide	10	53
	100	100
2,4-dinitrophenol	10	0
	100	0
8-hydroxyquinoline	10	0
	100	0
Acriflavin	10	0
	100	0

conclude that bromoperoxidase is most likely a hemeprotein.

Nucleophiles as halogen acceptors —Investigations were initiated in order to determine the types of substrates which bromoperoxidase could use as acceptors for the synthesis of halometabolites. Since brominated heptanones are the major halogen containing compounds in *B. hamifera* the beta-ketoacids, 3-ketooctanoic acid and 3-ketoadipic acid, were examined as potential biosynthetic precursors. Typical reactions involving an enzyme bound halogenium ion as an intermediate were formulated for the reactions as follows:

$$Enz{\sim}Br^+ + HO_2C-(CH_2)-\overset{\overset{\displaystyle O}{\|}}{C} - (CH_2)_4 - CH_3 \longrightarrow$$

$$\longrightarrow CO_2 + Br-CH_2-\overset{\overset{\displaystyle O}{\|}}{C}-(CH_2)_4 - CH_3$$

In addition, suitable precursors for halogenated acetones and aromatic compounds would be represented by acetoacetic acid, and benzylalcohol or aniline.

Each of these nucleophiles was subsequently examined as a substrate acceptor by incubating bromoperoxidase, hydrogen peroxide, and radioactive $^{77}Br^-$ with the acceptor molecule as described in Materials

163

and Methods. The results of these experiments (Table IV) demonstrated that bromoperoxidase is capable of catalyzing the conversion of radioactive $^{77}Br^-$ into an ether-extractable organic form when supplied with a variety of acceptor molecules. Although not all of the products of these reactions have been structurally defined, we feel it is safe to assume that beta-ketoacids and substituted phenols are precursors for two of the major classes of halometabolites found in red algae. These include brominated ketones and phenols.

Table IV
Radiobromination of Suitable Acceptor Molecules by Bromoperoxidase

Radiobromination experiments were performed according to the procedure outlined in Materials and Methods. Reaction mixtures 1-6 and 8 contained 0.1 mg of partially purified bromoperoxidase with a specific activity of 120 mcmoles/min/mg protein.

#	Compound	Ether Extractable Radioactivity c.p.m.	Net Incorporation c.p.m.
1	3-ketooctanoic acid	41,000	34,000
2	3-ketoadipic acid	38,000	31,000
3	Monochlorodimedon	22,000	15,000
4	Acetoacetic acid	14,000	7,000
5	Anisole	15,000	8,000
6	Benzylalcohol	8,000	1,000
7	Control 1*	6,800	
8	Control 2#	7,200	

*A control reaction which included 3-ketooctanoic acid as a nucleophile, hydrogen peroxide and $^{77}Br^-$.

#A control reaction which included bromoperoxidase, hydrogen peroxide and $^{77}Br^-$.

Radiobromination of bovine serum albumin—In addition to its ability to synthesize marine halometabolites, bromoperoxidase is capable of incorporating $^{77}Br^-$ into protein. Radiobromination of bovine serum albumin (BSA) was examined by incubating bromoperoxidase, hydrogen peroxide and radioactive $^{77}Br^-$ with the protein as described in Materials and Methods. The results of these experiments (Table V) demonstrated

Table V
Radiobromination of Bovine Serum Albumin (BSA)

Radiobromination experiments were performed as described in Materials and Methods. Reactions 1-3 contained 0.1 mg of partially purified bromoperoxidase with a specific activity of 130 mcmoles/min/mg protein.

#	Compound	Reaction pH	TCA Precipitable c.p.m.	Net Incorporation c.p.m.
1	BSA	5.4	49,000	47,000
2	BSA	6.0	46,000	44,000
3	BSA	7.0	25,000	23,000
4	Control*	6.4	2,000	

*The control reaction mixture contained 10 mg of BSA, hydrogen peroxide and 77Br-.

that the enzyme is capable of radiolabeling proteins at its pH optimum (pH 5.4) as well as pH values of 6.0 and 7.0. Radiolabeling of BSA was primarily the result of enzyme catalyzed bromination of the tyrosinyl residues of the protein. This has been demonstrated by measuring the rate of iodination or bromination of free tyrosine as monitored by the decrease in tyrosine fluorscence as a function of time (Fig. 8).

Discussion

Some progress has been made in the isolation and purification of bromoperoxidase from *B. hamifera*. However, the purification of this enzyme has been complicated by the association of large quantities of carbohydrate with fractions containing the partially purified enzyme. Ion exchange column fractions containing bromoperoxidase were found to contain a carbohydrate to protein ratio of 15:1 by weight. The chromatographic properties of these preparations suggest that the enzyme is covalently attached or tightly associated with an anionic polysaccharide similar in structure to plant alginates.

Previous results revealed that the general halogenation reaction catalyzed by the *B. hamifera* peroxidase can be written as follows:

$$X^- + H_2O_2 + HA \longrightarrow AX + OH^- + H_2O$$

where X^- represents bromide or iodide and HA represents a nucleophilic halogen acceptor molecule.

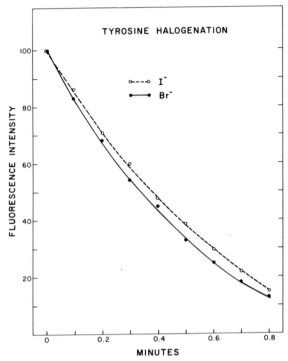

FIGURE 8. The rate of tyrosine halogenation as measured by the decrease in tyrosine fluorescence as a function of time. Assays were performed as described in Methods. The rate of bromination of tyrosine in a reaction which included 5 mcg of partially purified bromoperoxidase with a specific activity of 40 mcmoles/min/mg protein. The rate of iodination of tyrosine in a reaction which included 1 mcg of the enzyme. Tyrosine fluorescence was measured at 303 nm after irradiation at 275 nm.

Bromoperoxidase like chloroperoxidase has been shown to possess a broad specificity with respect to halogen acceptor molecules. However, radiobromination experiments revealed that beta-ketoacids and cyclic beta-diketones are particularly good acceptors whereas substituted phenols are significantly less effective. These findings were certainly not unexpected as brominated ketones are the predominant halometabolites of the algae (4). Larger scale reactions are currently being conducted with the aim of defining the precursor: production relationships that are essential for the biosynthesis of naturally occurring halometabolites. Utilizing GC-MS several of the reaction products from the enzymatic bromination of 3-ketooctanoic acid have been identified. These include 1-bromo-, 1, 1-dibromo-, and 1, 1, 1-tribromo-2-heptanones.

Bromoperoxidase has been found to be identical to all other heme peroxidases in its ability to oxidize iodide ion (15). However, unlike horseradish peroxidase and many other peroxidases, bromoperoxidase also utilizes bromide for enzymatic halogenation. In addition, bromoperoxidase differs from chloroperoxidase in two important aspects. First, the pH optimum for the halogenating activity of these enzymes is quite different. Bromoperoxidase has a pH optimum of 5.4 while chloroperoxidase is inactive above pH 4.5. Secondly, chloroperoxidase will oxidize chloride ion whereas bromoperoxidase will not. This latter difference entertains certain questions regarding the mechanism of synthesis of chlorine containing compounds in numberous species of red algae. We suggest that peroxidative halogenation with chloride is dependent upon the presence of an algal peroxidase capable of oxidizing Cl^- to Cl^+. However, based on the properties of other heme-peroxidases, an enzyme capable of oxidizing chloride ion should then also be capable of oxidizing both I^- and Br^-. Why therefore should chlorinated metabolites predominate? The predominace of chlorine containing compounds in some species of algae can be explained by the abundance and availability of chloride ion to act as a substrate. In seawater the molar ratio of halide ions is about 120,000:2,000:1 for Cl^-, Br^- and I^-, respectively (15). Assuming that a particular halogen ion is not selectively concentrated, an organism possessing a peroxidase capable of oxidizing chloride would, on the basis of substrate concentration, contain predominantly chlorine-containing halometabolites. Furthermore, in instances where the peroxidase cannot oxidize chloride but can oxidize bromide and iodide, brominated halometabolites should predominate. Such is the case with bromoperoxidase which is capable of oxidizing both I^- and Br^-. The selectivity of *B. hamifera* for the synthesis of brominated halometabolites must be a consequence of the intracellular ratio of Br^- to I^- which for seawater is greater than 2,000 to 1. Other factors undoubtedly enter into selective halogenation. For example, preferential membrane permeability, the affinity of the enzyme for halide ion, and the stability of the halogenated molecules themselves could be involved. However, the simplest explanation would be based on the relationship of oxidation-reduction potentials for the peroxidase coupled with the intracellular halide ion concentration. We reject the concept presented by Fenical (15) and others (16) that the explanation for selective halogenation lies in the formation of an enzyme-halogen complex which is capable of oxidizing bromide but incapable of oxidizing iodide. The final answer to this question will not obviously be resolved until a number of other algal halogenating enzymes have been purified.

In addition to its utility for understanding the synthesis of marine halometabolites, bromoperoxidase will also readily catalyze the incorporation of [77]Br into the tyrosinyl residues of bovine serum albumin in the pH range of 5.4 to 7.0. The rates of free tyrosine halogenation with either I^- or Br^- have also been monitored by measuring the decrease in tyrosine fluorscence as a function of time. Accordingly, future studies with bromoperoxidase will include optimizing conditions for radiolabeling proteins at physiological pH with carrier-free $^{77}Br^-$ (17). We conclude that bromoperoxidase-catalyzed halogenation reactions at physiological pH may prove to be of practical importance in the labeling of proteins for use in nuclear medicine (18).

Acknowledgments

We wish to thank Drs. K. D. McElvany, L. C. Knight, and M. J. Welch at the Mallinckrodt Institute of Radiology, Washington University School of Medicine for providing radioactive bromine. Financial support was provided by a grant from the National Science Foundation (NSF PCM 76-12547).

References

1. Hager, L. P., *et al.* (1976). A Survey of Organic Halogens in Marine Organisms. In *Proc. Food-Drugs From the Sea*, Marine Technol. Soc. Washington,D.C. pp. 421-428.
2. Robertson, D. (1896). *Trans. Nat. Hist. Soc. Glasgow* **41**, 1972.
3. Siuda, J. F. and DeBernardis, J. F. (1973). Naturally Occurring Halogenated Organic Compounds. *Lloydia* **36**, 107.
4. Siuda, J. F. *et al.* (1975). 1-Iodo-3, 3-dibromo-2-heptanone, 1,1,3,3-tetra-bromo-2-heptanone, and Related Compounds from the Red Alga *Bonnemaisonia hamifera. J. Am. Chem. Soc.* **97**, 937.
5. Burreson, B. J. and Moore, R. E. (1975). Haloforms in the Essential Oil of the Alga *Asparagopsis taxiformis* (rhodophyta). *Tetrahedron Letters* **7**, 473.
6. McConnell, O. and Fenical, W. (1977). Halogen Chemistry of Red Alga *Asparagopsis. Phytochemistry* **16**, 367.
7. Morris, D. R. and Hager. L. P. (1966). Chloroperoxidase: Isolation and properties of the crystalline glycoprotein. *J. Biol. Chem.* **421**, 1763.
8. Murphy, M. J. and O'hEocha, C. (1973). Peroxidase from the Red Alga *Cystoclonium purpureum. Phytochemistry* **12**, 55.
9. Murphy, M. J. and O'hEocha, C. (1973). Peroxidase Activity in the Brown Alga *Laminara digitata. Phytochemistry* **12**, 2645.
10. Murphy, M. J. and O'hEocha, C. (1973). Peroxidase from the Green Alga *Enteromorpha linza. Phytochemistry* **12**, 61.
11. Hager, L. P. *et al.* (1966). Chloroperoxidase: utilization of halogen anions. *J. Biol. Chem.* **241**, 1769.
12. Stallberg-Stenhagen, S. (1945). *Ark. Kemi. Min. and Geol.* **20A**, No. 19.

13. Deeb, S. S. and Hager, L. P. (1964). Crystalline Cytochrome b_1 from *Escherichia coli. J. Biol. Chem.* **239**, 1024.
14. Hager, L. P. (1974). The Mechanism of Enzymatic Halogenation and its Relation to the Labeling of Cell Surface Structures. *Miami Winter Symposia* **8**, 27.
15. Fenical, W. (1975). Halogenation in the Rhodophyta. *J. Phycol.* **11**, 245.
16. Pedersen, M. (1976). A Brominating and Hydroxylating Peroxidase from the Red Alga *Cystoclonium purpureum. Physiol. Plant.* **37**, 6.
17. McElvany, K. D., *et al.* (1977). Use of Bromoperoxidase, an Algal Enzyme, in the Preparation of Radiobrominated Proteins. Abst. from 9th International Seaweed Symposium, Santa Barbara, Calif. In *"Algae and Pharmaceutical Science"*, W. deGruyter Pub. Co., W. German, 1978.
18. Knight, L., *et al.* (1975). [77]Br: a new protein label. In *"Radiopharmaceuticals"*, Eds. Subramanian, Rhodes, Cooper, and Sodd, Society of Nuclear Medicine, Inc., N. Y., Publisher. pp. 149-154.

Silicon And Iodine Metabolites From Marine Plants

Dietrich Werner

University of Marburg Institute of Botony
Marburg, West Germany

Sea water as the major source for biological marine production includes more than 70 different elements in the solvent water (1-3), out of which about 25 are considered to be essential elements (4). The element concentrations span about 15 orders of magnitude (5.4 x 10^{-1} M Cl, to 3.5 x 10^{-16} M Ra). Eleven elements are considered as major elements and all others as minor constituents. Studies on the metabolism of two trace elements, silicon and iodine, are reported here, using diatoms and red algae as organisms, which use and accumulate these elements in unusual quantities.

Silicon Metabolism in Diatoms

The silicon content in sea water varies significantly, as that of other bioelements, between 5000 mcg/l and less than 1 mcg/l in various parts of the oceans and in different seasons (5). The diatom *Coscinodiscus asteromphalus*, with an SiO_2 content of 38% per dry weight (6) and 40 ng Si per cell (110 mcm valve diameter) (7) accumulates Si up to an amount of 100 g per litre. This means that the concentration factor is more than 10^8, based upon a utilization by the cells of concentrations less than 1 mcg/l. This is a much higher value than those found, for example, for nickel (10^3) and titanium (10^4) in *Fucus spiralis* or for zinc (1.4 x 10^3) in *Ascophyllum nodosum* (8).

In silicon metabolism of diatoms, we can separate three different aspects (Fig. 1): (i) Si(OH)$_4$ biochemistry which involves uptake of orthosilicic acid, (ii) its transport as unknown intermediate in the cell to silica depositing vesicles, and (iii) the direct connection to the biochemistry of other elements such as boron (9) and potassium (6). The regulation by silicate of other metabolic pathways and activities such as protein, DNA

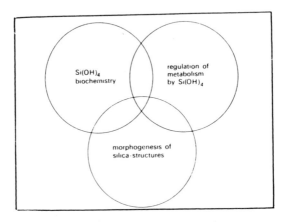

FIGURE 1. Scheme of interaction of silicate metabolism in diatoms.

and chlorophyll biosyntheses, chrysolaminaran utilisation, and fatty acid synthesis are exciting fields of research (7). The morphogenesis of silica structures with the formation of the highly ornamented valves and several other parts of the shells, is connected to $Si(OH)_4$ biochemistry and to several other metabolic pathways such as carbohydrate (diatopectin) and protein (protein-template) metabolism, and to cellular events that are involved in cell wall formation in general.

Shells of diatoms are deposited in enormous quantities on the ocean floor and cover an area of about 30 million km^2 (10). To estimate the changes this material has undergone during the geological periods of deposition, it seemed very desirable to analyze the element composition of cells and shell preparations of a pure culture of the large marine diatom with a new method known as proton induced x-ray emission spectroscopy, ("pixe"). Only these analyses from a defined stage of single species grown under controlled conditions can be the basis to find out the chemical changes this material may have undergone by dissolution (11) or by adsorbing dissolved material, and to see, whether cells or shells of big diatoms might be a source of accumulated trace elements.

The composition of cells of *Coscinodiscus asteromphalus* is summarized in table I. The cells were cultivated in the medium described (12), but with the addition of 0.02 M Tris-HCl, pH 8.0. and in continuously aerated culture in light thermostats at 25°C in a 14:10 hours light: dark regime (12,000 lux during the light phase). The average valve diameter was 135 mcm and the cells were harvested during the light period. Dried cell material was used for CHN and element analysis with "pixe". The silicon content was additionally measured with the molybdate blue reaction and used as a reference value for the other elements with atomic numbers above 14.

The cells are characterized by an equal content of carbon and silicon (each 17% per dry matter) and an unusually high oxygen content due to the $(H_2Si_2O_5 \rightarrow SiO_2)$ content of the thick shells in addition to the oxygen

Table I

Element Analysis of Cells of *Coscinodiscus asteromphalus* **(135 mcm valve-diameter) Determined by Proton Induced X-ray Emission Spectra.**

Element	Atomic No	ng/mg cell dry wt I analysis	ng/mg dry wt II analysis
H[1]	1	27 600	
C	6	170 500	
N	7	3 100	
O	8	450 000 — 500 000	
Si[2]	14	170 000	170 000
P	15	2 313	2 717
S	16	5 309	6 218
C1	17	68 064	77 746
K	19	33131	35 246
Ca	20	886	1 060
Ti	22	6[3]	10
Cr	24	8	7
Mn	25	22	25
Fe	26	283	334
Ni	28	21	23
Cu	29	55	69
Zn	30	45	53
Br	35	392	478
Rb	37	10	9
Sr	38	16	20
Ba	56	27	27
Pb	82	3	—

[1]Determined by CHN -analysis
[2]Determined additionally by chemical methods and used as reference value.
[3]The minimum amount detectable for elements above atomic no. 22 is about 2 ng.

content of the organic compounds. The rather low N content is in agreement with previous analyses of the biochemical composition of the cells (13) in which the potassium content was determined to be twice as high as the protein value, out of which about 1/6 is nitrogen. In the data in table I the potassium content is also about 12 times higher than the nitrogen value. The major anion is chloride. The sulphur content (sulphate and reduced organic sulphur compounds) is only 1/10 of the Cl. In the sea water medium, Br amounts to 65 ppm, about 0.34% of the Cl value (w/w), whereas to about 0.60% in the cells. This means that in the cells we find an accumulation of bromide compared to chloride by a factor of 2.

Calcium and K in the sea water are present in very similar amounts (400 and 410 ppm). In the cells, the accumulation of potassium versus calcium is about 80-fold. Assuming a 25% figure of the fresh weight (volume) per dry weight of the cell, we find calcium not enriched in the cells compared to the sea water. The iron concentration in the cells is 309 ppm per dry weight, and about 75 ppm per cell volume, compared to 0.56 ppm in the sea water medium — an enrichment by a factor of 134.

Copper is enriched about 7,000-fold, from about 2.25 ppb in the medium to 15 ppm (per wet weight) in the cells. However, Zn, due to its higher concentration in the medium (35 ppb) is enriched only about 340-fold. From the other elements also listed in table I, only titanium shall be stressed. The value of 6-10 ppm per dry weight is significantly above detection level. In relation to the 1 ppm found in sea water, we find a small accumulation of this element in the cells of *Coscinodiscus asteromphalus.*

The same elements were analyzed in a preparation of the shells of *Coscinodiscus asteromphalus* (Table II). To avoid any loss of trace elements from the shells, no strong mineral acids were used for purification. Instead, a plasmolyzing agent (60% sucrose) and organic solvents (acetone and methanol) were used.

As we can see from the CHN analysis, the purification of the organic material was incomplete; 84% of the carbon was removed but only a small part of the nitrogen, as we can see from the silicon/carbon and the silicon/nitrogen ratios, based on the dry weight of the cell and the shell preparation.

To evaluate the composition of the shell preparation, the relative increase or decrease of the other elements compared to silicon gives us some idea as to whether or not the elements were firmly bound to the shells or to the adherent cytoplasm fraction.

The potassium/silicon ratio (w/w) decreases from 1:5 to 1:1060, the ratio chlorine/silicon from 1:2.3 to 1: 420 and the ratio phosphorous/-silicon from 1:68 to 1:670. On the other hand, other ratios change much less: calcium/silicon from 1:175 to 1:630, and iron/silicon from 1:550 to 1:1000. Other elements, such as Zn and Cu even increased, perhaps by adsorption to the silica-shells.

Table II

Element Analysis of Shell-preparations of *Coscinodiscus asteromphalus* **(135 mcm valve-diameter), Purified by Plasmolysis (14 hours) in 60% Sucrose and Extraction with Acetone (3 x) and Methanol (1 x). Methods as in Table I.**

Element	Atomic No	ng/mg shell-prepar.2 I analysis	ng/mg shallprepar.2 II analysis
H[1]	1		10 600
C	6		27 500
N	7		6 200
Si[2]	14		420 000
P	15	655	603
S	16	2 643	2 145
Cl	17	1 055	940
K	19	450	328
Ca	20	695	638
Ti	22	18	13
Cr	24	8	5[3]
Mn	25	15	10
Fe	26	440	393
Ni	28	85	60
Cu	29	235	178
Zn	30	483	338
Br	35	-	5
Sr	38	10	8
Ba	56	50	38
Pb	82	45	33

[1]Determined by CHN -analysis.
[2]Determined additionally by chemical methods and used as reference value.
[3]The minimum amount detectable is about 5 ng in this sample.

Iodine Metabolites in Red Algae

The experiments reported here were as described by Knappe and Werner (14). We studied two generations of the same species, *Asparagopsis armata* representing the gametophyte, and *Falkenbergia rufolanosa* as the tetrasporophyte. Using trace methodology with ^{131}I, we could pursue the uptake by measuring the remaining activity in the supernatant (Fig. 2). Measured for an equal amount of thallus dry weight of both forms, the uptake in *Asparagopsis* was about three times as fast as in *Falkenbergia* during the first 24-hour period (starting from 4×10^{-7} M I$^-$ concentration).

Not only is the rate of uptake different in both forms, but so also is the I_o value (the concentration that cannot be used) or the concentration at a time when an equilibrium between uptake and excretion of the element is reached. This concentration is 2×10^{-9} M for *Asparagopsis*, and ten times higher for *Falkenbergia*. When we increased the iodine concentration in the medium by a factor of 13.5 (Fig. 3), we found very similar results. The uptake rate was more than twice as fast in *Asparagopsis* as in the tetrasporophyte, and both forms differ in the I_o value after several days. There was no difference of iodine uptake in both forms in the light and in the dark. Inhibitors of photosynthesis also did not inhibit iodine uptake in these red algae.

The extraction of the incorporated iodine in both types shows again remarkable differences (Table III). In general, a much higher percentage of the iodine was extracted from *Asparagopsis*. Only in ammoniacal

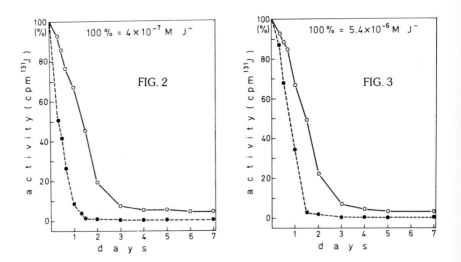

FIGURE 2. Decrease of iodine concentration in the culture medium (^{131}I-labelled with 50 uCi/10 ml, I-concentration 4×10^{-7} M) of — *Asparagopsis* — *Falkenbergia* calculated for the same dry weight matter of both forms. Culture conditions: 15°C, 14:10 hour light-dark regime, 38 foot candles for *Asparagopsis*, 19 foot candles for *Falkenbergia*.

FIGURE 3. Decrease of iodine concentration in the culture medium with a higher initial I concentration ($5:4 \times 10^{-6}$ M). Other data as described in figure 2.

methanol similar relative quantities were extracted from both the algae. With acid butanol, 15% of all iodine incorporated was extracted from *Asparagopsis*, but only 1.4% from *Falkenbergia*.

The high percentage of ^{131}I activity, left in the sediment after extraction with Tris-HCl-buffer (pH 7.6, 0.05 M), raised the question whether significant quantities could be solubilized by the action of proteinases (Fig. 4). During the first hour, about 40% of the iodine was in a form, that did not sediment at 1400 x g. After that time, another 20-30% became soluble only by the action of trypsin or pronase, not in the buffer control. We may assume that perhaps at least this percentage is bound to structural proteins linked to cell organells or cell particles that sediment at 1400 x g. Some preliminary chromatography experiments on Sephadex show at least 7 different protein fractions with ^{131}I label.

The ^{131}I labelled metabolites, that could be extracted by ammoniacal methanol (Table III) were chromatographed on thin layer cellulose plates in two dimensions, first direction with t-butanol-3% NH₃ (3:1) and second direction with s-butanol-acetic acid-H₂0 (4:4:1). In *Asparagopsis*, more than 99.8% of the radioactivity was concentrated in the spot A, which is most likely I⁻, as we can conclude from the location on a chromatogram in the system of Sofianides *et al.* (15) with iodinated amino acids (thyroid

Table III

Extraction of ^{131}I labelled substances from freeze dried material of *Asparagopsis armata* **and** *Falkenbergia rufolanosa*, **labelled during a 7 day period with 50 mcCi [131]I.** (The total activity in the freeze dried material was set as 100%, the percentage extracted by the various solvents are given below.)

Extraction with	Asparagopsis	Falkenbergia
1 N HCl (70°, 1 hour)	94	54
water (70°C, 1 hour)	88	43
t-butanol:25% HCl (1000:3) (22°C, 1 hour)	15	1.4
t-butanol:25% HCl (1000:3) (60°C, 1 hour)	16	2.2
methanol:3% NH₃ (99:1) (22°C, 1 hour)	17	18
Tris-buffer (pH 7.6, 0.05 M) (30°C, 1 hour)	36	13

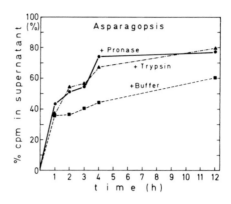

FIGURE 4. Treatment with pronase and trypsin of the sediments of *Asparagopsis* (centrifugation 5 min at 1400 x g) of tissues, ground in tris-buffer (0.05 M, pH 7.6. __ Incubation with trypsin at 30°C,. Incubation with pronase at 30°C;. control incubation in tris-buffer at 30°C) vertical axis: per cent of ^{131}I-activity, not sedimented at 1,400 x g for 5 min.

hormones). The other three small spots had less than 100 cpm. The result with the extract from *Falkenbergia* were quite different: here the radioactivity in the spot E was 4200 cpm, in F 11,700 cpm, in G 1,000 cpm and in H 12,000 cpm. The spots F and H were totally absent in the extracts from *Asparagopsis*. Whether the spot F is in fact identical with T 4 and G with T 3 from thyroids (16) remains open for further identification experiments. The spot H from the same form contains at least two different compounds, that are apparently not identical with any of the four substances on the chromatogram in the system of Sofianides *et al* (Fig. 5).

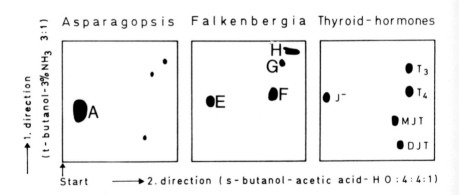

FIGURE 5. Autoradiogram of a two-dimensional thin layer chromatogram of extracts (1 % ammonia in methanol) from *Asparagopsis*, *Falkenbergia* and from iodinated amino acids and iodide, according to Sofianides *et al.* (15).

Besides further research on the function of these iodine metabolites in the two forms of the same species in red algae, it is proposed to test some of these unknown iodine metabolites from *Falkenbergia* in mammalian systems to see if any unknown physiological or pathological reaction might develop.

Summary

The role of the essential element silicon in diatoms is discussed in a scheme of interaction of silicon biochemistry, regulation of metabolic pathways by silicate and morphogenesis of silica structures. Elemental analysis of the cells and shell-preparations of the large marine centric diatom, *Coscinodiscus asteromphalus* by proton induced x-ray emission spectroscopy and CHN-analysis, gave the composition: C, Si, Cl, K, H, S, N, P, Ca, Br, Fe, Zn, Cu, Ni, Mn, Ba and Ti. These data have been discussed as enrichment of trace elements by diatoms as a source of minerals, considering the vast amount of diatomaceous oozes covering more than 30 million km^2 of the ocean floor.

The role of the essential element iodine has been compared in *Asparagopsis armata* and *Falkenbergia rufolanosa*, representing different generations of the same species of red algae. Remarkable differences in the uptake and in the extraction of iodine in both forms have been demonstrated. Two different low molecular weight iodine metabolites were isolated from *Falkenbergia* which were absent in the other generation of the same species. Some experiments have been proposed in mammalian thyroid gland metabolism, using the isolated metabolites from *Falkenbergia*.

References

1. Harvey, H.W. (1955). *The Chemistry and Fertility of Sea Water.* University Press, Cambridge.
2. Pytkowicz, R.M. and Kester, D.R. (1971). The Physical Chemistry of Sea Water. *Oceanogr. Mar. Biol. Ann.* **9**, 11.
3. Pytkowicz, R.M. and Hawley, J.E. (1974). Bicarbonate and Carbonate Ion Pairs and a Model of Sea Water at 25°C. *Limnol. Oceanogr.* **19**, 223.
4. Frieden, E. (1972). The Chemical Elements of Life. *Scient. Am.* **227**, 52.
5. Armstrong, F.A.J. (1965). Silicon. In *Chemical Oceanography Vol. 1* Eds. J.P. Riley and G. Skirrow. Academic Press, London. p. 409.
6. Werner, D. (In press). Regulation of Metabolism by Silicate in Diatoms.

In *Nobelsymposium Biochemistry of Silicon and Related Problems.* Ed. V. Runnstrom-Reio. Plenum Press, New York.

7. Werner, D. (1977). Silicate Metabolism. In *The Biology of Diatoms.* Ed. D. Werner. Blackwell Scientific, Oxford. p. 110.

8. Black, W.A.P. and Mitchell, R.L. (1952). Trace Elements in the Common Brown Algae and Sea Water. *J. Mar. Biol. Ass.* **30**, 575.

9. Werner, D. (1969). Silicoborate Als Erste Nicht C-haltige Wachstumsfaktoren. *Arch. Mikrobiol.* **65**, 258.

10. Fairbridge, R.W. (1966). Marine Sediments. In *Encyclopedia of Oceanography.* Ed. R.W. Fairbridge. Reinhold, New York. p. 462.

11. Kamatani, A. (1969). Regeneration of Inorganic Nutrients from Diatom Decomposition. *J. Oceanogr. Soc.* **25**, 63.

12. Werner, D. (1971). Der Entwicklungszyklus mit Sexualphase bei der Marinen *Diatomee Coscinodiscus* Asteromphalus. I. Kultur und synchronisation von entwicklungsstadien. *Arch. Mikrobiol.* **80**, 43.

13. Werner, D. (1971). Der Entwicklungszyklus mit Sexualphase bei der marinen *Diatomee Coscinodiscus* Asteromphalus. II. oberflachenabhangige differenzierung wahrend der vegetativen zellverkleinerung. *Arch. Mikrobiol.* **80**, 115.

14. Knappe, J. and Werner, D. (1975). Physiologische Unterschiede im Jodstoffwechsel von Asparagopsis and Falkenbergia. *Z. Pfl. Physiol.* **75**, 277.

15. Sofianides, T. *et al.* (1966). Separation and Quantitative Recovery of Iodinated Amino Acids and Iodide by Thin Layer Chromatography. *Proc. Soc. Exptl. Biol. Med.* **123**, 646.

16. O'Dell, B.L. and Campbell, B.J. (1971). Trace Elements, Metabolism and Metabolic Function. In *Comprehensive Biochemistry* Vol. 21 Eds. M. Florkin and E.H. Stotz. Elsevier, Amsterdam. p. 179.

Studies on Marine Sterols Using Chemical Ionization Mass Spectral Techniques

Ajay K. Bose, B. N. Pramanik, B. G. Pujar, and H. Fujiwara
Department of Chemistry and Chemical Engineering
Stevens Institute of Technology
Hoboken, New Jersey

In the past few years, Chemical Ionization Mass Spectrometry (CI-MS) has undergone remarkable growth; now it is the analytical method (1, 2) of choice for the study of a wide variety of compounds. The commonly used reagent gases for CI-MS studies are methane, isobutane and hydrogen. Under CI-MS condition these reagent gases produce Bronsted acids as shown by the following equations:

$$CH_4 + e \longrightarrow CH_4^+, CH_3^+, CH_2^+, CH^+, C^+, H_2^+, H^+ + 2e$$

$$CH_4^+ + CH_4 \longrightarrow CH_5^+ + CH_3$$

$$CH_3^+ + CH_4 \longrightarrow C_2H_5^+, + H_2$$

$$(CH_3)_3CH \longrightarrow (CH_3)_3C^+$$

$$H_2 \longrightarrow H_3^+$$

$$NH_3 \longrightarrow (NH_3)n^{H^+} \quad (n = 1,2, \text{ and } 3)$$

Each of the ions CH_5^+, $(CH_3)_3C^+$ and H_3^+ function as a Bronsted acid to the neutral organic molecule, and transfer a proton to produce a charged molecule $[M + H]^+$.

When ammonia is used as the reagent gas, the sensitivity of this mass spectral method is increased and strong pseudo-molecular ions, $[M + NH_4]^+$, are observed for multifunctional sterols and many of their derivatives.

On the basis of proton affinity values of methane, isobutane and ammonia (127 kcal/mole, 185 kcal/mole and 207 kcal/mole, respectively) it has been stated that ammonium ion addition requires less energy than protonation (3); hence more intense pseudo-molecular ions and less fragmentation can be expected in most cases when the CI-MS (NH$_3$) technique is used. In fact, one of the major practical advantages of this technique is the increased chance of observing the pseudo- molecular ion even when loss of water and other fragments is the predominant course in CI-MS (CH$_4$ or i-Bu). Dihydrocholesterol, cholesterol and their analogs display strong pseudo-molecular ions, $[M + NH_4]^+$. Proton transfer from NH$_4^+$ to the organic sample is also observed if the proton affinity of the compound is greater than that of ammonia (PA = 207 kcal/mole).

Most sterols (4) from marine sources (molluscs, sponges, etc.) now known, differ only in the number and/or position of the side chain double bonds or alkyl groups and are therefore not easy to separate on GC columns. When some of the components in a mixture to be analyzed are present in disproportionately small amounts, the corresponding GC peaks may be difficult to observe.

In the course of our research on sterol composition of marine organisms, we found it convenient to use CI-MS (NH$_3$) technique for the detection and identification of sterols. It provides pseudo-molecular ions for free sterols extracted from biological samples. Little purification is necessary for CI-MS analysis, because the impurities usually have a lower molecular weight range than the sterols and therefore present no problem in the 400-600 Dalton region where most sterol peaks appear.

Marine organisms often contain large amounts of various *delta*^{5}-sterols and comparatively small amounts of their dihydro derivatives. We found it convenient to subject such a mixture of sterols to reaction with AlBr$_3$ in ether to convert selectively the *delta*^{5}-sterols to 3-bromo-*delta*^{5}-steroids. The bromosteroids move much faster on silica gel TLC plate (benzene: hexane) and are easily separated from non-*delta*^{5}-steroids. The non-*delta*^{5}-steroids are then directly studied by CI-MS (NH$_3$) method for identification and structure determination. We have found this technique very convenient for sterol mixtures from non-marine sources too, such as sterols from gall stones, atherosclerotic plaques and other biological samples.

The 3-bromo-*delta*^{5}-steroids can be further separated on preparative TLC plates. Each fraction is then subjected to mass spectral analysis for structure determination. The location of the double bond on the side chain can often be determined from the mass spectral cleavage induced when a mixture of argon and ammonia is used as the reagent gas. Moist argon as the reagent gas in CI-MS is known to produce EI-MS type fragmentation.

We have developed an oxidation method with RuO$_4$ (Chart 1) follow-

Chart 1

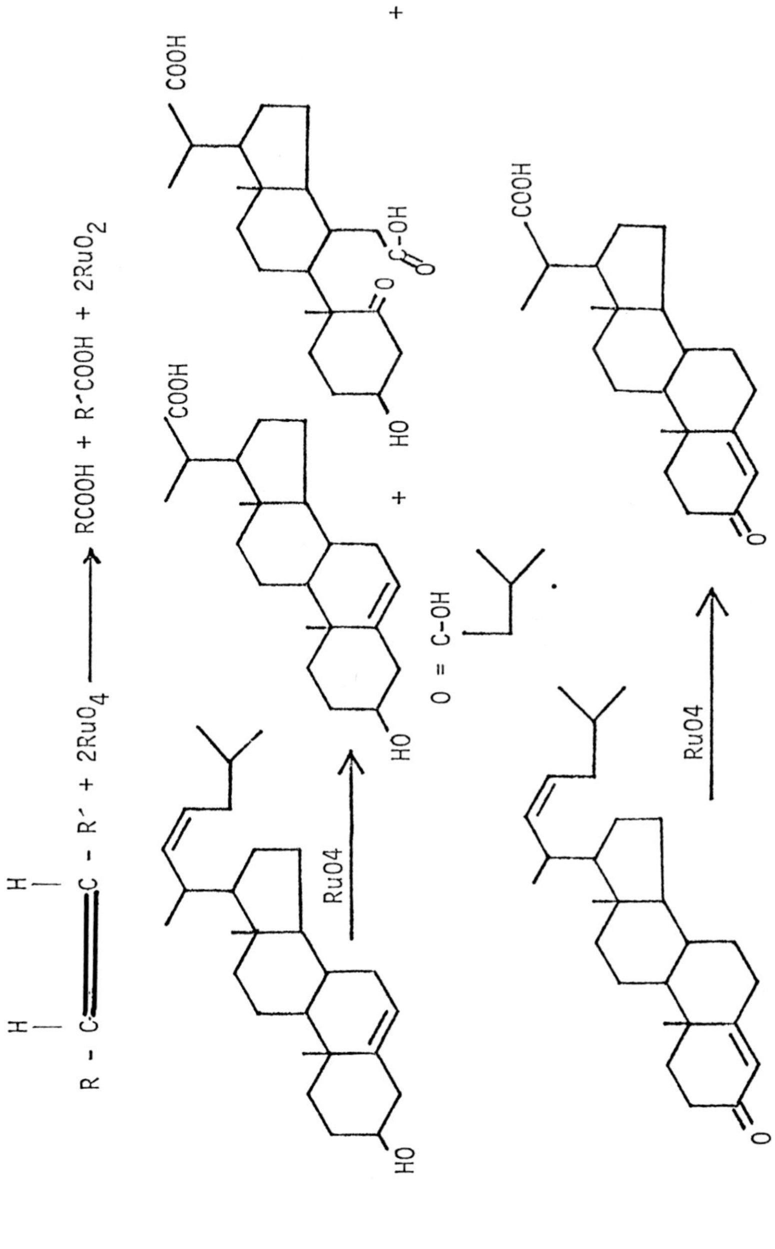

ed by CI-MS (NH₃) for the location of double bonds on the side chain of sterols. The major advantage here is that the reaction can be carried out on sub-microgram scale and the reaction product can be used directly for the CI-MS analysis. A second spectral recording after addition of diazomethane to the crude oxidation product shifts only the carboxyl peaks by 14 Daltons and helps identify them. We have also explored the analytical potential of negative chemical ionization (NCI) mass spectrometry for the detection of picogram quantities of compounds with appropriate functional groups. A derivatizing agent for sterols that is particularly useful is trichloroacetyl isocyanate. The chlorine containing urethanes (Chart 2) from sterols provide strong [M-1]⁻ peaks in NCI spectra in the 500–700 Dalton range which is free from background peaks. Also because of the chlorine isotopes, tell-tale ion clusters are observed.

To test the reliability of this CI-MS technique, we have analyzed the total sterol fraction from clams. The sterol composition of clams has been reported also by other workers. For our experiments, clams collected from Long Island Sound were used and sterols were isolated by standard techniques. The CI-MS of the sterol fraction showed cholesterol and its analogs (Spectrum 1). The 5-sten-3 *beta*-ols were selectively converted to their 3-bromo-derivatives. The mass spectrum of the bromo-derivatives indicated the presence of cholesterol, methylated cholesterol and dehydromethylated cholesterol. The bromosterols were separated on silica gel TLC plate. Methylated dehydrocholesterol was identified as 24-methylene cholesterol on the basis of the mass spectral fragmentation

Chart 2

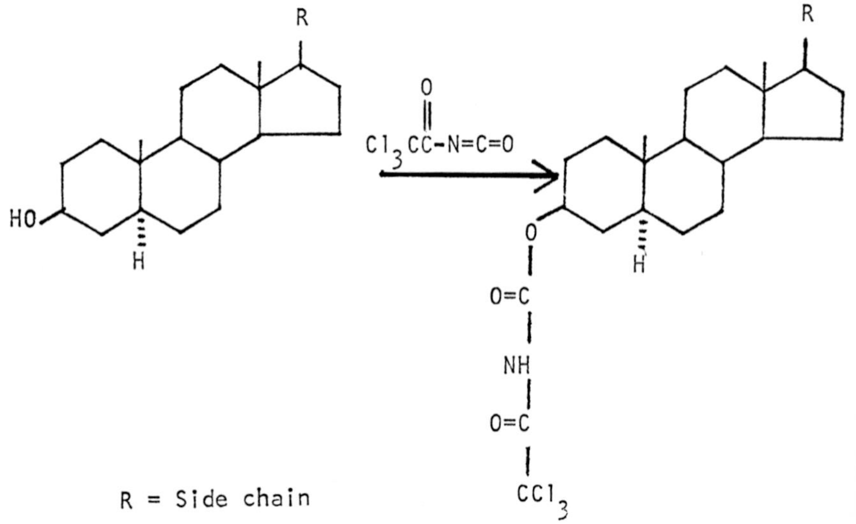

R = Side chain

(Spectrum 2) as shown in chart 3. The same *delta⁵*-sterols have been previously found in clams by other workers using GC-MS techniques.

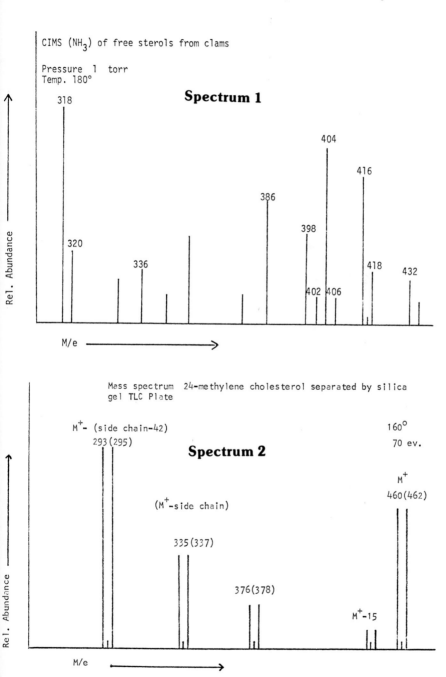

CIMS (NH₃) of free sterols from clams

Pressure 1 torr
Temp. 180°

Spectrum 1

Mass spectrum 24-methylene cholesterol separated by silica gel TLC Plate

Spectrum 2

Chart 3

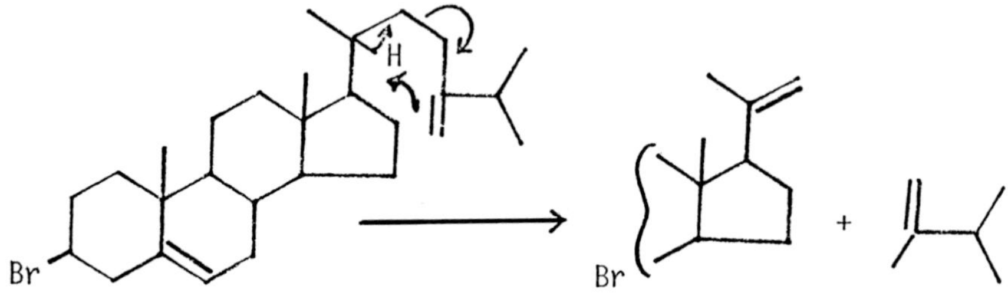

460(462)   376(378)

Acknowledgment

The CI-MS facilities used in this research were established with a grant from the Scherring-Plough Foundation.

References

1. Hunt, D.F. (1976). Selective Reagents for Chemical Ionization Mass Spectrometry. *Finigan Spectra* **6**, 1.
2. Chixhov, O.S., *et al.* (1976). Polysaccharide Sequencing by Mass Spectrometry: Chemical Ionization Spectra of Permethyl Glycosylalditols. *J. Org. Chem.* **41**, 3425.
3. Hunt, D.F., McEwen, C.N., and Harvey, T.M. (1975). Positive and Negative Chemical Ionization Mass Spectrometry Using a Townsend Discharge Ion Source. *Anal. Chem.* **47**, 1730.
4. Idler, D.R., Wiseman, P.M., and Safe, L.M. (1970). A New Marine Sterol, 22-trans-24-norcholesta-5,22-dien-3 beta-ol. *Steroids* **16**, 451.

New Compounds And Activities From *Laurencia* Species

Salvatore Caccamese[1] and Kenneth L. Rinehart, Jr.[2]

[1] *Institute of Industrial Chemistry*
University of Catania, Italy
[2] *Department of Chemistry*
University of Illinois, Urbana, Illinios

In previous reports stemming from our Alpha Helix Baja Expedition 1974 (1,2), we described briefly our use of combined gas chromatography–mass spectrometry (GC-MS) to identify constituents of *Laurencia* extracts. We have continued these studies and have now examined a number of *Laurencia* species by GC-MS techniques, both in a search for novel compounds and as a means of comparing species.

Chemotaxonomy Employing GC-MS

Table I shows the antimicrobial activity (3) and halogen content (4) of several *Laurencia* samples, while figure 1 compares the GC traces of four samples. Morphological characterization of this genus is rather difficult, as pointed out previously (5). The sample giving the upper chromatogram was originally identified as *L. johnstonii*, but its GC trace indicated it to be *L. decidua*, and that identification was subsequently confirmed by more careful morphological examination. On the other hand, authenticated samples of *L. decidua* collected at diverse sites in Baja California in June 1976 showed remarkably similar GC profiles.

Identification of Compounds

Crude extracts of *Laurencia* species have been examined by GC-MS directly to identify many of the components present, as noted above. In addition, it was necessary to employ a more extensive fractionation procedure to isolate a number of the compounds in order to study their mass spectra without interference from overlapping GC peaks, to provide

187

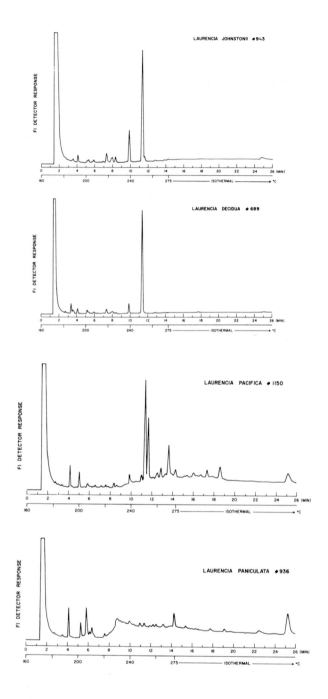

FIGURE 1. Gas chromatographic traces of four *Laurencia* extracts.

Table I

Halogen Content and Antimicrobial Activity
in *Laurencia* Species

SAMPLE NUMBER	SPECIES	LIPID WEIGHT, (% of alga)	TH[1]	*Bacillus subtilis*
943	*L. johnstonii*	1.01	39	+
689	*L. decidua*	1.25	33	+
1058	*L. Sp. A.*	0.61	43	+
1150	*L. pacifica*	0.84	36	
1056	*L. sinicola*	0.53	ND[2]	—
1059	*L. Sp.B*	0.71	ND[2]	—
936	*L. paniculata*	0.54	ND[2]	—

[1]Total halogen as chlorine in mg/g of lipid.
[2]Not detectable.

authentic samples, or to study their biological properties. This procedure employed gradient elution silica gel chromatography, exclusion volume liquid chromatography and reverse phase liquid chromatography. In examination of chromatographic fractions, three approaches have been employed: (i) trimsylation to identify hydroxyl-containing components by their shift in retention time and increase in mass by 72 amu, as illustrated in figure 2 (left side); (ii) examination of mass spectra for the presence of the M–68 (M– C_5H_8) and M–C_3H_5 (or M–C_3H_5–Br) peaks characteristic of compounds containing the laurane skeleton (1), as illustrated for bromolaurinterol (in which the position of the bromine *ortho* to the hydroxyl was established by synthesis) compared to bromoisolaurinterol in figure 3; and (iii) comparison of retention times of the components of fractions with those of known compounds, as well as coinjection of authentic samples with the fractions, as illustrated for bromolaurinterol in figure 2 (right side). Some previously known and new compounds (which double the number of known compounds with the laurane skeleton) identified in the studies are shown in figure 4; new compounds are enclosed in boxes. Structures of these compounds were assigned mainly by use of the three steps described above.

Oxidative Coupling Dimers of Laurinterol

Perhaps the most interesting new compounds found thus far in our *Laurencia* studies are oxidative coupling dimers of laurinterol and

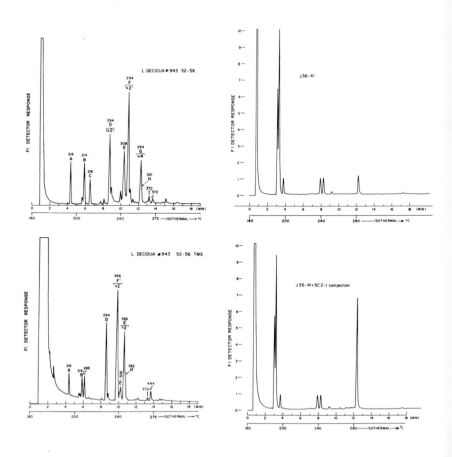

FIGURE 2. Left side: Gas chromatographic traces of *L. decidua* fraction 52-56 before silylation (upper) and after silylation (lower). Numbers above the peaks refer to molecular ions. Right side: Gas chromatographic traces of *L. decidua* fraction 36-41 (upper) and of the same fraction coinjected with bromolaurinterol (lower).

debromolaurinterol. These were first observed in extracts of *L. decidua* by the presence of weak ions at m/e 586 (2 x 294-2) and 508 (294 + 216-2) containing two and one bromine atoms, respectively. Following the extraction and separation procedure, the dimers were concentrated by chromatography and characterized by GC-MS of their trimsylated derivatives as containing both one and two hydroxyl groups (C–O and C–C coupling products, Fig. 5) and by mass spectral analysis (two C_5H_8 losses) as containing two laurane skeletons. The dimers were proposed to arise by standard phenolic oxidative coupling reactions at the position *ortho* to the pehnolic group. Mass spectra of GC peaks containing dimer IIa and the trimsyl derivative of dimer IIb are shown at the top and middle

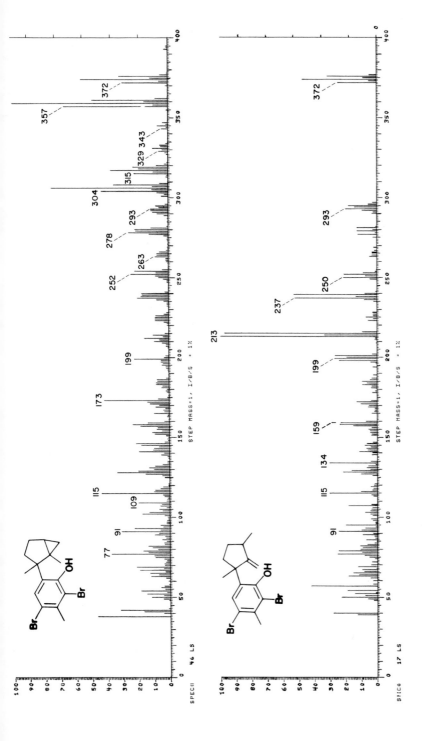

FIGURE 3. Gas chromatographic mass spectra of bromolaurinterol (upper) and bromoisolaurinterol (lower).

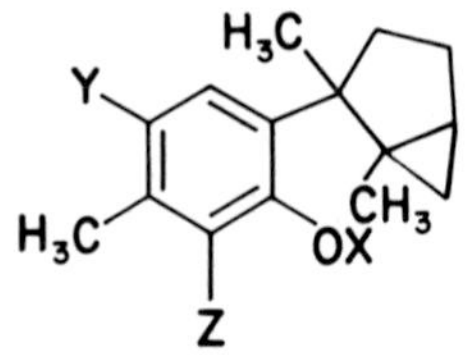

FIGURE 4. Structures of aromatic sesquiterpenoids found in *L. decidua.*

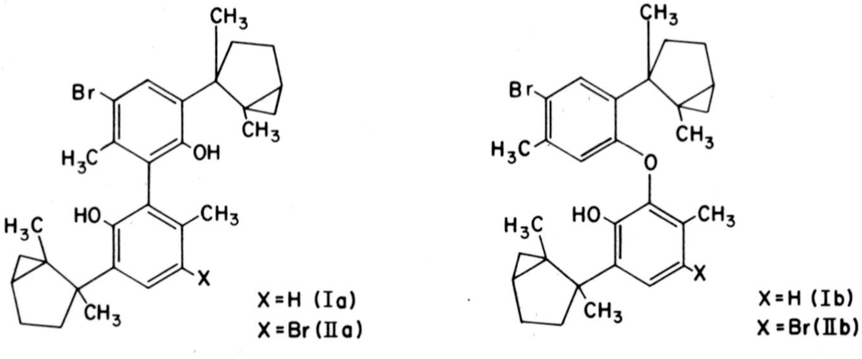

X	Y	Z	m.w.		
H	Br	H	294	1	laurinterol
H	H	H	216	2	
Ac	Br	H	336	3	
Ac	H	H	258	4	
H	Br	Br	372	5	

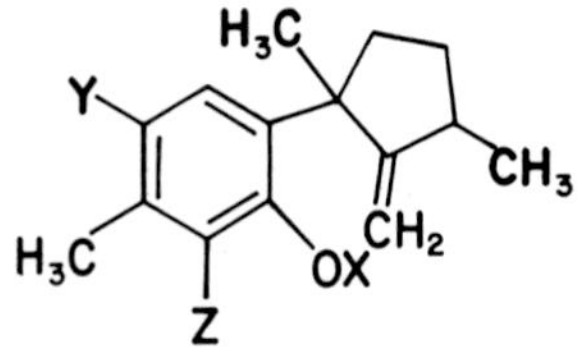

X	Y	Z	m.w.		
H	Br	H	294	6	isolaurinterol
H	H	H	216	7	
Ac	H	H	258	8	
H	Br	Br	372	9	

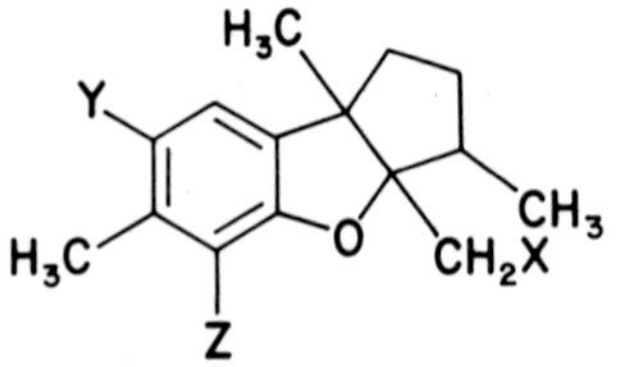

X	Y	Z	m.w.		
H	Br	H	294	10	aplysin
H	H	H	216	11	
OH	Br	H	310	12	
H	Br	Br	372	13	

X = H (Ia)
X = Br (IIa)

X = H (Ib)
X = Br (IIb)

FIGURE 5. Laurinterol dimers from oxidative coupling.

of figure 6, while the mass spectrum of a fraction containing the ditrimsyl derivative of dimer IIa is shown at the bottom of figure 6. Laurinterol was accordingly oxidized by ferricyanide and the products of the oxidation were purified by thin layer chromatography to give a mixture of the C–C and C–O dimers which was characterized by its ^{1}H nmr spectrum. The synthetic dimers were shown to be identical to the naturally occurring oxidative coupling dimers by identical mass spectra and GC retention times.

Halogenating Enzyme in *L. decidua*

Identification of the oxidative coupling dimers in *L. decidua* argues for the presence of oxidative enzymes in *Laurencia* species. More direct evidence was provided by an enzymatic assay (6) involving treatment of an extract of *L. decidua* (stored frozen) with 2-chlorodimedone, bromide ion and hydrogen peroxide while observing the diketone's ultraviolet absorption at 292 nm. A reduction of the absorbance from 0.98 to 0.82 during 4 min indicated the presence of a halogenating enzyme.

Isolation and Biological Properties of *Laurencia* Constituents

Laurinterol and aplysin have proved to represent the most common sesquiterpene skeletons in *Laurencia* species examined by us. These compounds have been isolated previously by repetitive column chromatography, but we find that high pressure liquid chromatography (HPLC) provides a more rapid, convenient procedure for their separation on either an analytical or a preparative scale (Fig. 7).

Laurinterol was previously reported to have potent antibacterial activity against *Staphylococcus aureus* and *Mycobacterium smegmatis*, lower activity against *Candida albicans*, and no activity against *Escherichia coli* and *Salmonella choleraesuis* (7). It has now been tested against a wider range of microorganisms and (Table II) laurinterol is indeed most potent against gram-positive organisms, slightly active against yeasts and filamentous fungi, and inactive against gram-negative organisms. In separate experiments the minimum inhibitory concentrations of laurinterol were measured as 10 mcg/ml against *Bacillus subtilis* and as 50–60 mcg/ml against *Saccharomyces cerevisiae*.

The antimicrobial activity shown by laurinterol appears to be largely a characteristic of its phenolic group. Aplysin and aplysinol, whose structure and absolute stereochemistry were recently established (8), which lack the phenolic group, are both inactive. Moreover, debromolaurinterol was earlier shown to be a less potent antibacterial agent (7), and we found

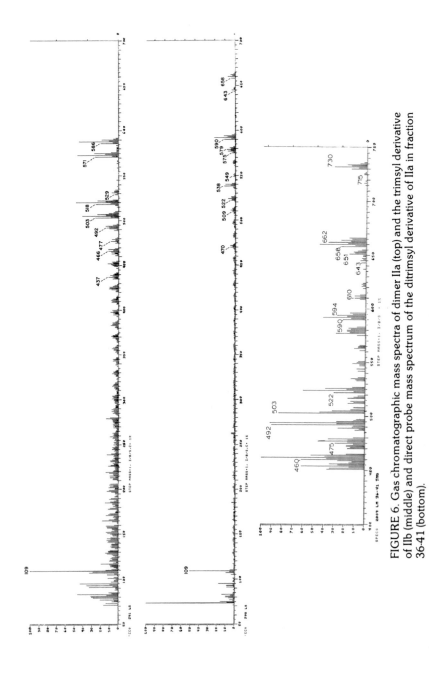

FIGURE 6. Gas chromatographic mass spectra of dimer IIa (top) and the trimsyl derivative of IIb (middle) and direct probe mass spectrum of the ditrimsyl derivative of IIa in fraction 36-41 (bottom).

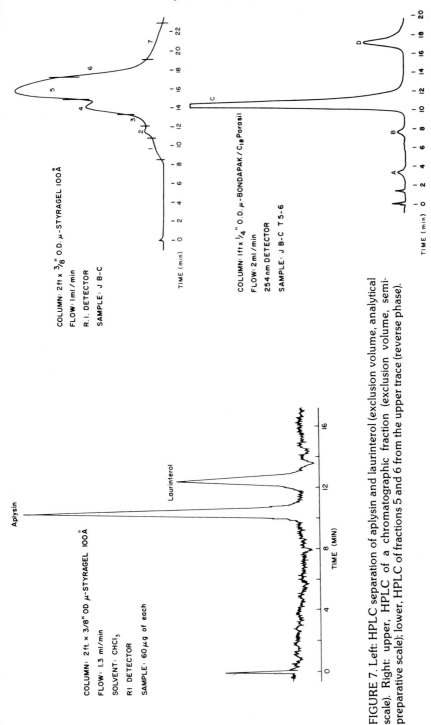

FIGURE 7. Left: HPLC separation of aplysin and laurinterol (exclusion volume, analytical scale). Right: upper, HPLC of a chromatographic fraction (exclusion volume, semi-preparative scale); lower, HPLC of fractions 5 and 6 from the upper trace (reverse phase).

Table II

Antimicrobial Screening of Laurinterol[1]

ORGANISM	ZONE SIZE (mm)
Sarcina lutea	25
Sarcina lutea sensitive	30
Staphylococcus aureus	28
Bacillus subtilis	25
Bacillus cereus	29
Streptococcus pyogenes	34
Mycobacterium avium	32
Klebsiella pneumoniae	Trace
Salmonella schottmuelleri	0
Salmonella gallinarum	0
Pseudomonas aeruginosa	0
Proteus vulgaris	0
Escherichia coli	0
Penicillium oxalicum	Trace
Saccharomyces pastorianus	Trace
Candida albicans	Trace

[1]12.7 mm discs saturated with 1 mg/ml solution of drug.

bromolaurinterol to be inactive. In the former compound the phenol is less acidic due to lack of the electron-withdrawing *para* bromine atom, while in the latter the phenol is also less acidic due to steric hindrance from the *ortho* bromine.

Acknowledgments

This research was supported in part by the National Institute of Allergy and Infectious Diseases (AI 04769). Mass spectrometric and gas chromatographic instrumentation employed in the present studies was provided by grants from the National Cancer Institute (CA 11388) and the National Institute of General Medical Sciences (GM 16864). We thank the Italian Research Council for a Fellowship to S.C. during his leave of absence from the University of Catania. We thank Dr. J. F. Siuda for assistance in performing the enzymatic assay and Messrs. G. E. Zurenko and C. Lewis, The Upjohn Company, for the antimicrobial assays in table II.

References

1. Rinehart, K. L. *et al.* (1975). Structures of Halogenated and Antimicrobial Organic Compounds from Marine Sources. In *"The Nature of Seawater"* Ed. E. D. Goldberg, Physical and Chemical Sciences Research Report 1, Abakon Verlagsgesellschaft, Berlin, p. 651.
2. Rinehart, K. L. *et al.* (1976). Identification of Compounds in Selected Marine Organisms by Gas Chromatography Mass Spectrometry, Field Desorption Mass Spectrometry, and Other Physical Methods. In *Proc. Food-Drugs from the Sea*, Mar. Technol. Soc. Washington D. C. p. 434.
3. Shaw, P. D. *et al.* (1976). Antimicrobial Activities from Marine Organisms. *ibid.* p. 429.
4. Hager, L. P. *et al.* (1976). A Survey of Organic Halogens in Marine Organisms. *ibid.* p. 421.
5. Fenical, W. and Norris, J. N. (1975). Chemotaxonomy in Marine Algae: chemical separation of some *Laurencia* species *(Rhodophyta)* from the Gulf of California. *J. Phycol.* **11**, 104.
6. Theiler, R., Siuda, J. and Hager, L. (1977). Bromoperoxidase from the red Alga *Bonnemaisonia hamifera.* This volume.
7. Sims, J. J. *et al.* (1975). Antimicrobial Agents from Marine Algae. *Antimicrob. Ag. Chemother.* **7**, 320.
8. McMillan, J. A. *et al.* (1976). Aplysinol from *Laurencia decidua:* Crystal structure and absolute stereochemistry. *Tetrahedron Letters.* 4219.

Natural Products Of Marine Sponges VIII: Partial Structure Of A Novel Compound Isolated From *Phakellia flabellata*

Gurdial M. Sharma, Gregory F. Schem and Albert T. Pastore

New York Ocean Science Laboratory
Montauk, N. Y.

The natural habitat of the marine sponge *Phakellia flabellata* is the Great Barrier Reef of Australia. This sponge is capable of producing a large variety of water soluble natural products. The interesting point, however, is that the concentrations of these compounds in the sponge vary a lot with seasons. This is well demonstrated by the results of the fractionation experiments on the aqueous methanol extracts of specimens collected in the winter and summer months of 1967, 1968, and 1969 by Burkholder (1). The fractionation data is summarized in figure 1. This data clearly suggests that the summer specimens are, on the average, poor in the water soluble components while the winter specimens are, in general, rich in natural products. In addition, the winter specimens contain an antibacterial substance which is absent in the materials collected in the summer.

We have initiated a program of research to characterize these compounds and to investigate the significance of the seasonal variations in the distribution of these molecules to biology, biochemistry and ecology of the sponge. The structures of one class of compounds, bromophakellins, isolated from *P. flabellata*, have been reported in our previous publication (2). In this paper we wish to report partial characterization of a yellow compound, m.p. 235-236°C, isolated by column chromatography of the aqueous or methanol extracts of the sponge over Sephadex G-10. This compound is present in the sponge mainly during the winter months.

Electron impact and chemical ionization mass spectra of the yellow compound were devoid of the molecular ion peak. The elemental analysis also did not yield satisfactory data. The best conclusion which could be derived from several combustion analyses was that the composi-

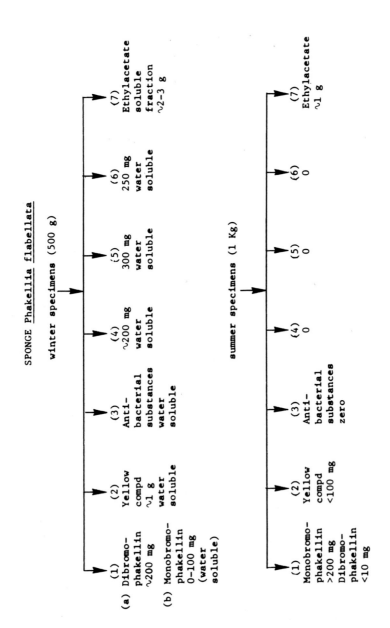

FIGURE 1. Fractionation summary on I *Phakellia flabellata.*

tion of the yellow compound was somewhere within the limits defined by the expression $C_{11-13}H_{9-13}N_5O_{4-5}.HCl$.

The ir, uv and nmr spectral data of the molecule revealed the presence of a 2,3-disubstituted pyrrole ring, two methylenes attached to two electro-negative groups, two or possibly more ketonic functions, and 4 D_2O exchangeable protons in the structure. The CD spectra showed no maxima above 200 nm which suggested the absence of chiral centers in the compound.

The yellow compound was recovered unchanged from a reaction with acetic anhydride-pyridine mixture at room temperature. Oxidation with alkaline potassium permanganate gave guanidine which was isolated as a picrate in about 5% yield. Hydrolysis with 2% aqueous sodium bicarbonate at 100°C gave a complex mixture from which a single compound having mp 284°C and elemental composition $C_8H_8N_2O_4$ was isolated by chromatography over Sephadex G-15. This compound is assigned structure *I* on the basis of usual spectroscopic data.

The hydrolysis product *I* and the guanidine unit together account for all the nitrogen atoms, 9 out of 11-13 carbon atoms, one out of possibly

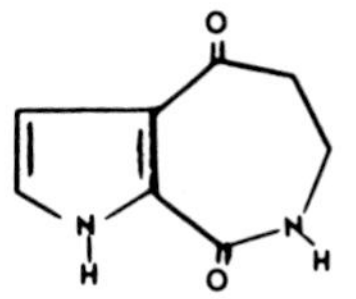

I

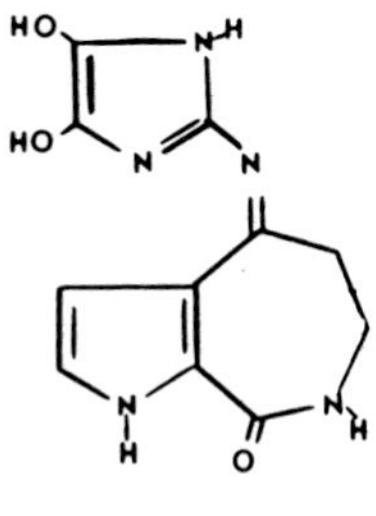

II

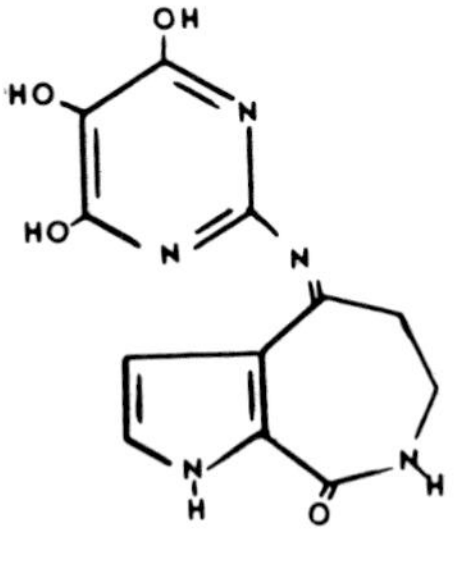

III

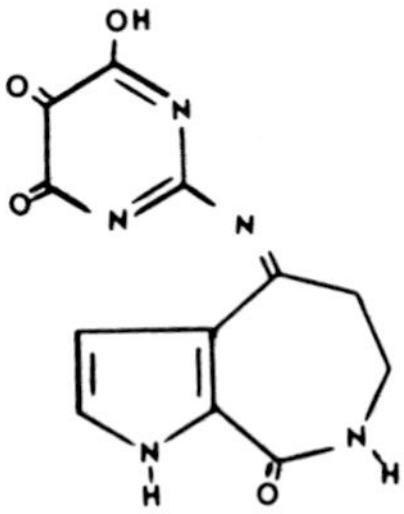

IV

four oxygen atoms, and nine out of 9-13 hydrogen atoms present in the yellow compound. The elucidation of the complete structure will require the determination of the exact molecular formula of the compound. Assuming that the elementary composition of the yellow compound is either $C_{11}H_{11}N_5O_3$ or $C_{12}H_{13}N_5O_4$ or $C_{12}H_9N_5O_4$ then, corresponding to each of these compositions, the trial structures *II*, *III* or *IV* may be written for this molecule. Further work on the characterization of this compound is in progress.

Acknowledgment

This is New York Ocean Science Laboratory Contribution No. 79.

References

1. Burkholder, P.R. and Sharma, G.M. (1969). Antimicrobial Agents from the Sea. *Lloydia* **32**, 466.
2. Sharma, G.M. and Burkholder, P.R. (1971). Structure of Dibromophakellin, A New Bromine-containing Alkaloid from the Marine Sponge, *Phakellia flabellata. Chem. Comm.* 151.
3. Sharma, G.M. and Magdoff-Fairchild, B.(In press). Studies in the Natural Products of Marine Sponges. Part IX. Structures of Weakly Basic Guanidine Derivatives, Dibromophakellin and Monobromo-phakellin. *J. Org. Chem.*

Low Basicities Of Phakellins

Gurdial M. Sharma

New York Ocean Science Laboratory
Montauk, New York

Phakellins are complex guanidine derivatives produced by the marine sponge *Phakellia flabellata* (1). In 1971 we we reported (2) that these compounds have structures *I–III* and their guanidine moiety exhibits pk$_a$ of about 8. This pk$_a$ is rather low when compared with the pk$_a$ values of 12 reported for all other guanidines. In this paper we wish to present an explanation for the anomaly in the base strength of phakellins.

The strong basicity of guanidino groups is a reflection of the high resonance stability of the cation produced by protonation of the CN$_3$ skeleton at the imine nitrogen (3). It may then be expected that the low basicity of phakellins is either due to the inability of these molecules to protonate at N-9, the imine nitrogen, or, if phakellins do protonate at N-9 then the resonance in the resulting cations (hereafter called phakellinium cations) is inhibited. To distinguish between these two possibilities, the following experiments were conducted.

The information on the site of protonation of phakellins was obtained by studying the nmr spectra of these molecules in trifluoroacetic acid (TFA). The spectra showed three singlets in the 7-9 ppm region. These singlets were assigned to the guanidinium protons because they were absent from the spectra determined in TFA-d$_1$. From low to high field these singlets integrated for 1H, 1H and 2H respectively. The integration and the singlet nature of these resonance suggests that phakellins, like all other guanidines, protonate at the imine nitrogen of the guanidino group. It now becomes important to determine whether resonance in phakellinium cations is inhibited or not. This was accomplished with the help of ir spectroscopy.

Resonance and Spectral Considerations

In a resonance stabilized guandinium cation there is no "true" imine group and the positive charge on the nitrogen atoms of the CN$_3$ skeleton is appreciably less than the positive charge on the nitrogen atom of an

I $R^1 = R^2 = Br; R^3 = H$

II $R^1 = Br; R^2 = R^3 = H$

III $R^1 = R^2 = R^3 = H$

IV $R^1 = R^2 = Br; R^3 = CH_3-C = O$

V

ammonium group. Because of this electronic description of the resonance stabilized guandinium ions the ir spectra of guanidine hydrochlorides exhibit two characteristic features (4). First the NH stretching frequencies occur above 3200 cm^{-1} (i.e. in the region of free amines) rather than below 3200 cm^{-1} where a typical ammonium group normally absorbs. Second, the C=N stretching frequencies disappear and are replaced by two bands in the 1700-1590 cm^{-1} region which correspond to the antisymmetric stretchings of the CN bonds within the guanidimium group. These features of the ir spectra of guanidine hydrochlorides should be of great value in diagnosing whether the guandimium group of a molecule has a resonance stabilized structure or not.

The ir spectra of phakellin hydrochlorides exhibit a broad band stretching from 3500-2900 cm^{-1}, indicating that in cations the positive charge is not evenly distributed over all the atoms of the CN$_3$ skeleton. The 1700-1590 cm^{-1} region of the spectra shows one band around 1650 cm^{-1} and another around 1695 cm^{-1}. The 1650 cm^{-1} band is due to the absorbtion by the amide carbonyl. Since there is no band around 1590 cm^{-1} the band around 1695 cm^{-1} is attributed to the absorbtion by the C = N unit which may still be present in the guanidinium system of phakellinium cations. In the ir spectra of phakellins the C = N absorbtion occurs around 1670 cm^{-1}. The increase in the C = N sketching frequencies upon passing from phakellins to their hydrochlorides suggests that in cations most of the positive charge resides on the imine nitrogen of the CN$_3$ skeleton. In other words, the resonance in phakellinium cations is inhibited. Since the four atoms of the CN$_3$ skeleton in phakellins are perfectly planar, the inhibition of resonance in cations will have to be attributed to some other structural features of the molecule.

The x-ray crystallographic data (5) of monoacetyldibromophakellin *IV* revealed that in phakellins the six-membered ring B is a half chair and the imidazoline ring (ring D) has a twisted conformation as shown in *V.* Inspection of the scale models indicated that ring D cannot be made planar because of the rigid geometry of ring B. It may then be expected that phakellins will resist all those transformations which require imidazoline ring to be planar either in the transition state or in the final product (5). This concept readily explains the inhibition of resonance in phakellinium cations if it is assumed that the efficient overlap of the nitrogen and carbon orbitals in the CN$_3$ skeleton of the ion might require the imidazoline ring to be planar. Since this ring cannot become planar, the resonance in the guanidinium system of phakellinium cations will be resisted and, in consequence, the phakellins will exhibit reduced tendency to add a proton. One way of testing this hypothesis would be to convert the tetracyclic skeleton of phakellins into a structure in which the imidazoline ring is planar. If the explanation offered for the inhibition of resonance in phakellinium cations is correct then the guanidine moiety of the transformation product should be highly basic and upon protonation this functionality should give a resonance stabilized cation.

Reaction of dibromophakellin *I* with a HNO$_3$—H$_2$SO$_4$ mixture gave compounds *VI* and *VII.* The molecular models of *VI* revealed that in this compound the six-membered ring is a boat with planar imidazoline ring strainlessly fused to the eclipsed bonds at the side of the boat. Thus, structure *VI* has all the characteristics needed for verifying the explanation offered for the inhibition of resonance in phakellinium cations.

In the ir spectrum of *VI* the NH stretching frequencies occured above 3200 cm⁻¹ and the 1700-1570 cm⁻¹ region showed two bands assignable to the antisymmetric stretchings of the CN bonds of a resonance stabilized disubstituted guanidinium cation. Thus, unlike the guandinium group of the phakellinium cations, the guandinium group of *VI* has a resonance stabilized structure.

Chemical Reactivity Aspects

Titration of *VI* in water with 0.01N NaOH revealed that this compound is a monoacidic base of pk$_a$ 7.9. Treatment of *VI* with one mole equivalent of sodium hydroxide gave the free base. Infrared spectroscopy revealed that those bands of *VI* which must be associated with a guanidinium group appear unchanged in the spectrum of the free base. This observation suggests that the deprotonation of *VI* upon titration with a base takes place at a site other than the guanidinium group. It is proposed that the other group which may dissociate with strongly acidic pk$_a$ 7.9 is the hydroxyl group at C-3 and the free base might have the zwitterion structure *X*.

Reaction of *VI* with methyl iodide under various conditions failed to yield the corresponding O-methyl derivative. Consequently, the normal basic function of *VI* could not be masked to determine the pk$_a$ of the guanidinium group.

When the aqueous suspension of *VI* was treated with concentrated ammonia a clear solution was obtained. Lyophilization of the solution gave an amorphous material. This material was crystallized from water and the pure compound was found to be identical in all aspects with *VI*. The results of this experiment suggest that the guanidinium group of *VI* has a pk$_a$ of at least greater than 9 because this functionality could not be deprotonated by reacting with a base of pk$_a$ 9.23. Thus, the guanidino group of *VI* is a stronger base compared to the same group of phakellins. The explanation offered for the low basicities of phakellins, therefore, appears to be correct.

The reaction of dibromophakellin *I* proceeds in the direction of *VI* because a change in the shape of the six-membered ring from half-chair to boat removes conformational strains in the imidazoline ring. The formation of *VIII* and *IX* upon treatment of *I* with hydrochloric acid further supports the view that most of the chemical reactions of phakellins will follow a course which removes angle strains in ring D.

Conclusion

In conclusion it may be stated that the low basicities of phakellins can be explained in terms of the twisted conformation of the imidazoline ring. Rigorous test of the adequecy of this view would require synthesis of the O-methyl derivative of *VI* and determination of the exact pk_a value of the guanidinium group. Until this is accomplished, explanation offered for the low basicities of phakellins may be considered to be only partially substantiated. This is especially so when it is realized that another factor, which may contribute to the lowering of the pk_a values of phakellins, would be the electron withdrawing effects of the pyrrole and amide nitrogen atoms attached to C-6 and C-10 of the imidazoline ring. If the pk_a of the guanidinium group of *VI* turns out to be greater than that of phakellins but less than that of other guanidine derivatives, then the inductive effect of nitrogen atoms identified above may also have to be considered.

Acknowledgment

This is New York Ocean Science Laboratory contribution No. 84.

References

1. Burkholder, P.R. and Sharma, G.M. (1969). Antimicrobial Agents from the Sea. *Lloydia* **32**, 466.
2. Sharma, G.M. and Burkholder, P.R. (1971). Structure of Dibromophakellin, A New Bromine-containing Alkaloid From the Marine Sponge, *Phakellia flabellata. Chem. Comm.,* 151.
3. Pauling, L. (1960). *The Nature of the Chemical Bond.* Cornell University Press, p. 286.
4. Goto, T., Nakanishi, K. and Ohashi, M. (1957). *Bull. Chem. Soc. Japan* **30**, 723.
5. Sharma, G.M. and Magdoff-Fairchild, B. (In press). Studies in the Natural Products of Marine Sponges. Part IX. Structures of Weakly basic Guanadine Derivatives, Dibromophakellin and Monobromophakellin. *J. Org. Chem.*

The Geographic Distribution of Ciguatoxic Fish In The Eastern Half Of The British Virgin Islands

William T. Davin, Jr., Norman J. Doorenbos
and William D. Longest
Bitter End Field Station Virgin Gorda, B. V. I.
and the Departments of Pharmacognosy and Biology
University of Mississippi
University, MS

Ciguatera, intoxification from eating affected marine fishes, is a problem in the tropical and sub-tropical regions of the Caribbean sea, and the Indian, Atlantic and Pacific oceans. Ciguatera is the dominate type of fish poisoning in the Caribbean. It has been reported that the largest concentration of ciguatera in the Caribbean is located in the Virgin Islands (1).

The toxin, although reported in 91 species of Caribbean fish (2), has been found to be more regionally specific than species specific in Pacific studies (3). Many reports from the Caribbean show that even around small islands, fishes from one sector may be dangerous to eat, while those of the same species from another area are safe. In reference to the poisonous fishes at Turk Island, Bahamas, Gudger (4) quoted Mowbray (5) as writing, " . . . the fish from one side of the island were much more dangerous than those on the other. This seems entirely preposterous, especially in the case of Grand Turk, an island only one and one-half miles wide by six miles long, but such a statement is met with over and over again in articles on West Indian Ciguatera."

In the British Virgin Islands, Brody (1) listed as toxic areas the islands and cays from Norman Island to Virgin Gorda, Necker Island Pass, the south-east side of Tortola, and the Anagada Reef near the Wreck of the Roccos. Later, Brody (2) added the east side of Virgin Gorda near the 100 fathom drop-off and the south side of Anagada. These areas and those reported by earlier authors are generally listed after a report of human intoxification was made to the health services on the islands. This leaves many cases unreported because, in the British Virgin Islands, the majority of the fish are eaten by the natives. Very few of those poisoned ever seek medical attention. Many local fishermen tell of being poisoned as many as ten times without ever having seen a doctor (personal communication from the fishermen).

The fishes that commonly cause intoxification are caught in depths of less than 30 fathoms. The carnivores, benthic herbivores, and detritus feeders are more apt to be toxic than are plankton feeders (2). The fishing industry in the British Virgin Islands is limited to personal use of the fish and sale to the local natives and resorts in the area. The method of capture is almost solely by means of fish traps, left for a period of 3 to 10 days and retrieved with small boats. The limited fish populations and the geography of the area prevent large scale fishing operations such as those found on the Gulf Coast of North America. Many think that the fishing industry could be greatly increased, however, if it were not for the problem of ciguatera (2).

A thorough understanding of the geographical distribution of the toxic areas would help the expansion of the fishing industry and may shed new light on the causative agent for ciguatera. It was thus decided to collect fish from the waters of the British Virgin Islands near our laboratory (Bitter End Field Station) on Virgin Gorda and test them for ciguatera. The field station is located on the property of Bitter End Yacht Club on John O'Point and is supported by Century America Corporation of Chicago. Collections to support this study on the distribution of ciguatoxic fish were carried out from September to December 1976.

The larvae of the brine shrimp, *Artemia salina* Leach, have been used as a bioassay organism for ciguatera (6), insecticide residues (7), fungal toxins (8), and dinoflagellate toxins (9). The brine shrimp are not affected when finely ground ciguatoxic fish is introduced into their media (3). It was found, though, that the shrimp larvae are very sensitive to certain organic extracts of ciguatoxic fish (6). Hence the brine shrimp larvae assay was used in this investigation.

Habitat

The study area was located in the waters of the British Virgin Islands, between 18° 15′ 00″ N to 18° 36′ 05″ N and 64° 09′ 55″ W to 64° 38′ 00″ W. The collecting stations are in shallow water bounded on the south and east by the hundred fathom drop-off as plotted on the Defense Mapping Agency Hydrographic Center's 1973 edition of map number 252243, Tortola to Anagada. They are bound on the north and west by Tortola from Slaney Point, Beef Island, Scrub Island, and the White Horses on the Anagada Reef (Fig. 1). The average depth in the area is 15 fathoms and ranges from 8 to 27 fathoms. The bottom geography is typically flat, with some large rock out-croppings, sloping slowly towards

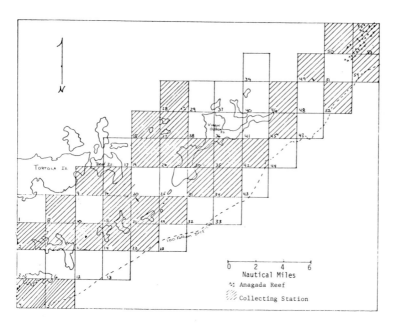

FIGURE 1. British Virgin Islands, collecting stations.

the 100 fathom drop-off and is covered by corals, volcanic rock, and stretches of sand.

The islands in the area are of volcanic origin except Anagada which is a coralline island. Shore lines are rocky with little sand and limited barrier reefs. There are no fresh water streams emptying into the sea of any size. Road Town Harbor, on the south side of Tortola, is the only major population center. The harbor has a large volume of small boat traffic and an occasional freighter. There is very little industry around the harbor, so pollution is minimal.

Materials and Methods

Stations—The area was divided into quadrants of 4 square nautical miles and numbered 1 through 54. Each of these represented a potential collecting station. From the 54 stations, 30 were randomly selected as collecting sites (Table I, Fig. 1)

Traps—The fish were captured with locally made arrow fish traps. The 25 traps consisted of a frame of white mangrove branches, *Laguncularia racemosa*, tied together with 12 gauge galvanized wire and covered with 18 gauge double dipped galvanized ¾" mesh chicken wire. The traps

Table I

Distribution of Ciguatoxic Fish by Station

Station	Total Capture	Toxic	Possibly Toxic	%
2	63	0	1	1
4	58	0	5	4
5	34	3	2	12
7	40	1	2	5
8	67	1	2	3
9	11	0	0	0
11	70	1	6	6
14	56	2	3	6
15	43	0	3	3
16	60	1	4	5
18	20	0	1	2
19	2	0	0	0
21	68	3	5	8
22	52	2	3	7
24	92	2	2	3
26	47	3	7	14
27	34	1	2	6
28	14	1	3	17
30	52	1	2	4
31	19	1	2	10
34	29	0	2	3
35	63	3	3	7
42	51	3	6	12
45	60	5	8	15
46	81	5	4	8
49	36	1	2	5
50	23	2	0	9
52	80	5	10	12
53	9	1	0	11
54	20	6	3	37
TOTAL	1354	54	93	7

were 100 cm long, 70 cm deep, and 80 cm wide (Fig. 2). Black 3/8 inch polyethylene line, 20 fathoms long, was spliced to the peak on the upper side of each trap. On the distal end of the line, two small ring floats, 5 cm high by 30 cm in diameter, and a numbered 30 cm bullet float were attached (Fig. 2).

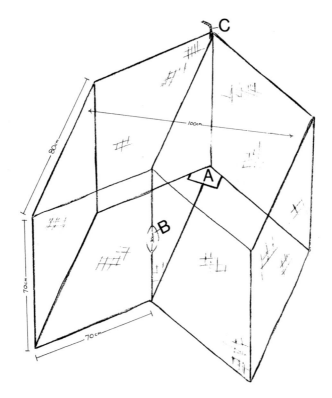

FIGURE 2. Diagram of a fish trap. (A) door. (B) funnel. (C) Float line.

Bait—The bait used in each trap included one-half kg of dusky anchovy, *Anchoa lyolepis,* one kg piece of a species of cactus, and one kg bundle of "West Indian Sage" branches that were collected locally. This combination was chosen after discussions with the local fishermen. Each item, when used alone, attracts certain types of fish. The fishermen thought that the three together would produce the broadest attraction.

Trapping procedure—Five fish traps, spaced approximately 150 m apart were dropped in each station. The traps remained in position for three to eight days, varying with the weather and availability of the "Reef Sampler," a vessel belonging to the Yacht Club. The fishes from each trap were separated by species and counted. A sample of each species, consisting of the five largest and one for each additional three, was retained and the rest released. Randall (10) stated that the larger fish of a given species are more likely to be toxic than the smaller ones. The fish from each trap were placed in separate plastic bags, numbered and packed on ice until they could be returned to the laboratory.

After returning to the laboratory, a permanent tag was attached to each fish giving the station number, trap number, and fish number. Each fish was then measured, weighed, identified and chopped into 2 to 4 cm slices. The pieces were placed in a bag and frozen.

Extraction—A 50 g sample composed of liver, viscera, muscle tissue and when possible brain, was taken from each frozen fish. Randall (11) suggested that the liver and alimentary tract are more toxic than the somatic muscles. The remainder of the fish was retained in the freezer. The sample was thawed and homogenized in 150 ml of 95% ethyl alcohol with a Waring blender. The homogenate was placed in a 250 ml flask, refluxed on a Barnstead steam bath for one hour and filtered through a Buchner funnel. The solid residue was then discarded. The alcoholic extract was concentrated under reduced pressure at 37°C until all the ethyl alcohol appeared evaporated.

The extract, which was about 15 ml, was defatted by extracting twice with 25 ml portions of n-hexane. The hexane fractions were stored for future study. The water fraction was extracted two times with 25 ml portions of diethyl ether. The combined ether extracts were washed with 5 ml water and dried over anhydrous Na_2SO_4. After filtering, the ether solution was concentrated to 10 ml and then placed in a tared, 4 dram screw capped vial for final drying, weighing and storage. The samples were stored at 8°C.

Bioassay—Freeze-dried brine shrimp eggs (Metaframes's San Francisco Brand) were hatched to get the larvae of *Artemia salina* used for the bioassay. The eggs were hatched in 150 by 15 mm petri-dishes containing 40 ml of 3.5% salt water. The salt water was prepared from Instant Ocean Brand sea salts without trace elements and distilled water. About 0.1 g of eggs were sprinkled on the surface of the water in five dishes, covered, and stored at 27°C for 24 hours. The ether extract was dissolved in 2.5% Tween 60 (Polyoxyethylene 20 Sorbitan Monosterate) to obtain a 50 mg/ml solution. A Bransonic 12 ultrasonic vibrator was used to mix the Tween 60 and extract to give an even suspension. This suspension was stored at 15°C until the larvae were ready to start the bioassay.

The shrimp larvae were separated from the unhatched eggs in a 150 ml seperatory funnel. The contents of the five plates were poured into the funnel and allowed to settle for ten minutes. The larvae suspension was then drawn off the bottom of the funnel into a 1000 ml beaker containing 50 ml of 3.5% salt water.

If the suspension was kept well mixed, it yielded between 75 and 150 larvae per ml when drawn from the middle of the beaker. This amount (1 ml) was put in each depression of a 12 depression pyrex deep-well spot plate. The 20 mcl samples (1 mg/ml) of three suspensions of extract were added in triplicate to each plate with an Oxford Sampler. The remaining three wells were used as controls; two with nothing added and one with 20 mcl of 2.5% Tween 60. The spot plates were covered, labeled and left undisturbed for 24 hours at room temperature. The larvae were examined for effects of ciguatoxin with a Bausch and Lomb 0.7X-3X binocular scope. The percentage of dead shrimp was recorded using a modified quadrant system (Table II).

Table II

Symbols and Percentage Equivalents

Symbol	% Kill	Symbol	% Kill	Symbol	% kill
0	0	2⁻	26-38	4	76-99
1	1-25	2+	39-50	4⁻	76-87
1⁻	1-12	3	51-75	4+	88-99
1+	13-25	3⁻	51-63	5	100
2	26-50	3+	64-75		

Preliminary screening was done on 1354 suspensions. Samples that rated 8 or higher, when the symbols for all three depressions were added together, were set aside. The bioassay was repeated on these bioactive suspensions using serial dilutions. The first depression received 20 mcl of suspension (1 mg/ml), the second, 10 mcl of suspension and 10 mcl of Tween 60 (0.5 mg/ml), and the third, 5 mcl of suspension and 15 mcl of Tween (0.25 mg/ml). Arbitrary levels of toxicity were determined as follows: (i) a suspension showing bioactivity at only 1 mcg/ml was considered non-toxic, (ii) a suspension showing activity of 1 mcg/ml and up to 50% kill at 0.5 mg/ml was considered possibly toxic, and (iii) a suspension exhibiting bioactivity at 0.25 mg/ml or above 50% at 0.5 mg/ml was considered toxic. Four of the toxic samples were rechecked by intraperitoneal injections (100 mg/kg) in Swiss white mice. The mice were observed continuously for one hour and checked again at 2, 3 and 24 hours. Spontaneous activity, muscle tone, reactivity, abnormal behavior, autonomic effects, reflexes, and rectal temperature were checked at 15 and 60 min.

Results

A total of 1,354 fish were trapped and tested. Of these, 54 fish were found to be toxic and another 93 possibly toxic (Table I). The distribution of these ciguatoxic fishes was highest at stations 54

(37%), 28 (17%), 45 (15%), 25 (1), 5 (12%), 52 (12%), 53 (11%), and 31 (10%). Only stations 9 and 19 produced no toxic fish (Fig. 3).

Some specimens of 22 species of fishes were found toxic. *Mycteropera venenosa* (Linnaeus), 1758 had the highest percentage; next was *Acanthurus bahianus* Castelnau, 1955. Individuals of two other species

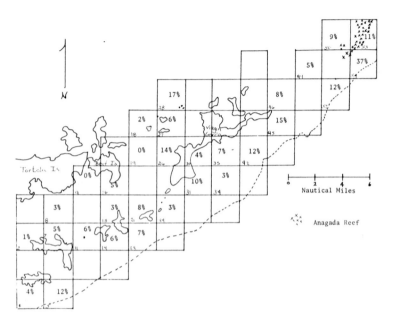

FIGURE 3. Percentage of toxic fish collected at each station.

of *Acanthurus* were also found to be toxic. *Holocentrus rufus* (Walbaum), 1792 was the fourteenth most toxic species and the second most commonly captured of the toxic fishes (Table III).

Average trapping depth was 13 fathoms, ranging from 8 to 21 fathoms. The greatest number of toxic fishes were trapped at 16 fathoms. There were more traps set at 16 fathoms than at any other depth.

The water temperature remained at 29°C during the entire trapping period.

Discussion and Conclusion

Although 54 of the fishes tested toxic and 93 possibly toxic, two factors may have affected the results. Ciguatera is the predominant form of fish toxin in the Virgin Islands (2), but not the only one. Some of the fish

Table III

Percentage of Toxic Fish by Species

Species	Number Toxic	Number Collected	%
Mycteroperca venenosa (Linnaeus), 1758	2	3	66
Acanthurus bahianus (Castelnau), 1855	2	6	33
Holacanthus tricolor (Bloch), 1795	1	4	25
Rhomboplites aurorubens (Cuvier)	1	5	20
Acanthurus coeruleus (Bloch and Schneider), 1801	14	74	19
Pomancanthus arcuatus (Linnaeus), 1758	5	30	17
Epinephelus striatus (Bloch), 1792	2	12	17
Lactophrys bicaudalis (Linnaeus) 1758	1	7	14
Scarus taeniopterus (Desmarest), 1831	1	8	12
Acanthurus chirurgus (Bloch), 1787	5	50	10
Chaetodon striatus (Linnaeus), 1758	3	51	6
Chaetodon capistratus (Linnaeus), 1758	1	20	5
Acanthostacion polygonius (Poey), 1876	1	18	5
Holocenterus rufus (Walbaum), 1792	6	135	4
Haemulon sciurus (Shaw), 1803	1	25	4
Balistes vetula (Linnaeus), 1758	2	63	3
Pseuduoeneus maculatus (Bloch), 1793	1	45	2
Lactophrys triqueter (Linnaeus), 1758	1	58	2
Calomus pennatula (Guichenot), 1868	1	83	1
Haemulon plumieri (Lacepede), 1802	1	65	1
Epinephelus guttatus (Linnaeus), 1758	2	150	1
Lutjanus syragris (Linnaeus), 1758	1	102	1

recorded as ciguatoxic may in fact have had another form of toxin that the brine shrimp were sensitive to. Another factor was the problem of an oily residue in some of the extracts. This residue, at 1 mg/ml, left a film over the water in the spot plate. It is possible that the film interfered with the respirator-process of the larvae and caused a higher mortality rate.

This study did not include the larger carnivorous fish that normally are not captured in fish traps. Although such fish are more likely to be toxic (2), they are less territorial and of little importance to the native fisherman. He avoids them because of their greater tendency to be toxic. The data from the smaller, territorial species, may be of value in locating the source of the toxin.

The three species of *Acanthurus* endemic to the British Virgin Islands were all found to be toxic. The members of this genus are herbivorous and have been found at the base of many ciguatoxic food chains (12). This genus, when toxic, could, therefore be considered an indicator genus for a toxic area. *Mycteroperca venenosa* has been reported many times as being toxic. Randall (11) stated that its scientific name may allude to its toxic properties so it was no surprise to find it the most toxic species. *Holocentrus refus*, on the other hand, has not been listed in the literature as toxic and is considered by many to be a safe fish to eat, no matter where it was captured (12).

The depth of capture of the toxic fish and the number of traps set at that depth are very closely related; so it appears that the depth is not a factor within the scope of this study.

Stations 54, 28, 45, 26, 5, 52, 53, and 31 had over a 10% yield of ciguatoxic fish. Of these, only stations 26 and 28 are not on or close to the 100 fathom drop-off. The drop-off is the only major variation in the marine habitat of the British Virgin Islands, with the possible exception of Anagada Reef. All the stations had coral formations of some magnitude. All the stations except 26 and 28 are on the south and east side of the islands, which leaves them unprotected during major tropical storms. These storms can denude portions of the bottom in the shallow waters of these stations. We have no explanation for the toxicity of areas 26 and 28.

The number of toxic fishes found in this study appears high in comparison to other published reports. Most reports are based on human poisoning. The brine shrimp assay may be sensitive enough to pick up traces of toxin that would have no effect on a human.

Summary

(1) The 100 fathom drop-off is in some way involved in the occurrence of ciguatera in the British Virgin Islands.

(2) The water on the windward side of unprotected islands is more likely to have toxic fish than the leeward side.

(3) There does not appear to be a correlation between the size of the fish or the depth of its capture (within the scope of this study) and its toxicity.

(4) The highest concentrations of ciguatoxic fish in the eastern half of the British Virgin Islands are in stations 54, 28, 45, 26, 5, 52, 53 and 31, which are located in the waters near the south tip of Anagada Reef, Seal Dog rocks, south east tip of Norman Island, and around Virgin Gorda Island at Pajoros Point, South Sound Bluff, Copper Mine Point, and Colesan Point.

(5) Possible method for establishing the distribution of ciguatoxic fish in reef waters has been studied and looks promising.

Acknowledgments

This work is a result of research sponsored by NOAA Office of Sea Grant, Department of Commerce through Grant No. 08(2) awarded through the Mississippi-Alabama Sea Grant Consortium. The U. S. Government is authorized to produce and distribute reprints for governmental purposes notwithstanding any copyright notation that may appear hereon. Appreciation is expressed to Mr. Myron Hokin of Century America Corporation for providing the facilities at Bitter End Field Station and to Norman O. Thomas and John Colmer for their help in collecting the fish specimens.

P. O. Box 5688, University, MS 38677, Dean, College of Science, Southern Illinois University, Carbondale, IL 62901.

References

1. Brody, R. (1971). Personal communication.
2. Brody, R. (1972). Fish Poisoning in the Eastern Caribbean. In Gulf and Caribbean Fisheries Institute Proceedings of the 24th Annual Session. Rosenstiel School of Marine and Atmospheric Science, Florida. p. 1.
3. Banner, A., *et al.* (1969). Observations on Ciguatera Type Toxin in Fish. *Ann. N. Y. Acad. Sci.* **9**, 770.
4. Gudger, E. W. (1930). Poisonous Fish and Fish Poisoning with Special Reference to Ciguatera in the West Indies. *Amer. J. Trop. Med.* **19**, 43.
5. Mowbray, L. L. (1916). Fish Poisoning (Ichthyotorisimus). *Bull. N.Y. Zool. Soc.* **19**, 1422.
6. Granade, R., Cheng P., and Doorenbos N., (1976). Brine Shrimp (*Artemia salina* L.) Larval Assay for Ciguatera Toxins. *J. Pharm. Sci.* **65**, 1414.
7. Tarpley, W. (1958). Studies on the Use of the Brine Shrimp *Artemia salina* (Leach) as a Test Organism for Bioassay. *J. Econ. Entomol.* **51**, 780.
8. Harwig, J. and Scott, P.M., (1971). Brine Shrimp (*Artemia salina* L.) Larvae as a Screening System for Fungal Toxins. *Amer. Soc. Microbiol.* **21**, 1011.
9. Trieff, N., *et al.* (1973). Biological Assay of *Gymnodinium breve* Toxin Using Brine Shrimp. *Texas Rep. Biol. Med.* **31**, 409.
10. Randall, J. (1961). Ciguatera: Tropical Fish Poisoning. *Sea Frontiers.* **7**, 133.
11. Randall, J. (1958). A Review of Ciguatera, Tropical Fish Poisoning, with a Tentative Explanation of its Cause. *Bull. Marine Sci. of the*

Gulf and Caribbean. **8**, 236.

12. Halstead, B. W. (1965). Class Osteichthyes: Ciguatoxic Fishes. In *Poisonous and Venomous Marine Animals of the World.* Vol. 2, U.S. Government Printing Office, Washington, D. C. p. 63

INTERLUDE

Food And Drugs From The Sea: A Perspective From The National Sea Grant Program

David H. Attaway

U.S. Department of Commerce
National Oceanic and Atmospheric Administration
National Sea Grant Program
Washington, D.C.

It was on this campus in 1960 that I had an acutely impressive introduction to marine drugs in the laboratory of Professor Leon S. Ciereszko where I had just begun my graduate research in chemistry. He and I had collected in Jamaican waters a number of samples of zoanthid, later identified as *Palythoa caribaeorum*. They were returned to the laboratory dry and Professor Ciereszko assigned an undergraduate student, William Reeburgh, the task of isolating their waxes by urea clathrate adduction. While Reeburgh ground the samples in preparation for extraction, all of us in the laboratory inhaled dust arising from the grinding. Professor Ciereszko and I returned to the laboratory the next afternoon and discovered we had had similar, strange experiences the previous night—severe chills, high fever, tightness in chest and back. Although Bill Reeburgh was unable to return for several days, he did recover. We made the correct association of our physiological changes with *Palythoa.* Later research here and at the University of Hawaii showed the genus *Palythoa* to be the elaborator of the most toxic nonproteinaceous substance yet found in nature. It is almost as toxic as botulin. The structure of palytoxin is still unknown, but it has interesting pharmacological properties some of which one of the chairmen of this conference, Dr. Pushkar Kaul, has documented. For example, it induces angina in mammals and therefore may be useful in studying that phenomenon. But enough reminiscing on those exciting days as a student, especially since my former colleagues and professors here probably were not so excited about my enthusiasm for graduate school.

Legislation establishing the National Sea Grant Program was passed in 1966; by 1968 the first grants had started to develop a program that was conceived as an instrument for enhancing marine and aquacultural resources along the lines of the Land Grant Act and its relationship to agricultural resources. The basis of the National Sea Grant Program is research, education, and advisory service centered at academic institutions. The objective is integration of these components into programs that identify and solve problems, and provide both formal and informal education to students, marine and coastal communities, and users of marine resources. Its primary charge is to bring academic expertise and innovation to bear on problems of development and wise use of marine and coastal resources. Cooperative work with industry and government is encouraged. Although most of the budget is spent in support of programs whose federal share ranges from $400,000 to $2,500,000, a significant share of the budget goes for individual projects at institutions, including inland institutions like the University of Oklahoma, that don't have institutional Sea Grant programs.

Obviously, participants in the program can and do endeavor in many types of research, education, and advisory service. Aquaculture, marine engineering, law, and economics are examples. The nature of the 28 major Sea Grant programs is shaped in large part at the state level where management is vested in non-federal administrators. The programs differ markedly in their content and emphasis. They reflect different problems, opportunities, resources of expertise on which to call, and different professional interests of the participants. This is not surprising because at least one third of the cost of each program must be provided by non-federal matching funds. Typically, these funds come from the university itself, the state or local industry. And there has been strong support for the matching fund concept: matching funds for most programs exceed the legal requirement and in some cases even exceed the federal share.

Several categories of research in our system of classification bear directly on food and drugs from the sea. They are aquaculture, biology and technology of commercial fisheries, and marine biomedicinals and extracts. Approximately $4,000,000 (15 percent of our budget) this year supports research in these areas. That figure will likely increase somewhat next fiscal year. Sea Grant research in other areas such as seafood science, biological oceanography, ecology, and coastal management bear indirectly on production of food and drugs from the sea. Thus, the National Sea Grant Program is strongly committed to research in these fields. The production of useful results of high quality through research such as we have heard about here over the past four days shows the wisdom of that commitment.

Food from the ocean is not now a major part of food production in terms of calories, but it supplies about half the intake of animal protein for half the world's population so as a source of essential amino acids it is indispensable. From the standpoint of calories it could become more important. Some experts have estimated the maximum sustainable yield of marine fisheries at as much as two billion tons per year. Others suggest more conservative yields of 100 to 200 tons. The worldwide harvest in

1974 was about 60 million tons. It is certain that there are still underutilized fishery resources, for example, squid and red crab off both our coasts, anchovies off the coast of California, and krill in the Antarctic. However, the recent "World Food and Nutrition Study" of the National Research Council points out that there also is overfishing of some stocks and increasingly damaging pollution in certain coastal areas, and that the catch of many commercial ocean species is at or near its sustainable maximum.

Increased research in capture techniques for underutilized species and development of acceptable products from them and from wastes of seafood processing could aid in improving world nutrition. About 30 percent of the total harvest is lost in processing for human consumption and about 10 million tons per year of incidental catch is discarded by fishing vessels. The report of the National Research Council suggests five requirements for making fuller use of the world fish catch:

1. improving methods of pick-up and transfer of fish at sea,
2. preprocessing incidental catch aboard ship,
3. processing fish used for fishmeal into protein for human consumption.
4. upgrading portions of fish now underutilized in order to formulate prepared food items for direct human consumption, and
5. developing intermediate processing technologies that are particularly applicable in developing countries.

Added to these could be many other items of importance such as improving technique of assessment of fishery stocks and improving managerial theory of fisheries.

Perhaps of more interest to a broader segment of this group is the role of aquaculture in increasing world food resources. It plays a minor role now; production is about five million tons per year and most of that is in fresh water species. It is likely that long-term selective breeding and complete control of reproductive cycles, so that they can be manipulated, will greatly increase its role. These developments must come through sophisticated research. Perhaps selective breeding can give us a herbivorous salmon or a microalgal alfalfa.

Research in marine aquaculture has really just begun. In this country aquacultural research with only a few species of animals is in progress and most of those are high-priced, gourmet species, such as oysters, shrimp, and salmon. Success with them will advance the states of art and science in aquaculture and will stimulate industrial aquaculture with the resulting accrued benefits, but research on low-cost, high-volume production of edible protein by aquacultural methods and associated research on development of acceptable products from it also is appropriate. Weatherly and Cogger point out in the July 29 issue of "Science" that since there is no general routine for testing the culture potential of new species, the prospects of discovering fish with superior characteristics of growth, productivity, robustness and flavor remain largely a matter of chance. They also opine that there has been insufficient exploitation of such techniques as systems analysis and cost-benefit analysis. They suggest that traditional methods of aquaculture such as polyculture in Chinese ponds and culture of milkfish in Indonesian brackish water are systems whose analysis with adequate techniques could provide important lessons for the entire aquacultural industry.

Research in developing food crops that can tolerate irrigation with brackish water or full-strength seawater is promising and may lead eventually to food production on currently unarable land as may related research from the opposite direction—modifying seed-bearing halophytes to make them suitable as food crops.

Increasingly rapid developments in marine natural products, as we have learned here, emphasize the importance of the sea's rich storehouse of novel organic molecules, which have many interesting and some useful bioactivities and pharmacological properties. The reports here of cardiotonic and hypotensive agents are particularly exciting and important examples of such developments. Promising antiviral properties of a marine alga have also recently been documented.

John Faulkner in his recent report in "Tetrahedron" says, "Marine natural products chemistry has experienced an explosive growth during the past five years." He goes on to make his point effectively with only a partial review of the field by concentrating on unusual molecules. He discusses a few hundreds of them.

Despite statistics that indicate marine organisms as a group contain more biologically active compounds than do terrestrial organisms, relatively few have undergone screening for useful properties. Those that are screened usually undergo only one or a very few bioassays. Maybe progress could be speeded if there were a federal commitment to aiding researchers of marine natural products in getting their extracts and isolates assayed for a broader range of bioactivities of critical medical importance. One approach would be in financially aiding researchers to exchange service in bioassay. One problem would lie in preventing such aid from becoming enormously expensive. Perhaps a wider variety of viral biocides and other drugs would be coming to clinical trials, had such a system of exchanging service been in operation the past few years.

The use of the sea in developing resources of food and drugs is still in its infancy. The potential of industry, government, and academia for nurturing growth past infancy is great. Exploitation of this potential is necessary for proper use of the oceans. Basic and long-term approaches in research for understanding and using marine resources of this type will be required to put exploitation and management on a sound footing. There is still considerable room for innovative ideas and well reasoned experimentation. The National Sea Grant Program will continue to be one of the players in this field. During its second decade the emphasis will be on maintaining and improving the quality and pertinence of the undertakings of the successful organizational structures developed during the first decade.

PART II

FOOD FROM THE SEA

SECTION I

Introduction

Food Production From The Sea

Carl J. Sindermann
U.S. Department of Commerce
National Oceanic and Atmospheric Administration
National Marine Fisheries Service
Sandy Hook, New Jersey

There is cause for reasoned optimism when considering food production from the world's oceans. We have seen during the last three decades a tripling of harvests from fisheries on natural populations, with an average annual increase in landings of about six percent. World food production from aquaculture constitutes about ten percent of total fisheries production, and there have been substantial advances in the technological base for aquaculture, for marine as well as fresh-water species.

There are, however, serious constraints on continued increases in food production from marine sources. A number of our stocks of traditional food species, such as cod, haddock, certain flounders, lobsters and redfish, are fully exploited, and have been in some instances overexploited. Costs associated with fishing—particularly fuel costs —have escalated alarmingly, and concern is expressed about impacts of coastal pollution on fisheries.

Further increase in world food production from the sea will depend more and more on utilization of natural stocks now underharvested or not harvested, on better utilization of harvested fish, and on solution of economic, environmental and institutional problems which now suppress expansion of marine aquaculture—particularly in the United States.

Some of the objectives of the conference on which this book is based were (i) to attempt a realistic assessment of the status of food production from the sea, including that from natural stocks as well as from aquaculture, (ii) to assess the present state of industrial development in aquaculture, and (iii) to consider research needs to increase contributions from aquaculture.

Emphasis has been placed on those species of greatest present interest to United States aquaculture—salmon, shrimps, bivalve mollusks, and certain fresh-water fishes—along with a detailed consideration of the major constraints on seafood production in the United States.

The history of salmon production on the west coast of the United States includes a number of dramatic changes— high levels of natural production in the early days of the 20th century; drastic decline due to overfishing, building of dams and increasing industrialization; partial rebuilding of stocks with the development of a system of public hatcheries; and most recently, the exploration of pen culture in sea water and the beginnings of private ocean ranching of salmon in the Pacific Northwest.

Shrimp production in the United States has long been dominated by the Gulf of Mexico fishery on penaeid species. Recent developments include expansion of shrimp fisheries elsewhere in the United States, gradual but significant annual increases in imports of shrimp, and initial attempts at commercial culture of penaeids as well as fresh-water shrimp of the genus *Macrobrachium*.

Molluscan shellfish production is still dominated by landings from fisheries on natural stocks, particularly from Atlantic surf clam populations. Oyster production methods have long employed simple culture techniques, but the development of commercial hatcheries as a source of seed is becoming an important method of augmenting production.

Aquaculture of trout and catfish in fresh water has been well established and commercially successful in the United States for several decades. Recent exciting developments in fresh water include the successful expansion of introduced populations of salmon in the Great Lakes, pilot-scale polyculture of fish in ponds, and the commercial success of crayfish and minnow culture in the southeastern states.

It is too easy to be elated by success stories or discouraged by failures when considering fish and shellfish production. A realistic assessment must include evaluation of the pluses and minuses. The attempt in this book to present and integrate information on the status of production from natural stocks as well as from aquaculture is somewhat unique, and we hope that this foods section of the book will represent a significant and current summarizing contribution to the literature on the status and potential of production from the sea.

The Contribution of Fisheries And Aquaculture To World And U.S. Food Supplies

John B. Glude

U.S. Department of Commerce
National Oceanic and Atmospheric Administration
Aquaculture Program Coordinator
Seattle, Washington

Surrounded as we are by an abundance of food and provided as we are to a greater or lesser extent with money to buy it, it is difficult to realize that the world needs more food. The world population is expanding so rapidly that every effort must be made to increase food production. Even so, according to some authorities the ultimate outcome will be that the human species, like some other animal populations, will outgrow its food supply, resulting in starvation and disease which will bring population and food supplies into balance.

As evidence for this concern a 1974 report by the House of Representatives Committee on Agriculture commented regarding grain supplies (1): "Since 1960, world grain stocks have fluctuated from a high of 155 million metric tons to a low of about 100 million metric tons. When these stocks drop to 100 million tons, severe shortages and strong upward price pressures develop. Although 100 million tons appears to be an enormous quantity of grain, it represents a mere 8 percent of annual world grain consumption, or less than one month's global needs—clearly an uncomfortably small working reserve and a perilously thin buffer against the vagaries of weather and plant diseases. As world consumption expands by some 2.5 percent annually, so should the size of working stocks; but over the past two decades, stocks have dwindled while consumption has continued to climb."

World supplies of aquatic foods, about 64 million metric tons (MMT) from capture fisheries and 6 MMT from aquaculture, represent only about 2% of the caloric requirements of the human race. However aquatic foods supply about 13% of the world's animal protein and this is essential to the survival of millions of people(2). In addition, aquatic foods provide balance and variety to the diets of many others.

This paper will examine the problem of increasing the supply of foods from fresh, brackish and sea water considering two main alternatives: (i) Increased landings of fish and shellfish captured by fisheries on wild stocks and (ii) increased production by public or private aquaculture.

The Seafood Supply Problem

Traditional stocks of marine species, once thought to be unlimited, are now estimated at a maximum sustained level of harvest 100 or 150 MMT (220 to 330 billion pounds) per year.

World landings tripled from 1948 to over 71 MMT in 1971, but decreased to 64 MMT by 1973 largely because of the decline in landings of Peruvian anchovy. Demand continues to increase and could reach 94 MMT before the year 2,000 according to FAO estimates.

On a worldwide basis, a shortage of fisheries products can be expected within the next decade as the human population increases.

U.S. commercial landings have increased little since 1948, from 1.95 MMT (4.3 billion pounds) to 2.13 MMT (4.7 billion pounds) in 1973, even though almost a fifth of the worlds marine resources are found within 200 miles of U.S. coasts (3).

With such riches at hand, the United States has not devised truly national approaches to the development of domestic fisheries and instead has relied increasingly on imported products to fill the growing U.S. demand. From 1948 to 1973 imports of edible products increased from 317 thousand metric tons (700 million pounds) to 2.13 MMT (4.7 billion pounds) on a round weight basis. Imports of industrial products, principally fish meal, grew even more rapidly, reaching a high point of 5.9 MMT (12 billion pounds) in 1968, declining thereafter as Peruvian fish meal supplies decreased. Now more than two-thirds of our edible fishery products are imported.

The wealth of fisheries resources off the U.S. coasts has attracted a vast influx of foreign fleets in the last fifteen years. By 1972 the foreign catch in waters off U.S. coasts had reached an annual level of 3.58 MMT (7.9 billion pounds). Of this total Japan took about 2 MMT (4.4 billion pounds) and the USSR more than 1 MMT (2.4 billion pounds); the remainder was shared by nearly twenty nations.

The Effect of Extended Jurisdiction

The Fisheries Conservation and Management Act of 1976 (FCMA), P.L. 94-265, extended U.S. fisheries jurisdiction from 12 miles to 200 miles off our coasts. Implementation of this act will make profound changes in the management of fisheries resources in this area and will provide increased opportunity for harvest by U.S. fishermen. Section 201 (d) of FCMA states that:

"The total allowable level of foreign fishing, if any, with respect to any fishery subject to the exclusive fishery management authority of the United States, shall be that portion of the optimum yield of such fishery which will not be harvested by vessels of the United States, as determined in accordance with the provisions of this act."

U.S. fishery scientists (4) have estimated the optimum yield for 1977 and 1978 for most species of fish and shellfish now harvested commercially in the 200 mile fishery conservation zone and the capacity of the U.S. fleet to harvest these resources and sell their catch. The difference between optimum yield level for each species and the U.S. harvesting capacity is considered as "Surplus" and is available for harvest by foreign fleets. This analysis considered those species which are not fully utilized by the U.S. fleet.

In 1977 the optimum yield total for all species considered was 2.6 MMT; US capacity was 0.5 MMT (19.4%). This left surplus of 2.1 MMT (80.6%) for harvest by foreign fleets, considerably less than the 1972 catch by foreign fleets of 3.58 MMT. The estimated optimum yield total for 1978 decreased 0.6% to 2.59 MMT; US capacity increased by 25.3% to 0.63 MMT leaving a surplus of 1.95 MMT (down 6.9%) for foreign fleets. Even with this increase in capacity, U.S. fleets will harvest only 24.5% of the allowable catch of these species in 1978 leaving 75.5% for fleets of foreign nations.

Major species considered in this analysis include:

Species	Est. Optimum Yield 1978
Alaska Pollock	1,118,800 M.T
Pacific Flounders	295,500 M.T.
Other fin fish, Atlantic	247,000 M.T.
Pacific Hake	130,000 M.T.
Other ground fish, Atlantic	102,900 M.T.
Silver Hake	115,000 M.T.
Pacific Cod	98,600 M.T.
Atlantic Squid	79,000 M.T.
Jack Mackeral	55,000 M.T.
Pacific Ocean Perch	47,500 M.T.
Tanner Crab	42,000 M.T.
Sable fish	35,500 M.T.
Pacific Rockfish	25,600 M.T.

The surplus species caught by foreign fishing fleets are generally sold in foreign markets. Only a small quantity of the foreign catch, principally pollock and Pacific flounders, enters the US market.

Implementation of the Fishery Conservation and Management Act of 1976 could increase US landings by 127,800 M.T., 6 percent of the US total landings of 2,136,000 M.T. (3) in 1978, and substantial increases can be expected in succeeding years as U.S. harvesting capacity increases.

With complete utilization by U.S. of all currently harvested species in the Fishery Conservation Zone, U.S. landings could be increased to over 4 MMT, nearly double the present level. This is not likely to occur, however, because the most probable species for increased harvest are those with least demand in U.S. markets. New product forms such as frozen breaded portions made from minced flesh of mixed species could expand the market for these species. However, it is unlikely that the US market could absorb all of the allowable harvest from our continental shelf in the forseeable future.

At the same time the U.S. demand for high-valued species, most of which are already harvested at maximum sustainable yield levels, is likely to expand. Imports have increased, but world demand is also growing. This situation is expected to limit the amount of high demand species available for export to the United States or to make it excessively expensive. Thus the demand for traditional seafoods in the United States will become critical within the next decade, resulting in physical shortages and increased prices for many products unless supplies from sources other than traditional marine fish stocks enter the market in the significant amounts (5).

The Status of Aquaculture

Worldwide output from aquaculture has approximately doubled during the last 5 years and now amounts to some 6 million metric tons (13.2 billion pounds), roughly 10% of world fish production. Some countries already rely upon aquaculture for over 40% of their total fisheries supply and expect production from aquaculture to increase.

Production by aquaculture in 1975 included the following species groups (5,6).

Finfish	4,000,000 M.T. (7)
Seaweeds	1,000,000 M.T.
Oysters	600,000 M.T.
Mussels	240,000 M.T.
Scallops	63,000 M.T.
Clams	38,000 M.T.
Cockles & other molluscs	30,000 M.T.
Shrimps & prawns	15,000 M.T.

Major aquaculture countries included the following: (5,6)

Mainland China	2,500,000 M.T.
Japan	945,000 M.T.
India	494,000 M.T.
USSR	210,000 M.T.
USA	151,000 M.T.
Indonesia	144,000 M.T.
Taiwan	126,000 M.T.
The Philippines	125,000 M.T.
Korea	83,000 M.T.
Thailand	83,000 M.T.
Bangladesh	76,000 M.T.

In the United States a significant portion of the supply of some species is produced by aquaculture. About 30% of our total landings of Pacific salmon and over half of the Columbia River salmon caught by commercial and recreational fishermen were reared in hatcheries before being released to grow further in rivers, lakes, and sea. Private aquaculture produces over 40% of our oysters, half of our catfish and crawfish, nearly all of our rainbow trout, and small quantities of several other species for a total of 78,000 metric tons (172 million pounds). This is about 3% of U.S. landings or 2% of U.S. total consumption of fishery products. U.S. aquaculture production by species groups is shown in table I.

The Potential for Increasing Food Production Through Aquaculture

On a worldwide basis, production from aquaculture can make a significant contribution to aquatic protein supplies. Pillay (5) described the goal of the Food and Agriculture Organization of the United Nations to increase aquaculture production from the present level of 6 MMT, 10% of world fish landings, to 30 MMT by the end of this century. The summary report of the FAO Technical Conference on Aquaculture, Kyoto, Japan, 1976 (7) included an estimate that aquacultural production would double to 12 MMT by 1985, with a possible production of 30 MMT by the end of the century.

The report of this major conference also recognized that in countries where aquaculture has been given national priority and the governments have set up legal and administrative machinery for promoting the development of aquaculture, notable expansion has occurred. The need for full recognition of the importance of aquaculture by governments was

Table I

Estimated Increase in Food Production Which Could be Achieved by Aquaculture
(Based on Table in Draft Outline for the National Fisheries Plan, Aug. 1974)

SPECIES OR SPECIES GROUP	CURRENT PRODUCTION TOTAL Thousands of Pounds	Thousands of Dollars	AQUACULTURE Thousands of Pounds	Thousands of Dollars	POTENTIAL PRODUCTION FROM AQUACULTURE IN THOUSANDS OF POUNDS [6] 1983	1988	1993	STATUS OF AQUACULTURE [1]	MAJOR PROBLEMS
Salmon, Pacific					[5]	[5]	[5]		
Public	213,000 [2] (1973)	125,116	60,000	35,244	70,000	90,000	120,000	1	Funding, smolt survival, space, permits, production costs
Private			1,000	587	14,000	60,000	120,000	2	Markets, imports, space, pollution, seed supply
Oysters	48,500 (1973)	35,153	20,000	14,496	40,000	80,000	200,000	1	
Shrimp, marine Penaeids	372,200 (1973)	219,400	500	482	7,000	23,000	43,000	2	Maturation in captivity, production technology and cost, seed supply
Pandalids	70 (1973)	67			100	1,000	5,000	4	Inadequate scientific knowledge, production technology, space
Freshwater Prawn	1,000 (1973 est.)	574	5	17	5,000	10,000	15,000	2	Market, cost-effective food, production technology

(Table I, continued)

SPECIES OR SPECIES GROUP	CURRENT PRODUCTION AQUACULTURE				POTENTIAL PRODUCTION FROM AQUACULTURE IN THOUSANDS OF POUNDS [6]			STATUS OF AQUA-CULTURE [1]	MAJOR PROBLEMS
	TOTAL		AQUACULTURE		1983	1988	1993		
	Thousands of Pounds	Thousands of Dollars	Thousands of Pounds	Thousands of Dollars					
Lobster	29,000 (1973)	41,867			1,000	5,000	10,000	4	Production costs, cannabalism, production technology, foods
Clams (hard and soft shell)	23,600 (1973)	24,664	2,600	2,717	5,000	10,000	25,000	2	Survival of juveniles, seed supply, space, permits
Scallops Sea	6,300 (1973)	10,689			NA [4]	NA	NA	5	Inadequate scientific knowledge
Bay	1,800 (1973)	3,459			500	2,000	5,000	3	Production technology, space, permits
Abalone	700 (1972)	1,355			500	1,000	5,000	3	Production technology, space, permits
Mussels	800 (1972)	237			1,000	10,000	25,000	4	Market, space, permits
Pompano	1,400 (1972)	1,651			100	500	3,000	4	Production technology, supply of juveniles
Sablefish	9,900 (1972)	861			NA	NA	NA	5	Market, production, technology

(Table I, continued)

Table I cont'd.

SPECIES OR SPECIES GROUP	CURRENT PRODUCTION TOTAL		CURRENT PRODUCTION AQUACULTURE		POTENTIAL PRODUCTION FROM AQUACULTURE IN THOUSANDS OF POUNDS [6]			STATUS OF AQUACULTURE [1]	MAJOR PROBLEMS
	Thousands of Pounds	Thousands of Dollars	Thousands of Pounds	Thousands of Dollars	1983	1988	1993		
Striped Bass	13,500 (1973)	4,240			NA	NA	NA	5	Production technology
Other Marine Fish	NA	NA			NA	NA	NA	5	Inadequate scientific knowledge
Tuna Baitfish	NA	NA			NA	NA	NA	5	Inadequate scientific knowledge
Crabs	154,700 [3] (1973)	27,722			NA	NA	NA	5	Inadequate scientific knowledge
Baitworms	1,490 (1972)	2,058			NA	NA	NA	5	Inadequate scientific knowledge
Marine Plants	NA	NA			NA	NA	NA	5	Inadequate scientific knowledge
Salmonid Trout Freshwater	30,000 (1973)	15,864	30,000	15,684	40,000	55,000	70,000	1	Production cost, market
Marine					1,000	5,000	10,000	2	Production technology, production cost, market
Catfish	84,600 (1973)	35,008	48,000	26,213	80,000	100,000	120,000	1	Production cost market; imports
Crawfish	16,000 (1973)	3,579	10,000	2,237	20,000	25,000	30,000	1	Market

(Table I, continued)

SPECIES OR SPECIES GROUP	CURRENT PRODUCTION				POTENTIAL PRODUCTION FROM AQUACULTURE IN THOUSANDS OF POUNDS [6]			STATUS OF AQUA-CULTURE [1]	MAJOR PROBLEMS
	TOTAL		AQUACULTURE						
	Thousands of Pounds	Thousands of Dollars	Thousands of Pounds	Thousands of Dollars	1983	1988	1993		
Low Cost Fishes	NA	NA			4,000	40,000	400,000	4	Production technology, market, processing methods
TOTAL	1,008,560	553,564	172,105	97,677	289,200	517,500	1,206,000		

[1] Status of aquaculture
1. Viable; could be expanded to meet demand
2. Some commercial ventures; viability expected in 3-5 years
3. No commercial ventures; will be ready for investment in 1-3 years
4. No commercial ventures; needs research or market development requiring 3-5 years
5. Inadequate biological or technical base for aquaculture, but has potential for the future

[2] Commercial landings only
[3] Excluding king and snow crabs
[4] NA not available
[5] Assumes adequate public funding
[6] Based on predicted state of technology assuming adequate funding for research and development. Excludes market considerations

seen as pre-requisite for orderly development of the industry. The need for increased investment for establishing and maintaining intensive culture systems was also emphasized at this session.

If landings from wild stocks increase to the estimated maximum sustainable level of 100 to 150 MMT by the year 2000, and if the FAO goal is achieved, aquaculture could add 20 to 30%.

In view of the known methods for improving the efficiency of traditional pond culture, and the potential for enhancing wild stocks by hatchery systems it is likely that worldwide aquaculture production could be greatly increased and that the FAO goal could be achieved.

In the United States, there is good potential for increasing aquatic food production by expanding hatcheries and other forms of public aquaculture and by encouraging private farming of fish and shellfish.

Procedures for rearing trout, salmon, catfish, and oysters are well known. With the solution of some biological, technological, institutional, or marketing problems, production of these species could be increased significantly.

Research and development can provide adequate biological and technological knowledge for aquaculture of additional species such as shrimp, scallops, clams, crabs, lobsters, and several marine fishes.

Although aquaculture in the United States has focused largely on species in high demand and limited supply, it is not restricted to high-valued products. Buffalo fish and various species of carp can be reared in ponds and processed into acceptable low-priced food products.

The extension of U.S. fisheries jurisdiction to 200 miles offshore provides an opportunity for increasing U.S. harvest of natural stocks. However, this is unlikely to provide significantly increased quantities of those species that might be grown by aquaculture.

Production records demonstrate the success of private and public aquaculture of several species and provide a basis for estimating their potential for expansion. Rainbow trout production by private growers has increased from just over 450 metric tons (1 million pounds) in 1954 to over 13,600 metric tons (30 million pounds) in 1972. With adequate markets and acceptable feed prices, production could be doubled during the next decade.

Private oyster farms produce 9,000 metric tons (20 million pounds) of meats annually. With adequate markets at satisfactory prices and space for oyster culture in the coastal zone, production could be quadrupled during the next decade.

Landings of Pacific salmon could be greatly increased with favorable benefit/cost ratios by expanding public aquaculture. Federal and State salmon culture experts estimate that landings attributable to hatcheries could be increased by half during the next decade if funds were made available for expanding hatchery production.

Private salmon aquaculture, a new industry based on technology developed from public hatcheries, is taking two forms: i. production of pan-sized or yearling salmon in floating net pens or in seawater ponds; ii. ocean ranching in which juveniles are released to feed in the ocean and are recaptured when they return to spawn. Private salmon aquaculture by the net pen and ocean-ranching systems is just beginning, but already there are ventures in Washington, Oregon, Maine, and several planned in Alaska. Production, which was less than 450 metric tons (1 million pounds) in 1975, could exceed 27,000 metric tons (60 million pounds) by 1988, if certain production problems can be solved and markets remain attractive.

Private catfish farming has been a viable industry for several years. About 2,000 farmers and 12 processing firms in 13 southern States produced over 23,000 metric tons (50 million pounds) round weight (1973). The expansion of catfish culture depends on production costs and market prices. With satisfactory profit potential, the industry could at least double its present production by 1988.

During the development of the National Fisheries Plan (8) a table was prepared showing estimated increase in food production which could be achieved by aquaculture. This table, based on best estimates of various government, university, and industry specialists, was included in the "Draft outline for the National Fisheries Plan" (9) and was widely distributed and discussed in a series of meetings in 1974. Comments received during that review process and later information were used to prepare the revised projection included in table I. This table assumes adequate funding for research, and development, and for operation of production hatcheries to enhance depleted natural stocks. It excludes market considerations such as demand, price, distribution systems and product form.

Finally the dates of the original prediction, 1980, 1985 and 1990, have been revised to 1983, 1988, and 1993 because of the elapsed time since 1974 without funding of an expanded aquaculture program.

With all of these caveats and assumptions this table should be considered as a bold attempt to make a realistic projection of the potential for aquaculture in the United States.

Total production for the 21 species groups included in table I, could increase from the present level of 78,000 metric tons (172 million pounds) to over 130,000 metric tons (290 million pounds) by 1983, 220,000 metric tons (517 million pounds) by 1988, and 547,000 metric tons (1.2 billion pounds) by 1993. Continuation of this trend could bring U.S. aquaculture production to nearly 1 million metric tons (2.2 billion pounds) by the year 2000.

Conclusions

1. The world needs more food as the population expands during the next few decades.
2. The world needs more fish. Demand is increasing rapidly and prices are increasing.
3. Landings of currently utilized species might be increased economically to perhaps 100 MMT.
4. New capture fisheries on unutilized or underutilized species could add large quantities (perhaps as much as 400-700 MMT) but technological and logistics problems of harvesting and processing as well as achieving market acceptance are important constraints.
5. Extended jurisdiction could add over 100,000 metric tons to US landings in 1978 with a good potential for substantial increases in succeeding years. Complete harvest of coastal stocks by US fishermen could double U.S. supplies. However, the species in abundance are not those in high demand on the US market.
6. The US demand for high-valued species is expanding and this trend is likely to continue. It is unlikely that this demand can be supplied from natural stocks.
7. Worldwide aquaculture production has doubled during the past 5 years and now is about 10% of landings from wild stocks.
8. There is good potential for doubling world aquaculture production by 1985 to 12 MMT and reaching the FAO goal of 30 MMT by the end of the century.
9. In U.S. aquaculture supplies only 3% of our aquatic products (78,000 MT) but could be increased to 130,000 MT by 1983, 220,000 MT by 1988, 547,000 MT by 1992 and might reach 1 MMT by the year 2000.
10. Public and private aquaculture can increase supplies of several high valued species such as shrimp, salmon, oysters and clams as well as lower priced products made from various fishes of low domestic market value such as the carps, buffalo fish, and tilapia.

References

1. Subcommittee on Department Operations of the Committee on Agriculture, "Malthus and America: A Report About Food and People," House of Representatives, (1974) p. 11
2. Idyll, C. (1977). Harvest from the Sea, NSF lecture, Pacific Science Center, Seattle.
3. U.S. Dept. of Commerce (1976). A Marine Fisheries Program for the

Nation: p. 72

4. National Marine Fisheries Service (1977). Economic Impact Analysis of the Amended Regulations Accompanying Preliminary Management Plans. (Draft).

5. Pillay, T.V.R. (1976). The State of Aquaculture: 1975 FAO Technical Conference on Aquaculture, Kyoto, Japan: Report R.36: p. 13

6. FAO statistic include weight of shell of molluscs.

7. FAO Staff (1976) Summary report of FAO Technical Conference on Aquaculture, Kyoto, Japan.

8. US Dept. of Commerce, (1977) A Marine Fisheries Program for the Nation. USDC, NOAA: p. 74

9. NMFS (1974) Draft Outline for the National Fisheries Plan. National Marine Fisheries Service: p. 225

SECTION II

Present Status and Potential Production of Mulluscs

The United States Molluscan Shellfish Industry

David M. Dressel and Donald S. FitzGibbon
U.S. Department of Commerce
National Oceanic and Atmospheric Administration
National Marine Fisheries Service
Washington, D.C.

As an orientation for those not familiar with our estuarine and coastal waters, a few biological notes on molluscan shellfish and water quality will follow to help put the industry and its history and potential in a better perspective.

General Biological Characteristics

As a group, oysters, clams and mussels have much in common. Their distribution covers wide areas from the brackish, low-salinity waters of most tidal rivers to the bays and adjacent coastal waters of the continental shelf, some beyond 3 miles from the Nation's coastline. The shallow estuaries and coastal areas adjacent to our shores provide favorable combinations of temperature, nutrients and light, and are among the most productive marine environments in the world.

Oysters, clams and mussels are harvested in 22 states. These bivalves are commonly known as filter feeders because they obtain food by using their gills to strain out and concentrate plankton as well as fine suspended and particulate matter from the water. In addition, they may concentrate micro-organisms (some of which may be potential pathogens), pesticides, and other contaminants found in trace quantities in their surroundings. For safe harvesting, shellfish waters must therefore be clean—even beyond the state of cleanliness used for swimming and other forms of contact recreation. Water quality is of paramount importance in understanding the resource and in projecting the future of the industry.

Water Quality and Pollution

Molluscs can be severely affected by adverse changes in their environment. Unlike fish, crabs, shrimp and other marine species, oysters, clams and mussels are sessile organisms incapable of movement to avoid adverse environmental conditions.

Water quality not only controls the productivity and survival of molluscs but also dictates their safeness for human consumption. Adverse water quality can result from natural processes, including flooding and hurricanes that lower salinities, scour bottoms, and silt-over oyster beds, or from local algae blooms that may produce toxins of paralytic shellfish poisoning (PSP).

Molluscs are also greatly influenced by pollution. The human population within 50 miles of our coastal shorelines has increased tremendously over the past 20 years. Man's activities alter and degrade the marine environment in countless ways. Industrial, agricultural and domestic wastes directly affect shellfish resources. The toxic discharges of heavy metals, chlorinated hydrocarbons and other industrial wastes can kill or damage the resources outright or make them unfit for human consumption. Oil spills and pesticides from agriculture and silviculture have similar potentially damaging effects. Urbanization often alters natural watersheds and runoffs, changes freshwater input into the estuary, produces silting from road construction and changes in natural ground cover, and contaminates waters with discharges from inadequate municipal waste treatment facilities, septic facilities, or pleasure boats. All of these can reduce the quality of these resources. Resources are also lost due to the dredging and filling of wetlands; harbor maintenance; and construction of dams, canals and other water diversions, all of which produce changes in nutrients, temperature, salinity, circulation and turbidity. These changes not only affect shellfish, but also alter the productivity and capability of the estuary and coastal waters to support other fisheries.

The future of our domestic molluscan shellfish industry will most likely be determined by the availability of waters of sufficient quality to allow the safe harvesting of molluscs for direct human consumption. Just over 50 years ago, a severe outbreak of typhoid, transmitted by the consumption of raw oysters, eroded public confidence in shellfish and the resultant drop in sales left the future of the industry in doubt.

In 1925, both the industry and the states petitioned the Federal Government to provide assistance in developing practices to assure that only pollution-free oysters reached the consumer. The National Shellfish Sanitation Program emerged as a voluntary Federal/State/industry program. As a result, guidelines were developed to insure that shellfish harvesting areas are safe and free of contamination prior to harvesting, and that products are handled and processed under conditions that prevent contamination and thereby assure product safety.

Today the harvesting of oysters, clams and mussels for direct marketing is allowed only in waters which are certified as safe. Under restricted conditions mildly contaminated stocks may be harvested and either moved to clean waters to purge themselves or cleansed in man-made facilities using treated seawater. The terms "relaying" and "depuration" are applied respectively to these practices.

Molluscan shellfish landings (meat weight) totalled 136.8 million pounds and were valued at $116.2 million in 1976. Landings of oysters have decreased from 90.0 million pounds in 1929 to 54 million pounds in 1976, but have increased in value from $13.3 million in 1929 to $53.1 in 1976. Landings of clams totalled 72.8 million pounds valued at $18.6 million in 1966, and ten years later the quantity increased to 81.0 million pounds, and the value increased to a record $62.7 million. The commercial harvest of blue mussels has fluctuated over the history of the industry. Record catches of over 3 million pounds were harvested in 1944 and 1945 at a value of approximately $175,000 compared to 1.4 million pounds in 1976 valued at $434,000.

In 1975, 22 states were involved in the harvesting of oysters, clams and mussels. Approximately 11,600 persons, including 8,700 full-time fishermen, were involved in oyster harvesting, 24,700 in clam harvesting and an undetermined number of fishermen were involved in the harvesting of mussels. (It should be noted that some fishermen may have harvested more than one species). Also in 1975, approximately 400 plants, employing 5500 persons, produced oyster products worth $86.5 million at the wholesale level. In addition, 3775 persons were employed in 130 clam-processing plants that produced clam and clam products valued at a wholesale level of $106.8 million. According to available records, no mussel products were processed in 1975. Therefore, no wholesale values have been established.

Evolutionary Trends

A general evolutionary pattern emerges in the historical review of the oyster and clam industries. The pattern appears to follow the sequence of: discovering and exploiting a new resource, and developing new techniques and equipment to increase production. This is followed by overfishing and resource depletion, and finally, attempts to rejuvenate the resource. The rate of progression is affected by the demand for the product and size of the resource, which is often reduced by natural disasters, predation, disease and pollution. Therefore, the effectiveness of resource management is a critical factor in reducing the rate of progression.

An historical review of the oyster industry will be made to illustrate this pattern, followed by a review of the clam and mussel industries.

The Oyster Industry

Oyster landings today are approximately one-third those of the very early 1900's and less than one-half of those 50 years ago. Traditionally seafood was a major source of protein prior to the emergence of the cattle industry. Oysters have always been highly valued, and booming harvests were taken from the waters of Long Island and the Chesapeake Bay in the early 1800's. The wholesale harvesting of vast oyster beds on the Atlantic coast began with the introduction of the English schooner and the first sail dredge around the time of the War of 1812. Long Island and New England waters received the heaviest early fishing pressures. In 1859, New York City residents spent more money for oysters than for meat. Some 7 million bushels per year were harvested from Long Island waters, which was the equivalent of 10 bushels of oysters for each New York City resident.

As northern productive areas were depleted, fishing pressure shifted southward to the Chesapeake region. By the time of the Civil War, nearly 650,000 bushels of Virginia seed oysters were being shipped to New England in an attempt to repopulate the beds. Few of these oysters were ever allowed to mature. Most were consumed prior to planting to meet high local demands.

When the first Government records and landings statistics were initiated in 1879, an annual harvest of 17 millon bushels of oysters was being taken from the Chesapeake Bay alone. This figure is over 5 times what the Bay now provides and is more than double the present total U.S. consumption of oysters.

The Chesapeake oyster boom occurred in the late 19th century. By 1880, there were 2,000 "larger dredging vessels" of local registry working the Bay, accompanied by 6,856 sailing "canoes" and other small craft. Today, the Chesapeake Bay is the largest producer of the American or Eastern oyster *Crassostrea virginica*, but as in New York, overfishing has taken its toll.

Natural Mortalities

Oysters are also susceptible to disease and predation. The haplosporidians *Minchinia nelsoni* and *M. costalis* (previously termed MSX and

SSO) were identified as the agents responsible for extensive oyster mortalities which began in the 1950's and continued for more than a decade in Delaware Bay, Chesapeake Bay and coastal areas of Maryland and Virginia. During this period, the oyster harvest in Delaware decreased from approximately 3.5 million pounds in 1953 to a negligible harvest of less than 44,000 pounds in 1968. Similar mortalities occurred in lower parts of Chesapeake Bay with salinities above 14 parts per thousand. Selective breeding for disease resistance appears to be a promising approach to repopulating beds. Other alternatives include selection of areas for oyster culture which are known to have low mortalities, and modification of culture methods.

The fungus *Labyrinthomyxa marina* devastates oyster beds in the Gulf of Mexico with the mortality rate often exceeding 30 percent per year, and in some cases 70 percent per year. Preventive techniques for this disease include planting of large seed, early harvesting, and reduced planting densities.

Predation by oyster drills, starfish, rays and crabs is another biological problem in some areas. Fortunately, oysters grow in areas having variable salinities that provide some protection against predators which are often less tolerant to salinity changes.

Hurricanes and floods are other forms of natural disasters which have lasting effects on oyster production. Reduced salinities and the silting of oyster beds from tropical storm Agnes in 1972 reduced the harvests in the Chesapeake Bay.

Aquaculture

Aquaculture has been employed as a method of repopulating depleted resources and for establishing resource populations in previously barren areas. The term "aquaculture" encompasses a variety of techniques ranging from the simple transplanting of immature seed oysters on new bottoms, to highly sophisticated hatcheries and closed grow out systems. Aquaculture is helping to replenish and stabilize some wild populations which have declined drastically from natural disasters, disease, and overfishing. Currently, 40 percent of the U.S. oyster production is dependent on aquaculture. Attempts to repopulate Long Island's overfished resources which began in the mid-1890's are still in progress today. Immature seed from Connecticut is planted on prepared bottoms on Long Island, periodically culled to remove predators and silt, and harvested 3 to 4 years later to supply a heavy raw bar demand.

Today the West Coast industry, like New York, is dependent on aquaculture. The industry is centered on two species: the native oyster, *Ostrea lurida*, and the larger Pacific oyster, *Crassostrea gigas*. Early attempts to introduce the American oyster, *Crassostrea virginica*, were initially successful at the turn of the century, but unexplained mass mortalities virtually eliminated the species. Production is almost entirely by aquaculture on private leased bottoms. Many seed oysters are still imported from Japan, a practice whch started in the 1920's. There is, however, an increasing reliance on local hatchery seed and some limited natural set occurs.

Industry Restraints

Today's oyster industry is faced with declining stocks, a lack of technology, and the need for new products and markets.

Water quality degradation in growing areas continues, with an annual 0.6 percent increase per year in the acreage closed to shellfish harvesting. These closures are caused largely by contamination from inadequate domestic waste treatment and uncontrolled runoffs. Resources are also lost from disease, predation, and natural disasters.

To conserve the resource, harvesting techniques are sometimes limited to inefficient labor intensive methods on public grounds. Private growers, however, can often use efficient escalator and hydraulic dredge boats capable of harvesting up to 2,000 bushels per day with a two-man crew. In addition, private oyster farmers can harvest their beds throughout the year; public areas are frequently closed 4 to 5 months of the year to conserve the resource.

A critical problem in increasing overall oyster production is the limited processing capacity. Except for steam-and-shake processing of canned oyster products, there is little mechanization. The processing of fresh shucked products is still a labor intensive manual operation. Maryland, the largest oyster producer, ships 70 percent of its harvest out of the state for processing because of the scarcity of skilled oyster shuckers. Processing mechanization is needed not only to overcome labor shortages, but also to create new product forms.

Traditionally, most oysters are marketed in their fresh shucked form. The demand for this product is at best static and many believe it is decreasing. Retail sales appear to be declining while institutional sales increase. This could indicate that oysters are losing out to retail sales of fast convenience foods. New product forms are needed to stimulate retail sales and reverse the decline in demand.

Unless positive action is taken to reverse the trends in water quality, processing, and demand, the decline of the industry will continue.

Clams

Clam exploitation. when compared to oysters, is relatively new. Several fisheries had their origin in bait production and did not convert to food production until the World War II years when red meat was scarce. Total clam landings have been heaviest in the past several years; the landings in 1973 begin 3 times those in 1950. Overfishing is common and when coupled with recent natural disasters, has nearly depleted several stocks.

Today, 14 species of clams are harvested commercially in 18 states. The majority of the clam industry is located on the East Coast and is concerned with the harvesting of four species; hard, soft, and surf clams, and ocean quahogs. These four species have accounted for 99 percent of the total U.S. clam landings over the past 10 years. The relative volume and value of these species are shown below:

	Percent Volume	Percent Value
Hard Clams	17	53
Soft Clams	12	20
Surf Clams	69	25
Ocean Quahog	1	1

Innovations and mechanization played an important role in the evolution of the clam industry. The industry did not really develop until the early 1900's when canneries were established. Exploitation was then often rapid, with depleted local stocks causing shifts to other species or locations. An example is the Pacific Coast razor clam which once supported high volume canneries until 1925 when the resource showed signs of depletion. Similar exploitation occurred in other species as well. A brief review of fisheries surrounding the four dominant species will illustrate the roles of innovation, new mechanization, changes in demand and overall resource availability.

Hard clams—The hard clam industry is the oldest of all the clam fisheries in the United States,dating back to colonial times. The industry has traditionally been concentrated on the East Coast, with less than 4 percent of production occurring on the West Coast.

The industry gained prominence in the early 1900's with the opening of canneries; the West Coast of Florida being a major producer of canned clams in 1913. In 1943, the largest clam bed in the United States covered a 150 square mile area off West Florida. These hard clams were so dense that a dredge towed for only 6 yards would yield a bushel of clams. The war and resultant meat shortages increased the demand for clams and in 1947 this same clam bed, once Florida's richest, was totally depleted.

In the same year, New England and Long Island were recording peak landings. The shallow nearshore habitat of the hard clam makes hand harvesting practical and subjects the resource to heavy harvesting from both commercial and recreational fishermen.

Most hard clams are consumed raw without any processing. This further necessitates the need for high water quality for safe harvests. However, the proximity of clam beds to urban areas often subjects them to intense domestic pollution, resulting in the closing of many productive clam beds. These condemned resources represent a significant loss in production, which increases in potential value as the resources in the major producing states of Maryland, Virginia, Delaware and New York, continue to decline from heavy harvesting. Hard clams, although still the most valued, are being displaced by other more abundant species of lesser value.

Surf clams—The surf clam fishery is located in the same states as the hard clam fishery. Its history dates back to 1870 when it was a bait fishery. The demand for meat in World War II shifted the use of surf clams from bait to food. The industry expanded rapidly in 1943 with the development of a drum washer to remove sand from the meats. Once this processing problem was overcome, a hydraulic jet cage dredge was created which increased harvests. As resources were depleted in various areas, the harvesting effort shifted to new locations.

Between 1945-54, the major harvesting effort was in New York, followed by a shift to New Jersey, which produced 96 percent of all surf clam landings between 1962-66. In the early 1970's, the fishing effort was concentrated off Virginia, and an automatic shucking machine was developed to help overcome hand labor shortages. About this time, efficient stern dredge vessels began entering the fleet. The industry recorded peak harvests in 1974 and 1975, which depleted many beds. In sharp contrast to the older traditional inshore clam and oyster fisheries, the offshore clam fishery had no legal restraints to prevent development of effective harvesting methods. The industry has always been progressive. Most plants use automated equipment for shucking, evisceration, washing, chopping, and packing.

The severest problem facing the industry today is depletion of stocks. The record landings in 1974 and 1975 depleted many beds and a massive clam kill in the summer of 1976 produced massive mortalities in some of the remaining stocks. Approximately 30 percent of all of the surf clams in New Jersey were killed by toxic waters resulting from vast phytoplankton blooms, their subsequent die off, and oxygen depletion.

Resource depletion led to price increases from $2.25 per bushel in October 1975 to $11.00 per bushel in October 1976, following the mass mortalities. The industry is now beginning to exploit the ocean quahog as an alternate resource.

Ocean quahogs—Ocean quahogs are presently underutilized, with large resources found beyond the 3 mile limit in 25 to 61 meters of water. During the war years, they were used as a red meat substitute, fostering a small fishery in Rhode Island in 1943.

The dark color and strong flavor of the meats are a deterrent to their utilization. They are hard to open and have only one-half the yield of surf clams. Advanced food technology is overcoming some of these problems. The tremendous investment in surf clam processing and the decline in surf clam stocks is promoting an intense search for a substitute resource, and the ocean quahog is a logical choice. Management plans are needed to prevent the overfishing that has been the plague of other segments of the fishing industry.

Soft clams—The soft clam fishery evolved from a bait fishery which was well established in the mid-1800's. The industry is centered in New England. Peak landings were in the late 1930's. The dramatic increase in demand during World War II years, and a major change in the local fin fisheries from bait to trawling, shifted the clam industry from bait to food production.

Intense harvesting to meet new demands resulted in New England waters being overfished by 1948-49. The emphasis then shifted to Maryland, where subtidal soft clam resources were not utilized until 1952 when the hydraulic soft clam dredge was introduced. Exploitation was then rapid, and from 1956 to 1970 the Maryland catch exceeded that of New England.

The Maryland stocks showed signs of overfishing in the 1970's, and in 1972 the severe flooding from tropical storm Agnes caused extensive mortalities in the remaining populations. At present, production is again concentrated in New England waters.

The Future

Only four of the 14 commercially harvested species have been reviewed in the paper. Even though these four species represent over 99 percent of the total clam landings in the past 10 years, an increased effort to utilize other species is likely, because once major stocks have been drastically reduced, a new source must be found. New technology and exploration should make additional species available for utilization. The sporadic occurrence of paralytic shellfish poisoning (PSP), caused by the rapid growth of certain phytoplankton species is a problem in areas of the Pacific Northwest and New England. It is predicted that the development of a rapid on-site test for the presence of PSP could allow the harvesting of vast new clam resources in Alaska. Preliminary surveys indicate that these resources could well equal the present entire U.S. clam production.

Mussels

Mussels are an underutilized species found on the West Coast from Alaska to California and on the East Coast from Maine to North Carolina. Harvesting is centered in Maine, Massachusetts, Rhode Island, and New York, with West Coast populations being relatively unexploited.

Mussels are not in demand in the United States as they are in Spain and the Netherlands, the world's largest producers. The mild flavor, occurrence of pearls in the meats, and short shelf life of fresh products are all a hindrance to the development of U.S. markets.

During 1929-1941, there was a small industry in New England. Wartime brought peak landings of approximately 2.6 million pounds annually in 1944 and 1945, when most of the mussels were canned for export. The number of processing plants increased from 3 to 15 during this period. Production nearly ceased after 1946. Only 1.4 million pounds are now harvested annually.

In some areas, mussels are considered a nuisance because they compete with soft clam stocks. New Hampshire even hires fishermen to dredge mussels off clam flats. Mussels are harvested throughout New England to meet small local demands; some mussels are shipped to a limited New York City market.

Mussels are normally harvested by hand using pitchforks at low tide. Some dredging in 20-100 feet of water is practiced. If demand were higher, there would surely be more interest in mussel harvesting. Investment is minimal, with high potential returns. Massachusetts shellfishermen receive $2.50 to $4.00 per bushel of sacked mussels. One man can gather 40-60 bushels in a day's labor of 4-5 hours. The potential is the same in Long Island, where the going rate is $4.00 per bushel and the beds are dense and overcrowded.

Several factors may influence the reluctance of watermen to enter this fishery. Unexplained mass mortalities are common; the most recent occurred in Rhode Island and Delaware in 1976. Pollution has closed vast, densely populated mussel beds in New Jersey, and the sporadic occurrence of PSP often necessitates the closure of large mussel producing areas in New England. In addition, hurricanes destroy beds, and there is often heavy predation by ducks, starfish and hermit crabs.

Most states do not have resource management plans for mussels because few are harvested. Should demand be increased, regulations would be needed to prevent overfishing. In addition to natural wild stocks, mussels are also being grown through aquaculture. The practice can yield larger mussels that are free of pearls and have better meat yields and flavor. These have a distinct market advantage over the small, often underdeveloped mussels found on densely populated natural beds. Unless new demand is created, mussels will continue to be a minor adjunct to other fisheries.

In summary, the major conclusions to be drawn from these data are that the future of our molluscan shellfish industry will depend on maintaining high water quality for safe harvesting, and on overcoming processing and marketing barriers that prevent a full exploitation of existing resources.

Acknowledgments

This paper is drawn in part from the "The Molluscan Shellfish Industries and Water Quality—Problems and Opportunities," a report by the Secretary of Commerce to the Congress, September 1977. Historical aspects were often extracted directly from three technical reports supporting the Secretary's report:"A Comprehensive Review of the Commercial Oyster Industries in the United States," and "A Comprehensive Review of the Commercial Mussel Industries in the United States," published under contract to NMFS in March 1977. Most historical aspects of the oyster industry were obtained from *The Beautiful Swimmers*, by William W. Warner, Atlantic-Little, Brown Books, Boston, 1976.

Shellfish Hatcheries, An Industry View

Stephen P. Henderson
International Shellfish Enterprises, Inc.
Moss Landing, California

This presentation will encompass a number of related aspects. After a brief view of the world of shellfish hatcheries as it exists today, we will describe our company from both technical and commercial viewpoints. Then we will highlight what we feel is the role of mariculture today, discuss the future of hatcheries as part of an overall fisheries complex, and conclude with a brief summary of our ideas and objectives.

This may seem like quite an order to meet, and indeed as far as we are concerned there is never enough time to do the subject full justice. However we sincerely feel that such an overview is important to the establishment of the proper perspective of hatcheries in the field of mariculture. As you will see, we are quite optimistic about the future of mariculture.

The World of Shellfish Hatcheries

It is thought by many that our modern concept of marine aquaculture, or mariculture, was actually begun with oyster culture in the days of the Romans. Others trace the history to the Orient some 3,500 years ago. Nevertheless, the art remained primitive until the 17th century when history records the discovery, in Japan, of the use of artificial means to collect larger numbers of oyster spat than would have survived under natural conditions. With this promising start, the Japanese have led the way in establishing effective and efficient culture methods for their native oyster. Indeed even today, the Japanese are considered the predominant suppliers of oyster seed to the world's growers. Although the Japanese have been and are experimenting with hatchery programs, their commercial techniques, appear to be somewhat traditional in that they primarily gather or "collect" oyster seed from the natural habitat--the ocean.

263

More modern thinking tends to favor the use of hatcheries as a method of producing more controlled outputs of molluscan shellfish, as well as those which possess desirable qualities.

Hatchery culture of oysters actually began in the United States back in the late 1800's and showed signs of only gradual success and refinement through the next 75 years. Beginning in the late 1940's and spurred by decreasing populations of natural oysters, a number of U.S. organizations laid the groundwork for model hatchery systems which produce consistent quantities of useable oyster seed. The concept of the shellfish hatchery became quite popular during the 1960's when various government agencies, both here and abroad, intensified their efforts to create effective hatchery systems which could augment the dwindling natural shellfish fisheries. At the same time, private interests began to see economic opportunity and found their way into a number of shellfish hatchery schemes.

In the wake of this flurry of interest, we have collectively discovered that the hatchery spawning and rearing of shellfish is a delicate process to initiate and to control, and that the hatchery product, when it has been available, is met in the market with mixed reaction. This reaction is mixed for a number of reasons—which primarily relate to the product.

Existing Shellfish Hatcheries

Traditional sources of shellfish seed to supplement natural reproduction in the growing areas have been cultch seed from Japan—collected on old shells in the prolific spawning beds in the northern part of the country. The Japanese have been and still are seed specialists to the world; however their product is slowing losing its appeal, and the beds are no longer as prolific as there once were.

Hatcheries have been trying to make up the difference. There exists today only a handful of working hatcheries. Some, such as those sponsored by the English government, have achieved only sporadic production over the past several years and continue, even today, on a non-predictable basis. Others, especially in the United States, have had success for one or two years, only to face production failures which have resulted in the redesign or ultimate closing of their facilities.

A couple of the most successful are in the states of New York and Washington. Operated primarily for continuous spat production for their private oyster harvesting business, the companies have proven that hatchery production of shellfish spat works, and works well.

Other hatcheries exist in the Southeastern and Northwestern parts of the United States. Some are privately owned although most are institutionally oriented.

Two years ago, one of the most promising commercial ventures, Sea Farms, in the state of Washington, was purportedly forced to close down due to water contamination beyond the company's control. Last year, our production in Moss Landing was stopped for the same reason. We feel that this must really be considered a reasonable risk of operation. Thus in the hatchery world we have a "mixed bag". Methods and technology are close at hand, and collectively we all appear to be on the threshhold of an important new phase of intensive, controlled, shellfish cultivation, yet we don't have a history of consistent or reliable production that is needed to gain market support. At the same time the world market, in face of rapidly diminishing natural stocks, is in great need of reliable supplies of seed shellfish—yet existing industry is at present not equipped to accept or handle the seed products that the hatcheries appear best suited to produce. We are seeing positive signs of resolution however and from this should come a brilliant future for hatcheries and their customers, the shellfish growers.

International Shellfish Enterprises, Inc.

Our company, International Shellfish Enterprises, is relatively new to the hatchery scene. Initial feasibility studies were begun in 1970 at the prompting of some environmentally-conscious residents of the San Francisco Peninsula.

Building on hatchery design concepts developed eariler in the United States, the founders were anxious to incorporate some of the progressive ideas developed at the famed Oyster Research Institute in Kesennuma, Japan. The director of the Oyster Research Institute, the late Dr. Takeo Imai, was retained by our founders to establish a hatchery site along the California Coast.

Our present site, in Moss Landing, lies along the shoreline of Monterey Bay in the central part of the state. There we were able to find a combination of factors which we feel have had a substantial influence upon our development and productivity, to date. First, Moss Landing lies adjacent to an immense, deep water marine canyon. We therefore benefit from copious amounts of consistantly good water. Near our facility is one of the worlds largest fossil-fuel electric generating plants, owned and operated by the Pacific Gas and Electric Company. This plant discharges huge quantities of warm water. Since the water is not treated or chemically influenced by the P.G. and E. operation, we can in theory use whatever amounts we want as a direct warm water source for the hatchery.

Finally we have at Moss Landing a natural slough which serves as an ideal environment for the handling and inventorying of our hatchery products.

The company was conceived as being a purely commercial venture. The intent of the founders was to create a new oyster fishery in California, using the production of the hatchery to provide a continuous and predictable supply of seed shellfish, to support an extensive grow out program. Under the guidance of Dr. Imai, and two marine biologists hired for the purpose, site preparation and hatchery design work was completed. Soon thereafter the construction of the most modern and efficient shellfish hatchery existing today was begun.

The facility was completed in early 1973, and after that came the difficult task of honing and balancing the individual systems to the point that they could sustain life.

It would seem that life was considerably easier for the oysters we were raising than it was for the personnel whose responsibility it was to put the facility into a production mode. Our efforts were continually frustrated by many technical setbacks, some of which have commonly thwarted most shellfish hatcheries, and others which were probably of our own design.

Nearly two years passed before we could produce shellfish seed with any degree of predictability. Even then our production levels remained substantially below our objectives. However, since early this spring (1977) we have been producing and marketing continually larger quantities of both clam and oyster seed and our progress curve suggests that we can be up to fully profitable production levels within the next six months.

Our hatchery design concept closely parallels what is known as the Milford Method. This method embraces the exclusive use of hatchery grown food to sustain animal life within the hatchery. The hatchery is divided into 5 divisions. The first is a conditioning facility where brood stocks are prepared for spawning. Spawning preparation includes water temperature controls, as well as lighting and dietary balances. Spawning is of course followed by fertilization and after fertilization the animals pass through a larval stage. This represents the second division within the hatchery. Here we have developed some of the most important handling techniques and controls within the system, and these probably account for much of our production success to date. We overproduce at this stage—in other words, we produce more than the remaining stages can handle—so that we can have the luxury of selecting only the very best larvae for further growth.

The third division is concerned with the "setting" of the oyster larvae. The word "set" refers to a brief, 24 hour metamorphic period when the larvae stop swimming about in the water and start assuming their identity as shellfish. The environmental balances necessary to support this stage, in the densities that make production economically viable, are extremely delicate. Also, it appears that the preselection of only the highest potential larvae is crucial to volume production.

All of this work gets us to the point where we have a large number of baby shellfish which need a great deal of tender loving care. Apart from the textbooks, formulae and laboratory techniques which guide our efforts, we seriously believe that a complete understanding of and full attention to the emotional and psychological needs of the young shellfish is an absolute necessity to the success of a hatchery operation. It is a predominant factor at this post-setting stage.

This begins our fourth division—the nursery phase. Here the spat grow from about 300 microns in size up to about 3 millimeters. They are continually fed, bathed and cuddled on a schedule which includes a full 24 hours each day. To make the system work at this stage we have had to depart from the more standard holding techniques and create facilities and equipment which can cater to all of the complex needs of the individual animals.

Finally, we remove the spat from the hatchery and transport it to the slough for introduction to the natural environment for conditioning before shipment to the growers.

The entire cycle consumes from 16 to 26 weeks, depending upon the species under cultivation, and on the pre-determined market size of the seed.

In concluding this brief technical review it should be pointed out that it has been relatively easy for us to follow the classical rules for hatchery production. However, the rules are not geared to high volume intensive production techniques. Indeed, many of the problems and variables are not even identified until a hatchery system has been "loaded", and this "loading" extends beyond the scope of most research or pilot study work. Thus, most hatcheries considering volume production must pioneer their own paths to technical achievement, or invest much time in bringing outside scientists up the learning curve of full-density production complexities.

Another way of saying this is to suggest that government and academic research efforts are not constructed in such a way as to have practical carryover benefits to the commercial sector. And, unfortunately, the capital limitations of a commercial enterprise prevent it from doing a satisfactory or even adequate job in the research and development sphere.

Persistence, patience, and the ability to sustain ones operation appear to be the main ingredients to successful production; and continual system balancing and refinement are the keys to the large volumes required to make a hatchery operation economically successful. It should be said here that we are still in the learning stage and probably face a variety of new problems as we push production even further up toward full plant capacity. All the same, we are now at about 50 percent production capacity, delighted with our achievements so far, and hope that the worst is behind us.

The Market

Since we are a commercial venture, we have business pursuits and interests which extend beyond the technical question of how well we make the hatchery work. Chief among these are growth and profit—though not necessarily in that order.

Our observation of the world market for shellfish seed has encouraged us to devote the major portion of our production to seed sales, and to adjust our thinking with respect to when we plan to enter the adult shellfish market. Clearly there is room for both but we feel that it dilutes our energies at a time when full attention to hatchery production offers the best return, in terms of both business and technical accomplishment.

Thus in 1975 we embarked upon a broad program of international seed sales. Our basic product line includes three species of seed oysters: *C. virginica, O. edulis* and *C. gigas*, as well as two species of clams, *M. mercenaria* and *Tapes semidecussata*. The oysters are offered in three size classifcations ranging from 3 to 40 millimeters while the clams are sold in two sizes, 3 to 5 mm and 6 to 10 mm.

Our dominant production has been in the small and midsize ranges of single or "cultchless" oyster spat. These are independent, individual oysters suitable for a broad range of both traditional and "new" culturing techniques.

Since our venture into international seed marketing, we have sold seed to more than 8 countries including such diverse locations as Tonga, in the South Pacific, and Casablanca, Morocco. Shipments in the United States have gone to six states on the east and south coasts as well as three on the Pacific coast. Our objectives are to sustain continuous capacity production on an increasing volume level. In order to maintain stability, however, we try to schedule orders and sales at the time of spawning, so as to reduce the risk and excessive inventory buildup. Fortunately the buyers are interested in securing advance contracts, so that makes it mutually desireable. We have learned, however, that unsold inventory is a hazard to normal production efficiency. We therefore encourage other hatcheries to develop an alternate program for use of un-sold seed, such as a dedicated grow-out program.

With the advent of year around production of hatchery seed, new avenues to oyster culture management are available to growers. Where in the past they have had to gear their plantings to the seasonal availability of seed they can now extend their planting season, which results in a longer harvesting period again diminishing curves in the adult oyster markets.

As mentioned, there is an extensive world-wide demand for seed. Part of the demand is cyclical, resulting from periodic crop failures. The better portion of it, however, is growing at an increasing rate, primarily resulting from two factors. The first is the need for more efficient culture management and the need for greater productivity of growing areas and labor. The second factor is the continuing decrease in natural shellfish reproduction caused by such things as over-fishing of natural beds, pollution of traditional growing waters, etc.

The net impact of all this is that we have identified a market which can accommodate an annual volume of 2 billion seed, from hatchery production. This number represents only 25 percent of the world annual adult harvest (as reported by FAO).

With such a demand you can expect that there will be a flurry of activity in the shellfish hatchery business. This is indeed coming about. Several improved techniques for hatchery development will soon be available—some sponsored by private industry and others by public funds. However, it will not come about over night, for two reasons. First, while it is possible for hatcheries to be erected in various locations, it will take considerable time for each individual hatchery system to be put into productive balance. Second, where-as the expressed interest of growers for hatchery seed is high, numbers of growers will be unwilling to take the conversionary steps necessary to adapt to hatchery seed until they are confident that hatcheries can produce continually and reliably, and that the hatchery products will adapt properly to their individual growing conditions. The industry is basically facing a transformation stage and with the cooperation of all parties it can be done smoothly and with good results.

The Future of Hatcheries

This brings us to the future of shellfish hatcheries and their role in mariculture. If we accept the fact that there is a large and growing demand for hatchery seed and that consistant supplies of seed will enhance the efficiency and productivitiy of oyster culture, then we must find a way to make this happen without the severe setbacks that have characterized the past.

We propose three steps for a smooth transition. First, the hatchery operators must establish a better level of communication among themselves. A mutual trust and understanding is required, along with a sharing of technological accomplishment. No one hatchery or even one company can or should control the market. And in turn the market will not materialize until the growers are assured that more than a single source of supply exists. Through the sharing of hatchery technology, hatchery operators can move through the hatchery conditioning stage more rapidly and with a lower degree of risk. It may be found that specialized functions of hatchery operations will develop. For instance, one hatchery may find that its particular conditions favor spawning and larval growth. While another hatchery may be more proficient in setting and nursery care. It would seem reasonable then, to share ultimate production capabilities to achieve the best results.

The second step for a smooth transition is better communication between hatchery operators and their customers, the shellfish growers. For instance it does not make much sense for a hatchery to produce seed that the grower cannot use, either because he cannot adjust to the seed style or adapt the species to his growing area. Yet we find that hatcheries have made a practice of producing what they produce best, often irrespective of the needs of the market. And the seed buyers, faced with only the decision of whether to buy seed or interrupt production, have often ended up being dissatisfied with their purchase and dubiuous as to the future contributions of hatcheries.

The shellfish growers know their problems and have a pretty good idea of possible resolutions. Yet for the most part they are not enlightened as to the potential of hatcheries for diverse production capabilities. Hatchery operators should take the lead in showing growers how to obtain the most benefits from hatchery products. And when they start that they can make innovative contributions to each other's businesses.

As a final step in our proposal for a smooth transition we suggest that hatchery operators develop a code of standards which can be used by the industry as a whole, and which will permit research organizations as well as various government regulatory agencies to develop a common understanding of the inherent risks and advantages of hatchery produced shellfish and their international distribution. As it stands today there is ineffective communication and sparse common understanding of the problems of shellfish culture — either on a national or international scale.

There should not be much concern that these things have not happened in the past since this is, in reality, a whole new field. What does seem important is that we exert every effort to make them happen now so that the oyster industry can achieve maximum benefit from this valuable new technology.

Once shellfish hatcheries establish themselves as reliable production facilities and achieve the operational balances that make them most efficient, we visualize a whole new array of by-products from hatchery operations. For instance the mastering of basic hatchery technology will pave the way for closed system shellfish culturing technology—thus eliminating dependency upon the sea.

There is also the promise of genetically improved strains of shellfish-hybrids particulary suited for their growing characteristics, disease resistance, shape, meat content, quality, taste, and similar other properties.

A properly designed and managed commercial hatchery should also be able to mass produce multiple species of shellfish seed simultaneously. This then gives the hatchery operator the capability of tailoring his product to the specific needs of each customer. For instance he can use a grower's adults as brood stock, assuring a genetic unity within the growers stocks, and he can precondition his nursery tanks to match the ultimate environment in which the seed will grow. Additionally, he should be able to set the same animals on a variety of different substrates—again tailoring the product to the specific use-needs of a variety of customers.

In a less commercial sense hatcheries should be able to make contributions to society in general. We see hatcheries devoting a portion of their production to the restocking of dwindling species of shellfish in natural habitats, to maintain or re-establish environmental balances. We see an opportunity for shellfish in a contained system providing a biological filtration process for contaminated water. The list goes on and on.

Finally we see hatcheries as the stepping stone toward other aspects of applied marine biology once predictability in closed-circuit, high-intensity breeding technology is obtained, there should be direct carryovers into other fields of marine science.

Conclusion

International Shellfish Enterprises wishes to participate in as many of these exciting new developments in mariculture as possible. In addition to providing a return to the founders of our company we hope to set an example for the industry which will both encourage the investment of more private capital in a broad array of mariculture disciplines, and which will result in the advancement of a much needed component in food production from the world's fisheries.

As mentioned at the outset we are quite optimistic about the future of mariculture and hope that you will share and sustain our enthusiasm.

Molluscan Shellfish Research In The United States With Emphasis On Controlled System Aquaculture At The University of Delaware

Kent S. Price, Jr.
College of Marine Studies
University of Delaware
Lewes, Delaware

The purpose of this report is to (i) review the scope of molluscan research in the United States, and (ii) highlight research activities that are specifically directed toward enhancing commercial production of bivalve molluscs. Whenever one attempts to synthesize information of this type, one can summarize activities by species group (oysters, clams, mussels, etc.), by disciplinary approach (nutrition, genetics, disease, etc.) or by institution (university, government, industry, etc.), to name the more obvious options. And, the compilation may take several forms. One can produce a digest (or handbook) of aquaculture research such as Aquaculture 1976 (1), which provides a summary of current aquaculture programs supported by NOAA through the Sea Grant Program, or a National Aquaculture Information System (NAIS) (2) for computer assisted access to a broad range of information (both published and unpublished) on growing marine, brackish and freshwater organisms. Other broad efforts that treat molluscan shellfish research from the perspective of some history, current scope, constraints, and recommendations for the future, include the NOAA Aquaculture Plan (3) and Aquaculture in the United States: An Assessment which is in preparation by the Committee on Aquaculture of the National Academy of Sciences Board on Agriculture and Renewable Resources. Glude (3) has effectively characterized the general scope of molluscan shellfish research in the funding patterns shown in his tables I and II and figures A5, B4, B6, and C1. Based on these indices we could probably build a convincing case that the United States has conducted a substantial amount of research on molluscs but that the development of solutions to industry problems is not keeping pace with the ever increasing difficulties related to shellfish production. Because of the availability of several research digests, overviews, and information retrieval systems, I chose not to provide you with a potentially boring list of research projects around the U.S.A., but rather to address the question "how can molluscan shellfish research more effectively support commercial shellfish production"?

Research on commercially valuable molluscan shellfish was initiated in the United States in the late 1800's by the Nelsons of Rutgers (4). Since that time many others have contributed to a substantial body of information as evidenced by the 3500 entries in the NAIS (2). Through an update of Aquaculture 1976 and a review of papers presented at the 1977 Technical Sessions of the National Shellfisheries Association one may identify key U.S. workers in the academic and federal research fields involving nutrition, genetics and breeding, disease, hatchery techniques and conditions, grow out techniques and environmental conditions, environmental systems control and economics and marketing for oysters (Table I), clams (Table II), mussels (Table III) and scallops (Table IV). For brevity only one individual per institution is identified by topical category. Undoubtedly some ongoing research was overlooked in this analysis. I would therefore appreciate your help in identifying oversights and omissions in these tabular summaries.

Several basic conclusions may be drawn from historical data and personal knowledge of shellfish research in the United States. The first is that about 12 million dollars has been spent on oyster research since 1938 and about two million dollars has been spent on clam research during a similar period (3). Only nominal amounts, too small to be tabulated by comparison, have been spent on research on mussels and scallops.

The second conclusion, which is more an observation on my part, is that most of the shellfish research in the U.S. has been conducted by biologists. Biologists tend to be fine professional scientists but do not often attack problems from the perspective of an engineer, economist, or industrial entrepreneur. Being a biologist, I feel that I can, in good conscience, level this criticism.

Trends And New Initiatives

It is my belief that the establishment of the Sea Grant Program in 1966 initiated a new trend in university-based shellfish research that will pay substantial dividends in the near future, i.e., the trend toward interdisciplinary team approaches to complex maricultural production and environmental control problems. A similar trend is also seen in the National Marine Fisheries Service. This trend, which is still in its infancy, is characterized by group development of program objectives, management

Table I
Researchers and Institutions Involved in Oyster Research

Nutrition	Epifanio	University of Delaware
	Dupuy	Virginia Institute of Marine Science
	Ukeles	National Marine Fisheries Service
Genetics and Breeding	Anderson	University of Georgia
	Lannon	Oregon State University
	Andrews	Virginia Institute of Marine Science
	Nakatani	University of Washington
	Longwell	National Marine Fisheries Service
Disease	Nakatani	University of Washington
	Rosenfield	National Marine Fisheries Service
Hatchery Techniques and Conditions	Hidu	University of Maine
	Krantz	University of Maryland
	Leibovitz	Cornell
Grow Out Techniques and Environmental Conditions	Hidu	University of Maine
	Seifert	Massachusetts Institute of Technology
	Breese	Oregon State University
	Manzi	South Carolina Marine Resources Research Institute
	Haskin	Rutgers
	Cooper	University of Rhode Island
	Eckmayer	Alaska Marine Research Laboratory
Environmental Systems Control	Bolton	University of Delaware
	Neilson	Virginia Institute of Marine Science
Economics and Marketing	Anderson	University of Delaware
	Krantz	University of Maryland

by initiative, creation of interdisciplinary teams selected for their appropriateness to a desired practical set of goals, and the operation of pilot scale projects for economic and process evaluation. As one means of developing program research objectives, industry representatives are asked to identify problem areas and their priority levels. Interdisciplinary teams involving biologists, chemists, engineers, lawyers, economists, etc. are assembled to do research on the identified problems. Research strategies are developed by the research team and its manager(s) and the research plan is put into effect if appropriate fiscal support is available.

Table II
Researchers and Institutions Involved in Clam Research

Nutrition	Epifanio	University of Delaware
	Castagna	Virginia Institute of Marine Science
Genetics and Breeding	Menzel	Florida State University
	Wall	George Mason University
Disease	Brown	University of Rhode Island
	Rosenfield	National Marine Fisheries Service
Hatchery Techniques and Conditions	Chew	University of Washington
Grow Out Techniques and Environmental Conditions	Haskins	Rutgers
	Whetstone	Clemson
	Rhodes	National Marine Fisheries Service
Environmental Systems Control	Bolton	University of Delaware
Economics and Marketing	Anderson	University of Delaware

Table III
Researchers and Institutions Involved in Mussel Research

Nutrition	—	—
Genetics and Breeding	—	—
Disease	—	—
Hatchery Techniques and Conditions	—	—
Grow Out Techniques and Environmenntal Conditions	Lutz	University of Maine/University of New Hampshire
	Myers	Abandoned Farms
Environmental Systems Control	—	—
Economics and Marketing	Slabyi	University of Maine
	Bonchard	Maine Department of Marine Resources
	Clifton	University of Maine
	Haley	University of New Hampshire

Table IV
Researchers and Institutions Involved in Scallop Research

Nutrition	—	—
Genetics and Breeding	Wall	George Mason University
Disease	—	—
Hatchery Techniques and Conditions	Castagna	Virginia Institute of Marine Science
Grow Out Techniques and Environmental Conditions	Hickey	Long Island University
Environmental Systems Control	—	—
Economics and Marketing	—	—

Once the knowledge base reaches an appropriate level, project engineers design and operate pilot scale efforts so that economic potential of the new system can be determined and both engineering and economic optimization may take place. The final step in the scheme is for the research institution to cooperate with industry or business to establish and operate a viable commercial shellfish production process based on the research and development previously described.

I am privileged to be part of such a team at the University of Delaware where over the past seven years we have taken a radical new research approach to the solution of declining natural production of bivalve molluscs. We chose to develop recirculated systems (Fig. 1) for growing mollusc shellfish under a high degree of environmental control somewhat analogous to poultry production schemes seen in the U.S. (5).

Advances in Closed Recirculated System Mariculture

With support from Sea Grant, the State, and industry, the University of Delaware team has been working to raise oysters and clams under controlled conditions. Delaware has demonstrated that these bivalves can be grown in a closed system and that they grow faster than they would naturally. Oysters that take at least 36 months to mature in natural

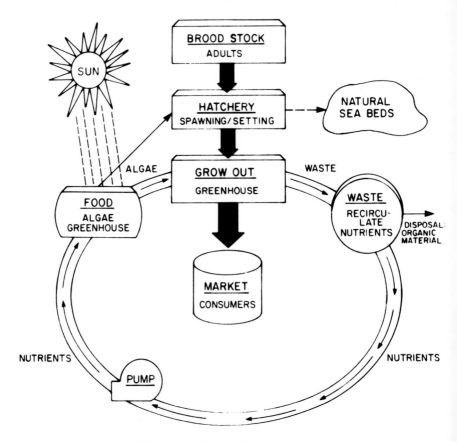

FIGURE 1. Closed (recirculated) system concept.

seabeds are now growing to market size in only 36 weeks in University of Delaware laboratories. The same degree of success has been achieved with clams, growing them to market size three to five times faster than in nature (Fig. 2).

Since the program's inception, the record has been one of continuing progress:

1968-1970   Biologists concentrated on manipulating parents to spawn at will. The bivalves were grown initially using natural plankton in a flow through system.

1970-1973   Clams and oysters reared in the laboratory were maintained in a recirculating system and fed various diets of algae, also grown in the laboratory. Clams grew 50 percent faster than they do in nature.

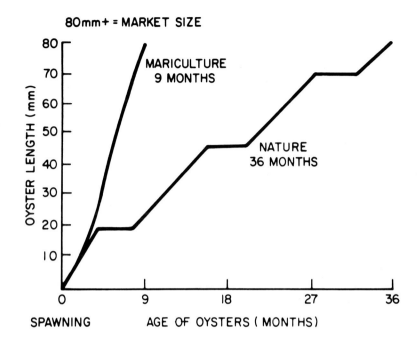

FIGURE 2. A comparison of natural and closed system oyster growth in Delaware.

1974-1975   Delaware's team became the first group in the world to successfully grow clams and oysters to market size in a recirculating seawater system.

Today   The system can now produce adult bivalves in less than a year from animals hatched and grown to maturity in the laboratory.

Outstanding achievements have been made with the algae needed to feed the animals. Delaware's mariculture scientists can now produce thirty times as much algae in a given volume of water than could be produced in 1973. Also, they have selected several types of algae that promote fast growth of the bivalves. At the current level of technology development, estimates indicate that commercial quantities of oysters produced using closed system techniques would range from $20 to $32 per bushel. Oysters raised naturally have been priced at $6 to $20 per bushel. However, with the extreme cold and freezing conditions which existed this past winter (1976-77) they reached a price of $45 per bushel. With the technology mastered, clearly the next significant hurdle is cutting costs to the point where commercial production will be profitable.

Specific Accomplishments

During the eighth year of research (1975-76), industry interest has been substantial, resulting in (a) eleven industries attending an MIT Opportunity Briefing at Delaware on closed system aquaculture, (b) Unilever Ltd. entering into a three-year industry partner agreement with the University of Delaware involving a $45,000 commitment by Unilever to closed system research and development work, (c) Campbell Soup Company agreeing to assist the University of Delaware in shellfish nutrition work by conducting nutritional analyses of bivalve shellfish feeds and contributing $45,000 to closed system research and development, (d) direct laboratory participation in the Delaware project by Amoco (Standard Oil of Indiana) in providing alternate shellfish foods (yeast) for testing, and (e) a considerable number of inquiries concerning the Delaware closed system mariculture program. Several patent disclosures concerning closed system shellfish culture have been initiated.

During the eighth year we also commenced testing a 50-bushel system on a natural day/night cycle in a simple greenhouse. A significant advance in algae culture has been achieved through careful control of gas mixtures to repress photosynthetically wasteful photorespiration. This results in culture densities of six million/ml in a semi-continuous culture mode in 10,000 liter cultures. Monocultures may be sustained and harvested for periods of 2-3 weeks. Fifty mg dry weight of algae/liter may be harvested daily. This compares favorably with the best laboratory culture production. Recycle has been increased from 70 percent to 90 percent with only a minor reduction of oyster growth.

Water quality monitoring techniques were refined to levels now in use in the recirculated system. Seven diagnostic water quality parameters can now be routinely analyzed by a simple procedure at a number of stations through the process and a large chemical data base is being accumulated.

Rapid growth response techniques provide results within a four week period for analysis of food and energy flow from algae species *Tetrasellmis suecicia* and *Pyramimonas* sp. clone PYR-2. Efforts are directed toward optimizing for nutritional quality of algae by selecting the optimal growth phase for harvesting.

Trace metal and mineral analyses in recirculated systems have now demonstrated that Ca and Fe are readily depleted. Significantly no toxic accumulations of other metals have been detected.

Techniques for examining shell ultra structure in relation to growth in controlled recirculated systems have been established. Differences in the crystallinity of shell structure in controlled system and wild oysters have been identified.

Macro-economic analysis of potential shellfish production firms has been completed. The analysis has already identified some high cost items that biologists have been able to eliminate through further research.

Intensive routine microbiological monitoring of all culture systems continues and to date no shellfish or human pathogens have been identified from the culture systems. Although an extensive protozoan fauna has been identified and associated with high organic loading, none have been pathogenic to shellfish.

Economic Aspects

Cultured oysters differ enough from "natural" oysters to be classified as a new product for the purpose of predicting potential sales revenue. Initially there may be some hesitancy to buy a commercially raised oyster, but most of the unique characterstics of these oysters should increase their price relative to commercially harvested ones. Quality control will be better, a constant output can be guaranteed, and meat yield per individual will be greater. (A bushel of maricultured oysters may contain up to twice as much edible meats). How much of a price premium these attributes will bring is not known at this time, nor is the size of the potential market. For one thing, there are at least three possible types of markets to enter: the ex-vessel market, the standard wholesale market, or contractual arrangements with large commercial processors. There is a wide range between the prices in the first two markets ($6 to $20 per bushel in 1976) with the likely price for the third to be somewhere between them, depending on the bargaining ability of the producer and the processor. There is no real information at present as to just how big each of these markets is because there have been no formal studies nor have there been any large increases in natural production.

The National Marine Fisheries Service estimates that the price elasticity of oysters is .6728, which means that for every one percent of increase in output, price will fall .6728 percent. Or to put it another way, if mariculture production were to increase output by 10 percent, the price would be about 6.7 percent less than it would be otherwise. But, of course, this does not take into account the positive attributes of maricultured oysters that may give them a premium price. In any event, what existng information there is does not indicate any apparent severe limits to the size of the market. Obviously, one cannot produce all the oysters one wishes without an effect on price, but there does appear to be room to grow especially as transportation and marketing channels adjust to increases in supply. The latter statement is especially true if one considers the potential of the essentially virgin markets in the inland parts of the country and the fact that mariculture operations may be possible in those locations.

It is extremely difficult to predict unit costs of maricultured oysters simply because the exact process to be used has not yet been determined. We know what must be done and how to do it in the laboratory and in very small test operations, but not how best to adapt this to large scale operations so that cost per unit of output is minimized. The Delaware Sea Grant Program is in the process of studying this very thing, but at the time of this writing no results have been obtained. A three-year old study using what appeared to be an efficient method given the state of knowledge at that time, indicated that costs would be somewhere between $20 and $32 per bushel in today's dollars. (Given the improvements that have been made since this study, these cost estimates should more than likely be considered as upper limits.) So on a strict comparison with commercially harvested oysters, it appears as if mariculture will be potentially profitable. If maricultured oysters are indeed able to obtain a premium price, then things look even better.

Anticipated Progress and Uniqueness

Due to the outstanding progress made during the past year, particularly in the control of mass algal cultures, and to the strong interest expressed from industry in the closed system process, we expect to enter into a cooperative industry-University pilot effort to demonstrate the commercial feasibility of closed system bivalve molluscs culture before the end of the 1977-78 grant year.

This Sea Grant supported research has reached a stage of technological development that is allowing us to design and build a pilot plant and associated mariculture research laboratory with capital construction support from the Economic Development Administration. The research and development facility should be completed and operational by 1 January 1979.

Such partnerships between industry, government and academia with relatively equal participation by all in a climate conducive to interdisciplinary studies will pave the way toward major improvements in our ability to produce palatable, healthful and inexpensive bivalve shellfish.

References

1. Jensen, K. (ed) (1976). Aquaculture 1976: A Digest of Sea Grant Research. Univ. of Del. DEL-SG-22-76: p. 44.

2. Lanier, J. A. (1977). Sea Grants' National Aquaculture Information (NAIS). Va. Inst. Mar. Sci. and Nat. Ocean. Data Ctr.
3. Glude, J. B. (1977). NOAA Aquaculture Plan. NMFS and Sea Grant. GPO #796-732: p. 42
4. Schuster, C. N. (1960). The Nelsons of Rutgers. Univ. of Del. *Estuarine Bull.* **5**, 12.
5. Price, K. S. (In press). Advances in Closed System Mariculture. *Mar. Tech. Soc. Jour..*

Shellfish Culture In Japan

William N. Shaw
U.S. Department of Commerce
National Oceanic and Atmospheric Administration
National Sea Grant Program
Washington, D.C.

The other papers in this volume have related to the shellfish industry in the United States, the ongoing shellfish research and a commercial shellfish hatchery. The purpose of this chapter is to describe shellfish culture in Japan of three major species—the abalone, the oyster and the scallop. The culture of these species in Japan differs drastically from methods typically used in the United States. Based on my past experiences, it is unlikely that our country will ever fully duplicate the shellfish culture systems now being practiced in Japan, unless certain social and economic barriers are overcome.

Abalone, *Haliotis discus*

The abalone is one of the major shellfish products in Japan. In 1973, a total of 5,939 tons were landed at a value of approximately 32 million dollars (1). Major efforts in research have been centered around techniques to produce artificial seed and methods to improve the coastal habitat. Natural populations of abalone have been supplemented with seed produced in hatcheries. Sanders (2) reported that there are 16 laboratories in Japan artificially producing two to three million seed abalone annually.

Research has concentrated on spawning techniques and on trying to improve survival of newly metamorphosed larvae. In a major breakthrough Kikuchi and Uki (3) found that seawater irradiated with ultraviolet rays induced spawning. Presently, the Japanese can spawn abalone at will. Methods of conditioning mature adults for spawning have been determined. The post larvae survival, however, is still a major problem. Present techniques involve the placing of special plastic collectors in outdoor, flow through tanks (Fig. 1). After a few days a film of diatoms

FIGURE 1. Special plastic sheets used to collect diatom film.

forms on the collectors. When the abalone larvae are ready to metamorphose, the collectors are placed in the setting tanks. Once the abalones
set, they begin to feed on the diatom film. Apparently this is the most
critical period in the abalone's early life and high mortalities (over 95%)
can occur at this time. Yet, because abalone are prolific, the hatcheries
have been able to withstand these losses. As the abalone grow they
switch diets from diatoms to seaweeds such as *Undaria pinnatifida* and
Eisenia bicyclis. After eight months to one year, the abalone are approximately 2.5 cm in size when they are sold to fishermen for planting on
natural grounds. About three years later, the seed abalone grows to 14.0
cm or the market size.

   In order to speed up the growth rate of young abalone, one hatchery is
located at a power plant in Sendai, Japan (Fig. 2). Hatchery techniques
are basically the same, but the newly settled abalone are maintained in
canvas-lined raceways, which receive heated water from the power plant.
The young abalone (Fig. 3) grow four to five times faster than in the
natural environment.

   Because of the increased demand for abalone, there has been a need
for more suitable grow-out areas. Many areas along the Northern Pacific
Coast of Japan are desert-like, or lack macroalgae. A successful program

FIGURE 2. Power plant showing abalone culturing tanks, Sendai, Japan.

FIGURE 3. Young abalone seed ready for transplanting to natural environment.

on afforestation has been underway. In combination with long-line kelp culture and removal of predators, low production areas have been converted into areas supporting sizeable populations of abalone (1).

Oysters, *Crassostrea gigas*

The Pacific or Japanese oyster, *Crassostrea gigas* is the most important shellfish grown in Japan. During the past 20 years, production has fluctuated between 175 thousand tons (with shell) in 1959 to 267 thousand tons in 1968 (Table I). Up to the early 1920's, oysters were grown on the botton similar to the methods practiced in the United States. In 1923 "hanging" culture was initiated in Kanagawa Prefecture. The advantages

Table I
Oyster Production in Japan

Year	Meat (A)	With shell (B)	A/B	Oyster shell	Scallop shell	Other collectors
	PRODUCTION FOR FOOD (tons)			PRODUCTION OF SEED x 1000 ren[1]		
1953	12 453	106 658	11.7	-	-	-
1954	13 556	102 398	13.2	-	-	-
1955	14 423	98 040	14.7	-	-	-
1956	16 725	114 386	14.6	-	-	-
1957	18 648	144 037	12.9	2 307	374	64
1958	20 051	151 212	13.3	1 963	483	66
1959	24 555	174 926	14.0	1 643	757	3
1960	25 977	178 276	14.6	1 534	744	41
1961	23 352	176 046	13.3	1 539	699	-
1962	30 075	214 468	14.0	1 060	634	-
1963	34 109	240 144	14.2	2 343	513	-
1964	35 221	240 564	14.6	1 448	558	-
1965	32 333	210 603	15.4	1 740	232	-
1966	35 313	221 139	16.0	2 108	496	-
1967	36 288	232 200	15.6	1 326	467	-
1968	41 798	267 388	15.6	1 872	275	-
1969	36 988	245 458	15.4	1 329	350	-
1970	35 713	190 799	13.5	1 505	329	4
1971	27 865	193 846	14.4	1 957	712	11
1972	33 861	217 373	15.6	2 931	414	4
1973	34 634	228 639	15.6	1 373	352	52

[1] The collectors are strung on "rens" of wire, rope, etc.

of this method of culture over bottom culture were found to be the following (4):

   (i)   The crop of oysters per unit area of sea bottom is greatly increased as a result of vertical suspension;

  (ii) more food can be ingested by the oysters because the water supply is continuous. The resulting growth rate is about twice that obtained by other methods; consequently, even with the culture period reduced to six months, a growth can be attained which is equal to that of the sowing and stick culture methods;

 (iii) the grower can culture his oysters without regard to the character of the water depth. This permits expansion of the culture area to deeper water away from the restricted shore area;

 (iv) the oysters can be cultured in clean, unpolluted seawater. The resulting meat is of much better quality than that produced by the sowing methods; and

  (v) the oysters are out of reach of predators.

Today almost all oysters are cultured by the hanging technique, from either rafts (Fig. 4), long-lines, or racks (Fig. 5). Only a few oysters are grown by the stick method or on the bottom (see Table II).

FIGURE 4. Oyster rafts in Hiroshima Bay.

Table II

Changes in Oyster Culture in Japan

Region	Year	Production (with shell) tons	Total No. of growers	RAFT		LONG-LINE		RACK		STICK		BOTTOM SOWING	
				No. of growers	No. of rafts	No. of growers	No. of long-lines	No. of growers	Area (x 1,000 m²)	No. of growers	Area (x 1,000 m²)	No. of growers	Area (x 1,000 m²)
Total	1964	227,554	8,784	3,662	12,198	913	5,472	2,669	2,298	386	5,115	1,154	7,859
	1973	232,723	5,783	3,034	17,108	1,329	12,588	1,180	3,933	23	168	217	1,550
	73/64	1.02	0.66	0.83	1.40	1.46	2.30	0.44	1.71	0.06	0.09	0.19	0.20

FIGURE 5. Oyster racks in Matsushima Bay. Upper right of photo shows seaweed culture.

Japan depends almost totally on natural setting. Key areas for collecting seed are in Hiroshima and Miyagi prefectures. The hanging technique is utilized to catch the seed. Shells are strung on galvanized wire, each shell separated by a 2.6 cm bamboo spacer. The strings of shells called "rens" are suspended from wooden racks at the time larvae abundance is the greatest, usually in July (Fig. 6). Following setting, the shells with the attached spat (oysters) are transferred directly to either rafts, long-lines or racks and are grown to market size (one year culture). In the two year culture system, the spat bearing shells are draped over wooden racks in the intertidal zone for six months (hardening period) and then suspended from floating structures (Fig. 7).

The method of suspending the spat bearing shells is simple but labor intensive. The strings of shells are transferred from the setting racks to the growing grounds. The shells are removed from wires and restrung on new wires up to 15 meters in length. Each shell is separated by a 22 cm bamboo spacer. The strings are then attached to the rafts for growing to market size when they are removed either by hand or a boom and transferred to processing plants similar in many ways to those found in the United States.

Another part of the oyster industry is the exporting of seed to foreign countries. A portion of seed, caught by methods described earlier, is box-

FIGURE 6. Oyster seed racks in Hiroshima Bay.

ed and shipped either by air or boat to countries like the United States, France and Spain. This is a large business, although the costs for seed have been increasing steadily and the U.S. market has dropped off considerably (Table III).

The problems that face the oyster industry in Japan are much like those in any country. Industrial and domestic pollutions are effecting some of the growing grounds. Consequently, the Japanese have expanded the long-line method which can utilize more open waters relatively free from pollution. Another problem is the cost of labor. The Japanese have solved part of this problem by utilizing the elderly, especially women. Also, the growers and shuckers are "all in the family", so basically costs are reduced because the family is working for itself. Yet, labor costs have played a serious role in the seed export business. Thus, the U.S. market has been reduced considerably.

Scallop, *Patinopecten yessoensis*

Scallop culture has steadily developed over the past few years, especially in areas like Aomori, Hokkaido and Iwate Prefectures where 95% of Japanese scallop production occurs. Between 1940-60 scallop

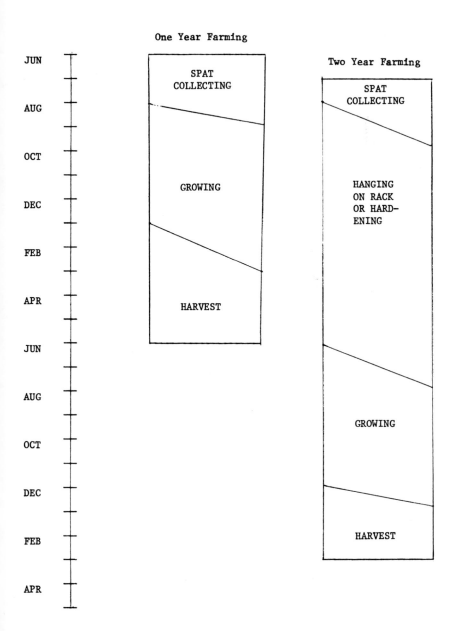

FIGURE 7. Seasonal activities of one and two year oyster farming in Japan (Fujiya, 1970).

Table III
Annual Seed Oyster Shipments to the State of Washington and the Pacific Coast.[9]

	STATE OF WASHINGTON DISCHARGE[1]						PACIFIC COAST TOTAL
SEED YEAR	MIYAGI PREFECTURE		BROKEN/ UNBROKEN	KUMAMOTO PREFECTURE	OTHER[2]	TOTAL	
	BROKEN	UNBROKEN					
1947	13,240	27,242	-	20	=	40,502	56,619
1948	8,951	18,308	-	80	30	27,369	32,869
1949	22,968	17,031	-	1,000	27	41,026	46,036
1950	22,578	13,715	-	548	20	36,861	46,726
1951	23,806	12,710	-	150	2	36,668	51,901
1952	53,881	14,422	-	600	61	68,964	83,290
1953	52,731	10,370	-	682	32	63,815	70,113
1954	55,159	9,269	-	250	1	64,679	65,528
1955	41,378	4,924	-	334	44	46,680	54,216
1956	63,221	10,246	-	507	85	74,059	100,634
1957	39,102	9,296	-	133	332[3]	48,863	60,063
1958	37,893	8,737	-	1,202	30	47,862	61,119
1959	18,870	13,600	15,875	606	33[4]	48,984	61,555
1960	17,101	2,224	15,779	1,200	-	36,304	44,291
1961	14,643.5	4,337	7,494	1,004	-	27,478.5	37,128.5
1962	13,450	4,597	13,610	1,141	1	32,799	41,499
1963	15,409	6,643.5	18,598.5	1,740	1	42,392	53,416
1964	12,148	2,522	13,975	1,890	-	30,535	41,160
1965	4,000	2,139.5	18,905	2,238	-	27,282.5	37,128.5
1966	5,740	1,000	6,186	1,995	-	14,922	16,102
1967	5,803	3,192.5	24,780	454	-	34,229.5	43,557.5
1968	3,500	1,000	21,915	1,670	-	28,085	38,415
1969	4,000	1,125	27,375	1,100	-	33,600	44,707
1970	5,250	500	15,321	1,142	-	22,213	26,079
1971	5,300	1,405	18,423	261	97[5]	25,486	30,337
1972	-	375	6,247	699[5]	-	7,321	7,321
1973	-	-	7,085	1,260[5]	1[2]	8,346	8,346
1974	-	1,455	10,431	520[5]	-	12,406	12,406
1975	-	-	7,816	-	100[6]	7,866	10,856
1976	-	3,445	11,575	-	800[7]	15,820	15,820
1977	-	5,152[8]	25,087	-	100[7]	30,339	30,339

[1] Including transshipments to Oregon, California, and British Columbia.
[2] Experimental boxes and samples of new types of cultch.
[3] Includes clam seed (197 cases), adult Kumamoto (31 cases), experimental (12 cases), and Suminoe (92 cases).
[4] Hiroshima
[5] Kumamoto seed packed in Miyagi Perfecture.
[6] 100 plastic cases, equivalent of 50 standard cases.
[7] Large-sized spat
[8] 2300 half-cases scallop shell
[9] Source of Table: Mr. Ron Westley, Department of Fisheries, Shellfish Laboratory, Brinnon, Washington.

landings fluctuated between 10,000-20,000 tons. From 1960-70 annual production had dropped to 4,000-10,000 tons. As a result of utilizing aquaculture techniques, production between 1970-75 has increased to over 62,000 metric tons (personal communication, Tokyo Embassy).

One of the greatest reasons for this increase is the development of culture techniques to capture scallop seed. Collector bags containing used gill netting are suspended from long-lines in early May (Fig. 8). The number of seed collectors utilized in Mutsu Bay, plus total number of spat caught from 1966-1974, are shown in table IV.

Before the young scallops lose their byssal threads, they are removed from the bags and placed in pearl nets (Fig. 9). As the scallops grow, they are transferred to new pearl nets with larger mesh size. At about 4 cm, the scallops are either planted on the bottom or placed in circular or book nets and suspended from the long-line. The suspended scallops reach commercial size 10.5 to 11.0 cm, in about two years. It costs the fisherman approximately 14 yen ($.05) per scallop to raise it to market size by the long-line method. In turn, he can sell the scallop for 30 ($.10) to 60 ($.20) yen a piece (5).

Initially scallops were consumed near the areas where they were produced. Now fresh scallops are marketed in Tokyo and other large cities.

FIGURE 8. Plastic net bag containing used gill net used to catch scallop seed.

Table IV

Seed Collection and the Yield of Scallops in Mutsu Bay (6)

		1966	1967	1968	1969	1970	1971	1972	1973	1974
Number of long lines used for spat collection		101	228	683	1,000	2,049	2,067	2,144	2,761	2,834
Number of collectors	$(\times 10^4)$	3	10	30	58	151	249	206	302	378
Number of spat per collector		201	1,012	2,089	405	10,124	10,732	31,023	616	44,907
Total number of spat	$(\times 10^6)$	3	176	893	229	15,725	38,283	58,024	1,480	197,573
Total number of spat used	$(\times 10^6)$	1	75	352	85	1,594	2,087	931	124	
Utilization of the seed	Bottom culture $(\times 10^6)$		52	324	150*	1,197	1,531	469	0	
	Hanging culture $(\times 10^6)$		2	23	27	78	132	288	321*	
	for sale $(\times 10^6)$		4	17	31	88	165	122		
Yield of scallops (with shell)	(metric ton)	715	1,781	1,125	5,936	11,770	8,621	24,003	34,042	

*Includes seed which were bought from Hokkaido

FIGURE 9. Pearl nets used to grow young scallops.

Shelled, boiled and canned scallops are also being marketed in increasing quantities. The processing of scallops is simplified in Japan since they eat the entire scallop meat, while we in the United States eat only the muscle.

Conclusion

Shellfish are just one type of marine product that is farmed in Japan. In 1973, 855,000 tons of salt and freshwater fishes were produced by aquaculture (6). Principal species included yellowtail, oysters, seaweed, trout and carp. In view of the Japanese need for fishery products, both Federal and state governments have committed substantial financial assistance, especially in the form of research facilities and extensive seeding programs.

Very early in the Japanese aquaculture history, coastal waters were zoned to favor aquaculture with recreation and even transportation taking a "back seat." Today, total bays and estuaries are covered with aquaculture structures (rafts, long-lines, floating pens, etc.). Thus, one can understand why Japan is a leader in this field.

In the case of abalone, there are U.S. hatcheries on the West Coast somewhat similar to those in Japan. The exchange of information between the two countries is just beginning. The application of seeding and afforestation now practiced in Japan could be applied in the United States.

For many years researchers and industry in the U.S. have been aware of oyster culture techniques in Japan. Attempts to duplicate them have had some success. Yet, the general public is against the utilization of our waters for floating aquaculture. Therefore it is unlikely, except in a few isolated areas, that off-bottom oyster culture will expand in the United States.

To date, the United States has done little in farming the sea scallops. Whatever research has been done in scallop aquaculture has been centered around a smaller variety, the bay scallop *Argopecten irradians*. Still the potential for culturing the sea scallop in areas like Puget Sound, protected area in Alaska and in Maine are great. Research in this area should be initiated to test the biological feasibility of sea scallop culture. Of course, the economic and environmental problems must be examined, for these could be the biggest hurdles.

References

1. Kan-no, H. (1976). Recent Advances in Abalone Culture in Japan. In *Proceedings First International Conference on Aquaculture Nutrition,* October, 1975: K. Price, W. Shaw and K. Danberg, eds. University of Delaware. p. 323.
2. Sanders, M.J. (1971). Australian Studies Japanese Fish Culture Techniques. *Australian Fisheries.* **30**, 3.
3. Kikuchi, S. and Uki N. (1974). Technical Study on Artificial Spawning of Abalone, genus *Haliotis.* II. Effect of irradiated seawater with ultraviolet rays on inducing to spawn. *Bull. Tohoku Reg. Fish. Res. Lab.* **33**: 79.
4. Koganezawa, A. (1976). The Status of Pacific Oyster Culture in Japan. FAO Tech. Conf. Aquaculture, Kyoto, Japan. **E. 69**: 9.
5. Fujiya, M. (1970). Oyster Farming in Japan. *Helgolander wiss. Meeresunters,* **20**, 464.
6. Ito, Susumu, Kanno Hiroki and Takahashi Katsunari. (1975). Some Problems on Culture of the Scallop in Mutsu Bay. *Bull. Mar. Biol. Sta. of Asamushi,* Tohoku University, **15**, 89.
7. Shaw, W.N. (1973). Aquaculture of Sea Scallops and Abalone in Japan. *Proceedings Third Annual Workshop World Mariculture Society,* p. 303.
8. Japan Fisheries Association. (1975). *Fish farming in Japan.* Akasaka 1, Minato-ku, Tokyo, Japan.

SECTION III

Present Status and Potential Production of Shrimps

Economic And Production Aspects Of The Gulf Of Mexico Shrimp Fishery

John P. Nichols, Wade L. Griffin
and Vito Blomo
Department of Agricultural Economics, The Texas Agricultural Experiment Station
Texas A&M University, College Station, Texas

The shrimp fishery of the United States, while accounting for only a small share of total landings, is the most valuable fishery in the country. In 1975 shrimp landings were 7 percent of total pounds landed but accounted for nearly a fourth (23.3 percent) of the ex-vessel value of all landings. While its status as one of the most important of U.S. fisheries is not expected to diminish, numerous changes are occurring in this fishery which have significant economic and management implications. The purpose of this paper is to describe the important trends in the industry with special reference to the Gulf of Mexico shrimp fishery.

Focus is placed on the Gulf of Mexico for several reasons. First, this shrimp fishery constitutes the largest share of total value of U.S. shrimp landings (79 percent in 1975). Secondly, much more detail is available regarding fishing effort and economic trends in the Gulf shrimp fishery. Beyond this, the impact of the worldwide trend toward extended jurisdiction over fishing is having an important impact in the Gulf. Mexico has established a 200 mile extended jurisdiction zone and negotiated a phase-out of U.S. shrimp trawling within that area thus shifting fishing effort back into U.S. waters. With these points in mind we now turn to a review of recent industry trends.

U.S. Shrimp Industry

Landings of shrimp have increased significantly in the last 25 years, doubling from 1950 to the mid-1970's (Table I). As a share of total supply, however, domestic production has actually declined over the same period. In 1950 domestic production accounted for 74 percent of supplies, with the remainder made up of imports. In 1975 over one-half (53

Table I
Production of Shrimp in the U.S. and Gulf of Mexico, and U.S. Imports in Millions of Pounds (Heads-off Weight).

YEARS	PRODUCTION UNITED STATES	PRODUCTION GULF OF MEXICO	U.S. IMPORTS
1950	113.9	90.3	40.2
1960	148.5	122.5	119.1
1965	152.3	122.9	179.0
1966	148.3	112.8	194.9
1967	190.0	141.4	202.1
1968	184.1	128.2	210.1
1969	195.0	126.5	218.7
1970	224.3	145.3	245.7
1971	238.1	143.1	213.9
1972	235.9	143.9	253.1
1973	229.4	114.8	229.3
1974	224.4	117.1	267.5
1975	207.6	107.1	231.0
1976	244.1	132.2	270.0

Sources: *Shellfish Market Review and Outlook*, NOAA, NMFS, U.S. Department of Commerce, June 1977.
Basic Economic Indicators, Shrimp 1947-1972, NOAA, NMFS, U.S. Department of Commerce, June 1973.

percent) of all shrimp consumed in the U.S. came from imports (Fig. 1). Imports have increased nearly seven-fold during this last quarter of a century.

Shifts have also occurred in the geographical source of domestic production. The Gulf of Mexico, long the leading shrimp fishery, has not shown any real increase in landings since the peak production of the mid-1950's. Other producing regions, particularly the Pacific area, have become important producers. New England has also established a shrimp fishery although its level of production has been erratic in the last few years. In terms of pounds landed the Gulf fishery has declined from 79 percent of total U.S. shrimp landings in 1950 to 52 percent in 1975.

Despite this decline in share of landings, the share of total value of landings coming from the Gulf has not changed greatly. The increased landings from the Pacific and New England have been primarily in small-sized, lower-valued shrimp. The value of these landings on a proportional basis has been offset by a decline in share of value from the South Atlantic shrimp fishery. The Gulf of Mexico shrimp fishery lands primarily brown, white and pink shrimp of generally larger sizes which enter

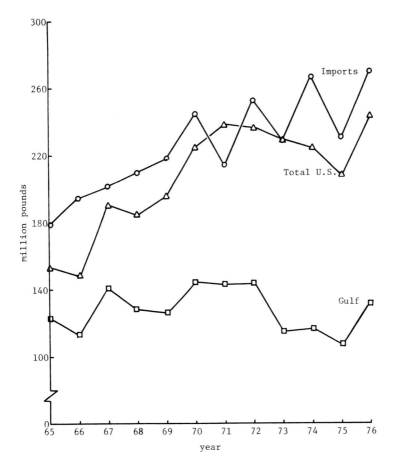

FIGURE 1. Landings of shrimp in the United States, share from Gulf of Mexico and U.S. imports 1965-1976 (heads-off weight).

markets that return a much higher price. Demand has been strong in these markets, thus ex-vessel prices and total value of landings continue to increase.

The trends in domestic production and supplies may be summarized in three general statements: (i) imports have been increasing relatively faster than domestic production, while domestic production has been increasing, (ii) domestic production is dominated less by the Gulf of Mexico fishery, (iii) share of value of landings from the Gulf is remaining fairly constant.

Gulf of Mexico Shrimp Fishery

As noted above this fishery has been the major component of U.S. production. In terms of value of production it continues to dominate the entire U.S. shrimp fishery. In this section a detailed review of production and economic trends is provided. The major aspects examined are fishing effort, landings, catch per unit of effort and costs and returns. These trends are presented separately for U.S. and Mexican waters where the data are available.

The analysis is based primarily on data drawn from National Marine Fisheries Service (NMFS) records of landings at U.S. Gulf ports by all vessels of five gross tons (GT) or larger. This provides the basic information on landings, value and effort. Also, economic data on costs and returns was collected through personal interviews with vessel owners. These data are summarized in tables II, III and IV.

Trends in Fishing Effort

There are several measures of fishing effort available which are important in understanding changes in the fishery. Number of vessels in the fishery is one such measure of the trend in fishing effort. The number of vessels of 5 GT and larger landing shrimp at U.S. Gulf ports is presented in table 2. In 1962 the number of vessels was 2,542; in 1974 their number had increased 28 percent to 3,247. Vessels account for about 70 percent of shrimp landed from U.S. waters. The remainder was landed by smaller boats, primarily from in-shore and near-shore areas. Shrimp caught in Mexican waters are landed exclusively by the larger vessels with most of these having home ports in Texas and Florida.

A second measure of fishing effort is the total number of days fished. This series for U.S. and Mexican waters is indicated in figure 2. Each day measured represents a full 24 hours fishing on the shrimp grounds. Days fished in U.S. waters has increased substantially since 1962 (50 percent) while decreasing by over 50 percent in Mexican waters. In total an increase in days fished is evident. Subsequent to the recently negotiated agreement, fishing by U.S. vessels in Mexican waters is expected to be phased out entirely in three years.

Most observers agree that the total number of days fished is a rather rough measure in that it fails to account for changes in the nature of the vessels in the fleet over time. Intensity of fishing effort should be increasing as vessels upgrade their potential productivity with larger horse-power engines and net size. A precise mathematical formulation for expressing

Table II

Number of Vessels and Selected Effort Statistics for U.S. Vessels (5 gross tons and larger) Fishing in the Gulf of Mexico Shrimp Fishery, U.S. and Mexican waters, 1962-1974.

YEAR	NUMBER OF VESSELS	U.S. Waters			Mexican Waters		
		DAYS FISHED (thous)	TOTAL EFFORT UNITS (thous)	INDEX (1962 = 100)	DAYS FISHED (thous)	TOTAL EFFORT UNITS (thous)	INDEX (1962 = 100)
1962	2,542	88.5	144.0	100	38.0	61.7	100
1963	2,653	112.9	181.8	126	26.3	43.6	71
1964	2,795	114.4	186.3	129	31.9	51.6	84
1965	2,804	113.7	187.6	130	28.0	46.6	76
1966	2,924	113.7	190.5	132	17.5	29.8	48
1967	3,098	116.0	201.7	140	14.6	33.2	54
1968	3,346	121.5	218.1	151	23.0	42.4	69
1969	3,362	147.8	273.6	190	16.9	31.8	51
1970	3,298	134.6	249.1	173	15.5	28.3	46
1971	3,282	137.0	259.0	180	14.8	28.9	47
1972	3,496	146.8	282.6	196	16.8	32.8	53
1973	3,280	140.0	269.7	187	17.7	34.7	55
1974		132.4	243.6	169	18.7	25.2	41

Table III

Catch, Value, Catch Per Unit of Effort and Price, U.S. Vessels (5 gross tons and larger) Landing Shrimp from U.S. and Mexican waters, 1962-1974.

U.S. Waters

YEAR	CATCH (heads off weight) million lbs.	VALUE million $	CATCH PER UNIT EFFORT lbs.	PRICE PER POUND $
1962	45.4	33.4	315	0.74
1963	77.0	41.5	423	0.54
1964	71.0	40.7	381	0.57
1965	80.1	49.1	427	0.61
1966	78.3	61.9	411	0.79
1967	99.7	68.5	494	0.69
1968	83.7	68.4	383	0.82
1969	82.4	74.3	301	0.90
1970	96.1	81.4	386	0.85
1971	91.3	100.8	352	1.10
1972	94.3	120.1	333	1.27
1973	71.0	118.6	263	1.67
1974	73.9	99.8	303	1.35

Mexican Waters

YEAR	CATCH (heads-off weight) million lbs.	VALUE million $	CATCH PER UNIT EFFORT lbs.	PRICE PER POUND $
1962	19.1	15.7	309	0.82
1963	14.0	10.2	322	0.73
1964	17.4	11.4	337	0.64
1965	16.3	11.7	350	0.71
1966	10.1	9.1	339	0.90
1967	10.8	9.1	325	0.91
1968	14.4	13.9	338	0.97
1969	8.3	8.9	262	1.07
1970	9.1	9.1	320	1.00
1971	9.1	11.5	313	1.26
1971	11.7	16.0	357	1.37
1973	10.1	18.8	291	1.85
1974	10.2	15.0	405	1.47

Table IV

Annual Costs and Returns for Gulf of Mexico Vessels of Steel and Wood Constructions, 51 to 80 feet in Length, and 104 to 425 Horsepower.

	1971	1973	1974	1975
RETURNS:				
Gross Receipts from Shrimp Sales	60,742	74,135	78,864	101,324
Lbs. Landed	50,656	39,907	46,270	44,070
Price/Pound	$1.20	$1.86	$1.70	$2.30
COSTS:				
Variable Costs:				
Ice	1,387	1,579	1,541	1,766
Fuel	6,561	9,539	18,976	19,114
Nets, Supplies, Groc.	2,358	6,747	8,885	11,211
Repair & Maintenance	11,708	9,953	9,337	11,643
Subtotal Variable Costs[1]	22,014	27,458	39,739	43,734
Crew Shares	19,437	23,723	26,593	32,422
Payroll Taxes	388	474	1,547	1,815
Packing	2,411	1,899	2,428	2,905
Total Variable Costs	44,250	53,554	70,307	80,876
Returns Above Variable Costs	16,492	20,581	8,557	20,448
Fixed Costs:				
Insurance	3,632	4,291	4,306	4,840
Depreciation	5,333	8,177	11,228	12,607
Overhead	0	2,415	3,201	3,073
Interest	2,256	2,611	5,604	6,984
Total Fixed Costs	12,221	17,494	24,339	27,504
Total Costs of Operation	56,471	71,048	94,646	108,380
Total Profit/Loss from Operations	4,271	3,087	-15,782	-7,056
Number of Vessels in Class	25	103	109	101

[1]Not proportional to catch.

relative fishing power of vessels based on horsepower and net size has been presented elsewhere (1). The impact of adjusting for this change in relative fishing power over time (days fished to real days fished) is illustrated by the effort series (Fig. 3). Fishing effort (real days fished) in U.S. waters is increasing faster than is indicated by the days fished measure. While days fished increased by 65 percent from 1962 to a peak in 1972, total effort increased by 96 percent during the same time. The difference is due to the gradual increase in vessel horsepower and net sizes used in the industry reflecting increasing fishing power by the average vessel.

Effort in Mexican waters has decreased as observed above in the days

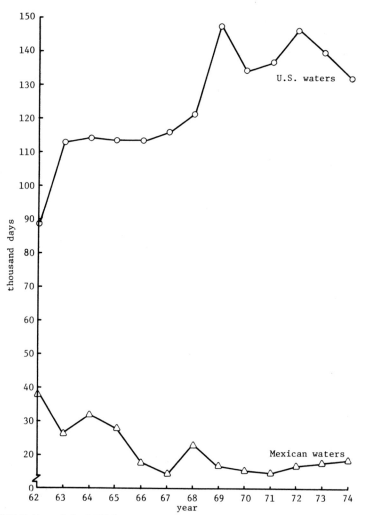

FIGURE 2. Days fished (24 hour equivalent) by U.S. shrimp vessels five gross tons and larger in U.S. and Mexican waters of the Gulf of Mexico, 1962-1974.

fished series (Table II). The decline in total effort appears to be slower than the decline in days fished, again reflecting an increase in fishing power of the average vessel.

Trends in Landings

Total landings of shrimp by both vessels and boats from the Gulf is presented in table 1. Little change is noted in the past decade. Brown, white and pink shrimp comprise nearly all of these landings. The most noticeable shift among these has been a relative decline in landings of pink shrimp from 22 percent in 1965 to 15 percent in 1975. Brown shrimp landings have increased in share from 51 percent in 1965 to 57 percent in 1975.

Shrimp landings by vessels in U.S. ports also shows some evidence of a slight positive trend in landings from U.S. waters, although not nearly as great as the increase in effort noted above (Fig. 3 and 4). Year to year

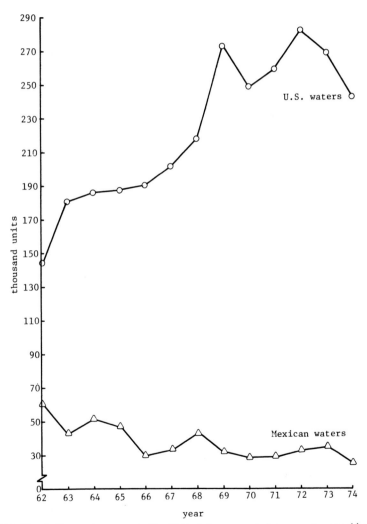

FIGURE 3. Total effort units expended by U.S. shrimp vessels five gross tons and larger in U.S. and Mexican waters of the Gulf of Mexico, 1962-1974.

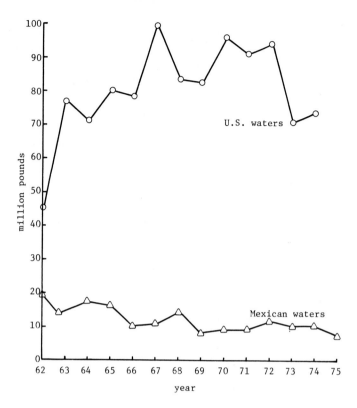

FIGURE 4. Landings of shrimp by U.S. vessels five gross tons and larger from U.S. and Mexican waters of the Gulf of Mexico, 1962-1974 (heads-off weight).

variations in total catch are significant and are influenced by poor environmental conditions in some years which prevent either adequate growth in the shrimp biomass or the shrimp fleet from fishing. The catches in 1962, 1973, and 1974 serve as examples of large variations in yearly catch when river discharge was high (2). The decline in shrimp landings from Mexican waters, however, is entirely consistent with the decrease in total fishing effort in Mexican waters over time. Evaluation of U.S. shrimp landings from the Gulf of Mexico as a whole shows no clear increasing or decreasing trend over the 1962 to 1974 period.

Trends in Catch per Unit Effort

Catch per unit of effort (CPUE) is calculated by dividing the appropriate catch statistic for vessels by its corresponding total effort statistic, as developed above. The trend in CPUE for U.S. and Mexican waters as well as total is illustrated in figure 5. For U.S. waters, it shows a general decline since 1962 with variation occurring from year to year. The years of unusually low production (1962, 1973 and 1974), related to environmental factors, appear to distort this relationship somewhat.

The CPUE for U.S. vessels in Mexican waters shows a less clear trend and significant variation. Both effort and catch from Mexican waters declined over the period. The trend for the total is dominated by the activity in U.S. waters and reflects the general decline observed there. While much variation exists in the data, the evidence indicates a general decline in CPUE during this period. A yield function further describing these relationships may be found in (2).

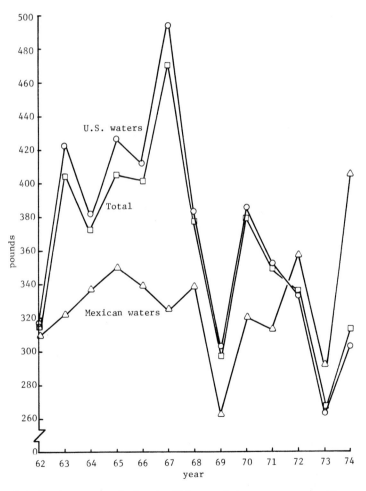

FIGURE 5. Catch per unit of effort for U.S. vessels five gross tons and larger, U.S. and Mexican waters of the Gulf of Mexico, 1962-1974 (heads-off weight).

Trends in Costs and Returns

Attention is now turned to the individual vessel's costs and returns for operating in the Gulf of Mexico. While the number of vessels interviewed make up a very small sample of all vessels, the data presented in table IV generally reflect changes felt by all vessels. Average gross receipts ranged from a low of $60,742 in 1971 to a high of $202,324 in 1975. Average landings per vessel were highest in 1972 at 50,656 pounds, with lower landings in the following years. The average price per pound received for shrimp landed by these vessels almost doubled from $1.20 in 1971 to $2.30 by 1975.

Costs are divided into three categories: fixed costs, variable costs proportional to catch, and variable costs not proportional to catch. Variable cost items not proportional to catch include ice, fuel, nets, supplies and groceries, and repair and maintenance. These expense items almost doubled during 1971-75, with fuel tripling and nets, supplies, and groceries increasing by 5 times. Costs proportional to value of catch include crew shares, payroll taxes and packing charges.

Total variable costs for these vessels almost doubled from $44,250 in 1971 to $80,876 in 1975. Returns above variable costs remain relatively constant from 1971 to 1975 at approximately $20,000 except for 1974 when it dropped to only $8,557. Thus, in 1974, after paying for variable costs, very little was left over to pay for fixed costs.

Fixed costs include insurance, depreciation, overhead and interest. Of these, the significant increases occurred in depreciation and interest since these two items reflect the cost of a new vessel (3). Thus, based on new vessel prices, depreciation and interest more than doubled. This caused fixed costs to more than double from $12,221 in 1971 to $27,504 in 1975.

Total costs (variable plus fixed) doubled during this 5-year period from $56,471 to $108,380. Since revenues increased at a slower rate than costs, this caused negative returns in 1974 and 1975 of $15,782 and $7,056, respectively.

Rates of increase in the cost components and in total revenue are illustrated in figure 6. Costs and revenues are in the form of indices (1971 100) which are calculated so that they reflect the nominal percentage increase in each item. The rapid increase in total cost, exceeding revenue increases, is very noticeable. Particular impact was felt in 1974 when costs jumped by 56 points while revenue increased by only five points on the index.

Discussion and Implications

In reviewing the Gulf of Mexico shrimp industry status, as revealed in these trends, several generalizations appear valid:

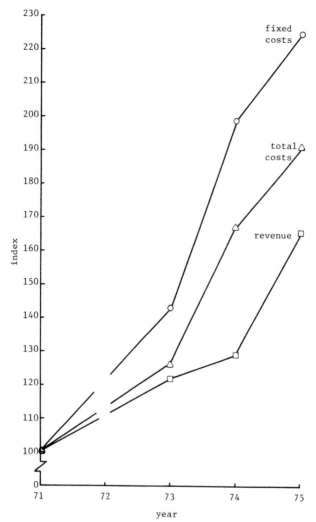

FIGURE 6. Indices of costs and revenues for U.S. shrimp vessels operating in the Gulf of Mexico, 1971 and 1973-1975 (1971 100).

1. Total landings of shrimp have not increased greatly in the last 15 years. Landings by U.S. vessels from Mexican waters have declined substantially.
2. Total fishing effort has increased significantly while effort by U.S. vessels in Mexican has declined.
3. Catch per unit of effort has shown a general decline. Increases in effort are associated with less than proportional corresponding increases in catch.

4. Ex-vessel prices for shrimp have increased greatly reflecting a strong market demand.
5. Imports of shrimp into the U.S. market have increased at a much faster pace than the total U.S. production.
6. Costs of owning and operating a shrimp trawling vessel have increased rapidly, particularly from 1971 to 1975.
7. During the 1971 to 1975 period total revenues generated by the average Gulf shrimping vessel did not increase as rapidly as costs, thus contributing to decreased net revenues and losses for many.

While data are not yet available to extend many of these trends through 1976, a casual observation of the industry would indicate that, in economic terms, improvements have occurred. Landings recovered in 1976 after three relatively low years and in 1977 are running at a rate somewhat above 1976. At the same time demand has remained strong and prices in general have not declined greatly in the face of this increased supply. A number of new vessels are being constructed and are scheduled to enter the fleet during the next year.

It appears likely that as long as demand continues strong, domestic production will not be sufficient to meet that demand. Imports will likely remain a dominant force in supplying U.S. markets. While prices remain strong continued expansion of effort may result. It is questionable, however, that this increased effort will result in major increases in landings. The shrimp fishery on the Pacific coast has shown rapid increase in size in recent years which may help meet the growth in demand in specific markets. Erratic production on the Atlantic coast, however, cannot be counted on to provide any increases in supplies.

The significance of imports in supplying the U.S. market is a particular problem for the industry. Dislocations in the world market for shrimp will greatly affect prices paid to U.S. shrimpers. A significant increase in imports can have a devastating impact on ex-vessel prices. While import controls have been discussed in the industry it doesn't appear likely that these will become a reality in the near future. If import limits were exercised, caution would have to be taken not to damage the growing consumer demand for shrimp by inducing restrictively high prices.

Maintaining economic viability in the face of rapidly escalating costs is a major challenge to shrimp vessel operators. The signficance of fuel as a large component of total variable costs is a particular problem in an environment where all energy costs are likely to escalate in the future. The development of regional fishery management councils creates a structure through which some industry problems may be addressed. Whether any significant management programs result from this for the Gulf shrimp fishery remains to be seen. It is clear that changes in either firm strategies or industry-wide strategies must be evaluated within a framework that recognizes the interdependencies among biological and economic relationships existing in the shrimp industry.

Acknowledgments

Technical Article No. 13673, The Texas Agricultuural Experiment Station, Texas A&M University. The research reported here has been partially supported through the Texas A&M Sea Grant Program and the Southeast Region of the National Marine Fisheries Service.

References

1. Griffin, W.L., Cross, M.L. and Nichols, J.P. (1977). Effort Measurement in the Heterogeneous Gulf of Mexico Shrimp Fishery. Department of Agricultural Economics, the Texas Agricultural Experiment Station, Texas A&M University, *Dept. Tech. Rept.* No. 77-5.
2. Griffin, W.L., Lacewell, R.D. and Nichols, J.P. (1976). Optimum Effort and Rent Distribution in the Gulf of Mexico Shrimp Fishery. *Am. J. of Agri. Econ.* **58**, 644.
3. Griffin, W.D., Wardlaw, N.J. and Nichols, J.P. (1976). Cost and Return Analysis by Selected Vessel Characteristics: Gulf of Mexico Shrimp Fishery, 1971-1975. The Texas Agricultural Experiment Station, Texas A&M University, MP-1253c.
4. United States Department of Commerce. (1973). Basic Economic Indicators: Shrimp 1947-1972, NOAA, National Marine Fisheries Service.
5. *ibid.* (1977). Shellfish Market Review and Outlook. NOAA, National Marine Fisheries Service.

Constraints on Food Production From Wild Penaeid Shrimp Stocks in the Gulf Of Mexico

Edward F. Klima and Michael L. Parrack

U.S. Department of Commerce
National Oceanic and Atmospheric Administration
National Marine Fisheries Service
Galveston, Texas

The shallow water shrimp resources of the Gulf of Mexico support two major trawl fisheries. The Northern and Eastern Gulf of Mexico inshore fishery produces small shrimp for canning, drying, salting, bait, and home consumption. The offshore fishery throughout the Gulf produces larger shrimp for sale as food, both fresh and frozen. Part of the harvest of both major trawl fisheries is discarded as undersized shrimp, for legal and/or economic reasons. Recreational harvest is thought to represent a significant part of the inshore catch.

Three major species comprise 99% (by weight) of the reported commercial catch: brown shrimp (*Penaeus aztecus*), white shrimp (*P. setiferus*), and pink shrimp (*P. duararum*). Three minor species of non-*Penaeus* shallow water species are taken in much smaller commercial quantities; seabob (*Xiphopeneus kroyeri*), rock shrimp (*Sicyonia brevirostris*) and sugar shrimp (*Trachypenaeus similis*).

Distribution

Shallow water shrimp are found in all Continental Shelf waters in the U.S. Gulf of Mexico shallower than 60 fm. The greatest portion of the reported offshore catch of brown shrimp is taken in 11-20 fm., that of white shrimp in 5 fm. or less, and that of pink shrimp in 11-15 fm. Highest offshore densities of brown shrimp occur off the Texas coast (Fig. 1), while highest densities of white shrimp occur off the Louisiana coast (Fig. 2), and of pink shrimp off the southwest coast of Florida (Fig. 3).

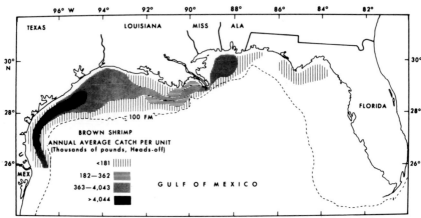

FIGURE 1. The distribution of brown shrimp in the Northern Gulf of Mexico.

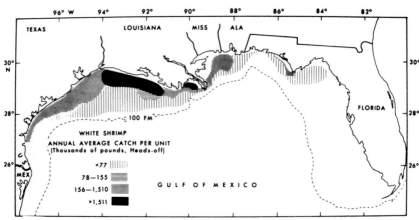

FIGURE 2. The distribution of white shrimp in the Northern Gulf of Mexico.

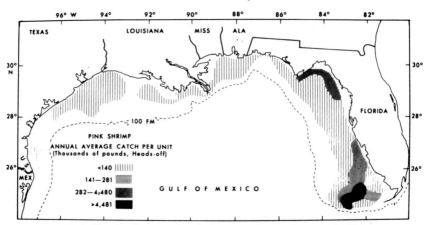

FIGURE 3. The distribution of pink shrimp in the Northern Gulf of Mexico.

The Relationship between Season and Size Caught

Season, shrimp size, and water depth are related. Reported catch records indicate that most small brown shrimp are caught in depths of less than 5 fm. during May. As brown shrimp grow larger, they move into deeper waters so that peak catches of large individuals occur in 11-20 fm. in July or August. Smaller catches of large individuals occur in winter months. Small white shrimp are caught in depths less than 5 fms. during September, and in depths of 6-10 fm. in October. Large white shrimp are caught in depths less than 5 fm. in April and in depths of 6-10 fm. in May. Low catches of white shrimp occur in mid-winter months. The peak reported catch of pink shrimp ususally occurs in January at 11-15 fm.

Effects of Life Cycle

The geographical distribution of shallow water shrimp is related to a large extent to their life cycle (Fig. 4). Adults spawn offshore on the bottom. Eggs hatch in 10-12 hours into planktonic larvae. During the next 12-15 days these larvae metamorphose through additional planktonic stages into postlarvae. These juvenile shrimp then become benthic and

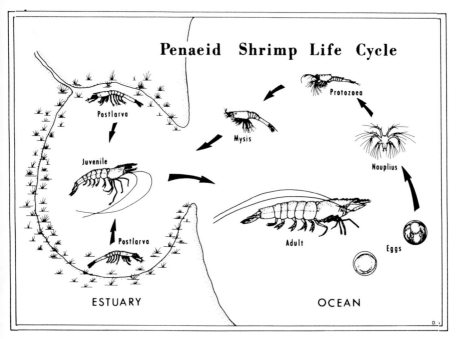

FIGURE 4. The life cycle of shallow water shrimp in the Gulf of Mexico.

enter the estuary. Within the estuary, the juveniles grow rapidly for 1-1½ months before emigrating offshore. During this estuarine phase, the males become sexually mature (contain spermatophores), while the females do not, although they do develop ovaries that contain large numbers of immature eggs. Apparently the females develop ripe eggs only after they leave the estuary.

Effects of Currents

Larvae presumably are carried toward the estuary by wind-driven currents. Juvenile shrimp appear to take advantage of tidal currents to carry them from place to place in the estuary. Likewise, newly adult shrimp take advantage of tidal currents to carry them out of the estuary and beyond. There is evidence that the factor or factors responsible for these movements with currents may be something other than currents themselves (e.g., moon-phase, light vs. dark, temperature, salinity, hydrostatic pressure, and biological rhythms).

Effects of Temperature and Salinity

The effects of temperature and salinity on shrimp distribution are complex; however, shrimp seem to be able to withstand cold temperatures if salinities are moderate to high. Brown and pink shrimp appear to be similar in that they move to deeper, colder more saline waters upon emigrating from the estuary. White shrimp generally move to deeper more saline waters with the onset of cool fall weather.

Effects of Food

Larval stages of shrimp require phytoplankton and zooplankton for food. Major peaks in spawning activity coincide with spring and fall blooms of phytoplankton and zooplankton in the Gulf. Juvenile shrimp ingest large quantities of organic detritus (dead and decaying particulate plant matter) in the estuary. It is thought that they gain nourishment from the microbes and associated microfauna adsorbed on or associated with this detritus. In the northern Gulf, the detritus is produced primarily from marsh grasses, and in the south Florida area, from mangrove leaves. As the shrimp grow larger and leave the estuary, they become omnivorous.

Environmental Effects

Cold spells, floods, droughts, hurricanes, and other climatological extremes or catastrophes are believed to affect distribution and abundance of shrimp, but the relative importance of these factors is not well known or documented.

Man-caused Environment Effects

Man's manipulations and alterations of the coastal environment affect the estuarine substrate, circulation, stream discharge, pattern of distribution, and water quality. The extent to which these changes influence shrimp distribution and abundance is poorly understood, but the loss and degradation of shrimp habitat, especially the estuarine habitat, through man's activities should be a matter of great concern in the management of shrimp fisheries.

Fishing Trends

The average annual shrimp landings from 1965 to 1974 were about 53,000 metric tons. However, these landings have fluctuated from 45,000 to well over 60,000 tons (Fig. 5). Specific information concern-

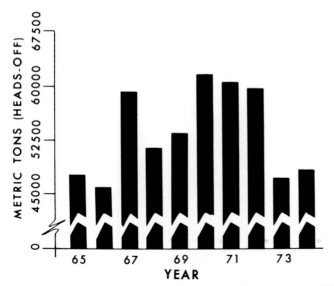

FIGURE 5. The landings of shallow water shrimp in the Northern Gulf of Mexico.

ing the brown, white and pink shrimp fisheries are shown in figures 6, 7, and 8. The brown shrimp landings have averaged about 31,500 metric tons annually; however, landings have fluctuated drastically from 23,000 tons to about 45,000 tons. Fishing effort has increased whereas catch-per-unit effort has decreased. The relationship between annual landings, fishing effort and catch- per-unit effort indicates that the resource is affected by the increase or decrease in fishing pressure, as can be seen in 1969 and 1970. The increased fishing pressure in 1969 was reflected in a significantly decreased catch-per-unit effort and subsequently lower annual landings. The high fishing pressure in 1971 and 1972 may in part account for the lower annual landings in 1973 and 1974.

The white shrimp fishery annual landings have averaged about 15,000 tons and have fluctuated between 10,000 and 19,000 tons. Peak annual landings occurred from 1969 through 1972, with a peak in catch-per-unit effort in 1969. Fishing effort increased from 1969 to a peak in 1973; however, from 1969 to 1973, the corresponding catch-per-unit effort

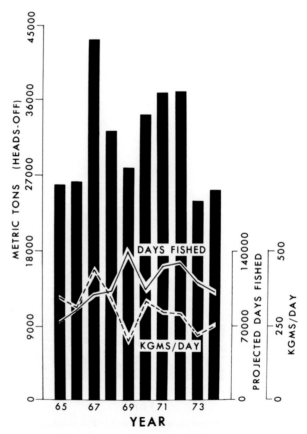

FIGURE 6. Brown shrimp landing in the Northern Gulf of Mexico.

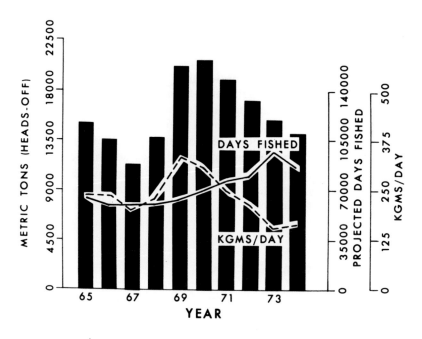

FIGURE 7. White shrimp landing in the Northern Gulf of Mexico.

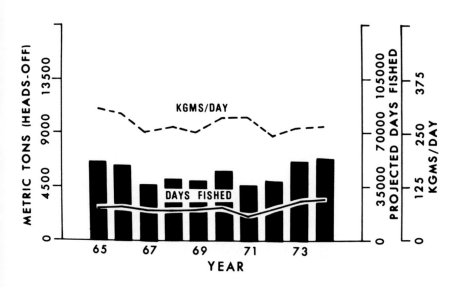

FIGURE 8. Pink shrimp landing in the Northern Gulf of Mexico.

decreased. The increase in white shrimp fishing effort in 1973 is probably due to a shift to the white shrimp fishery from the brown shrimp fishery because of the low brown shrimp abundance. That inter-relation between the brown and white shrimp fisheries is quite evident from figures 6 and 7, especially in the years 1973 and 1974. During that period, brown shrimp catches and fishing effort were low, concurrent with high fishing effort in the white shrimp fishery. The basic trend in the white shrimp fishery has been a decrease in the catch-per-unit effort, coupled with an increase in fishing effort from 1969 to the present. Continuation of this trend will certainly affect the economic conditions in the fishery.

Unlike the white and brown shrimp fisheries which fluctuated widely, the pink shrimp fishery in the south Florida area has been fairly stable through the study period, averaging close to 5,000 tons annually with very little deviation. Fishing effort was relatively stable, as was the catch-per-unit effort.

Maximum Sustainable Yield

The classical approach to determining the production potential for any fisheries resource is to estimate the relationship between catch and fishing effort. The top of the curve representing the relationship is commonly referred to as the maximum sustainable yield (MSY) and has been defined (1) as "the largest average catch or yield that can continuously be taken from a stock under existing environmental conditions". The MSY concept is based upon the assumption that a stock produces its greatest harvestable surplus when it is at an intermediate level of abundance, not at a maximum abundance. Under reasonably stable natural conditions, the growth of an unfished population is balanced by natural deaths. Harvesting individuals from the stock increases production by decreasing competition for the food supply and by decreasing the number of older slower-growing individuals, so that a larger proportion of the stock is composed of young fast-growing individuals. The net effect is that fishing creates a surplus to be harvested. Hence, the fishing or the thinning out of the population creates the production which maintains the harvest operation.

As a first estimation of the total potential, we have examined this relationship and have estimated the MSY for the total U.S. shrimp stocks in the Gulf of Mexico, excluding the Mexican coast. We feel that this is a reasonable approximation of the production limit of the shrimp resource in the U.S. portion of the Gulf of Mexico.

We estimated MSY by Schaefer's method (1957) utilizing annual effort and landings (1956-76) in tail weight for the area from Key West to Brownsville in the Gulf of Mexico. These landings include catches of brown, white, pink, sugar, and rock shrimp. The measurement of fishing effort was days fished in these areas and we assumed that this effort was directed at the shallow water shrimp resources. It should be pointed out that these annual landings do not account for the shallow water shrimp caught and discarded at sea. At present we do not have a reliable estimate of this portion of the catch. If the magnitude of the discarded shrimp at sea has changed over time, the proposed model is inaccurate. Furthermore, we have not tried to adjust fishing effort data for increases in fishing gear technology. If, in fact, fishing effort has increased in efficiency through time, it will affect the proposed model. Annual data for 1957, 1961, and 1962 were not included in this model. During those years, major hurricane activity occurred and we feel that these years do not reflect a steady state of the fisheries and further, these points fell well outside the bulk of the other data. We have estimated the equilibrium state of the fishery to be quantified by the model $L = F (A + BF)$.

where $A = .45528$, a constant,

$B = .93870396 \times 10^6$, a constant,

$F = $ days fished, and

$L = $ landings.

The model predicts a maximum sustainable yield of approximately 55,000 metric tons tail weight (approximately 88,000 metric tons round weight) with 225,000 days fished (Fig. 9). The annual landings and total fishing effort have been fluctuating around that maximum since 1970, indicating that the Gulf of Mexico shallow water shrimp resources have been fully exploited in recent years. Landings in 1976 indicate that this trend is continuing.

Size and Yield Relationship

MSY can be achieved by limiting fishing mortality by controlling either fishing effort or catch. However, if the fishing strategy of the fleet is such that it harvests fish or shrimp before they reach an optimum size, a decrease in the potential yield is very likely. In essence, what must be attained is a balance between the rates of growth and mortality. Animals grow at a very fast rate when young; as they age, that rate decreases. The rate of natural death, however, is usually fairly constant throughout the juvenile and adult life stages. Harvesting very young animals results in a loss of potential weight gain since the growth rate is faster than the loss rate attributed to mortality for young animals. Harvesting animals older

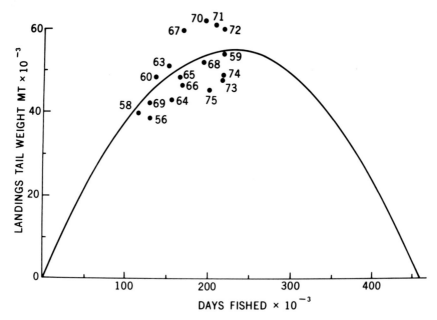

FIGURE 9. The relation between fishing effort and landings of shallow water shrimp in the Northern Gulf of Mexico.

than the age at which the growth and death rates are equal results in weight losses because mortality is removing biomass faster than it is being replaced by growth. Data on hand indicated that these two rates balance at 6-9 months of age or at a size of 20-30 shrimp tails per pound.

Shrimping regulations vary by states along the Gulf coast and, in fact, the harvesting strategy differs significantly between the states of Texas and Louisiana. These two states produce approximately 75 percent of the shrimp landed in the northern Gulf of Mexico. In Texas, the shrimping regulations generally restrict the catch of small shrimp, whereas in Louisiana there are few restrictions on the catching of small shrimp. The overall results of these two diametrically opposed regulatory schemes is that in Texas the bulk of the catch comes from an offshore fishery and consists mostly of large shrimp. In Louisiana there is a substantial inshore fishery which produces a large amount of both small and large brown and white shrimp. The average ex-vessel value per pound for brown shrimp in 1976 dollars was $2.22 per pound in Texas as compared to $1.36 in Louisiana (2). Furthermore, the annual total weight and value of brown shrimp landing has been greater in Texas than in Louisiana (Fig. 10).

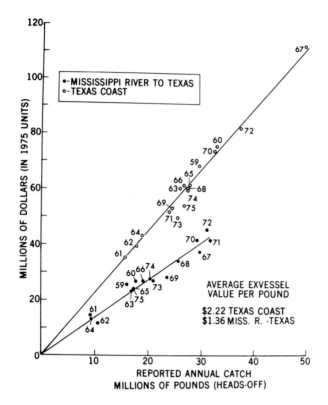

FIGURE 10. The relation between the ex-vessel value of shrimp landings and the annual landings for the Texas coast and the Louisiana coast.

Environmental Management

It is possible that increased productivity of the stocks might be achieved by altering the harvesting management strategy, but the specific ways in which this might be accomplished remain to be determined. Restricting the size at first harvest may increase the yield and the ex-vessel value, but could also eliminate jobs for most of the inshore fishermen. It is also possible that manipulation of the environment (i.e., controlling and directing man's impact on the environment) might be used to some benefit. For example, it is quite possible that alterations in the quantity and distribution of fresh water discharge into the estuaries might be done in such a way as to enhance shrimp productivity. Studies of the relationships among shrimp yield and environmental factors should provide part of the technical information base necessary for such actions.

Laws

Existing laws and regulations have been directed primarily toward limiting the quantity of small shrimp landed. These laws include restrictions on mesh size of the trawl nets, the number of trawls used, minimum legal sizes, and closed areas during certain seasons. While these regulations are effective to some extent, they do not prevent the taking of undersized shrimp (e.g., some are caught and discarded dead offshore and represent a waste of part of the resource).

Economic Factors

The shrimp industry in the Gulf of Mexico underwent a difficult transition period from 1971 to 1975 (3). Low shrimp prices coupled with rapidly escalating prices for fuel and other input items brought about a cost-price squeeze that severely affected vessel owners. Average annual landings were approximately 49,000 pounds. The break-even ex-vessel price for normal production is estimated to be $2.60 per pound. Net profit was calculated to be $0.40 per pound with loan payment and $0.80 without loan payment. Net profit was $1.00 per pound if vessel depreciation and insurance costs were not considered. Since in 1975 production was slightly below normal, and the ex-vessel price of shrimp averaged only $1.66 per pound, vessel owners did not meet their cash expenses. We have reviewed the average price based on the mid-August price in Texas and have estimated the 1977 average price to be approximately $2.26 (Table I). Under this situation then, if 1977 is a normal year, the fleet will,

Table I
Average Price Per Pound of Shrimp Based on Size, Price and Percent by Size

Size (Heads off per pound)	Price (Dollars) Mid-Aug. 77	Percent of 1975 Landings
Under 15	4.09	.02
15-20	3.79	.11
21-25	2.88.8	.16
26-30	2.47	.12
31-40	2.10	.23
41-50	1.74	.14
51-67	1.54	.13
Over 68	1.26	.09

Average price = (size price per pound x % size) = $2.26

be in a much better position than they have been in past years. All preliminary indications are that in 1977 the average price per pound will increase to a figure higher than $2.26 and that shrimp production will be slightly above normal. The prospects for profit appear to be good.

The major economic constraint along the Gulf coast is overcapitalization. A good fishing year followed by another good fishing year produces an increase of the number of vessels being constructed. Since 1976 and 1977 appear to be two good years with high prices, the fleet will expand; hence, in 1978, excess vessel capacity will exist. However, if in 1978 shrimp abundance is low, then severe economic hardship can be anticipated. This sequence is a visible historical trend in shrimp fisheries in the Gulf of Mexico.

Social Factors

The inshore shrimp stocks support very large and increasing numbers of recreational and commercial fishing units and fishermen. The magnitude of the recreational catch is unknown; however, in the last decade the number of boats registered as commercial has increased considerably. It is assumed that the recreational catch of shrimp has also increased significantly in the last decade. The offshore fisheries of Louisiana, Mississippi, and Texas have been expanding, and they represent far fewer fishing units and fishermen than does the inshore fishery. The inshore fishery likewise harvests on an average smaller and less valuable shrimp than that offshore fishery (2). The curtailment or restriction on the inshore fishery with its many small boat and vessel operators can cause severe hardships. Many of these inshore fishermen rely heavily on this income although it may not be their primary source of revenue. The secondary industries likewise are dependent upon these producers. The canning industry of Mississippi and Louisiana depends upon small shrimp landed primarily by inshore boat operators. Management actions which impinge heavily upon this population must be thoroughly analyzed prior to promulgation. However, on the other side of the coin, fishing on the inshore shrimp stocks must be controlled. Continued expansion of this fishery may eventually lead to biological depletion or at the very least, to economic hardship for both the inshore and offshore fisheries. Since unrestricted fishing in the inshore area does affect revenue production by the offshore segment of the fleet, this complex problem needs to be analyzed not only from a biological standpoint but from economic and social aspects as well.

Also of concern is man's effect on that part of the coastal environment which produces the shrimp resources—the estuaries. Continued alteration of the environment by man's activies may result in far greater reduction in productivity than over-fishing. Management of the resource must take into consideration the primary nursery habitats of the shrimp stocks of the Gulf of Mexico. This brings into direct conflict the oil and gas producing areas and the nursery areas in many of the coastal marshes along the entire Gulf coast. Housing development likewise is in direct opposition to the maintenance of estuaries as nurseries. The social conflicts arising from these conflicting uses must be resolved on an equitable and fair basis not only for this generation but for future generations as well. The resources of not only the Gulf but of the world are not just for the use by the present generation, but for future generations as well, and we should look to these resources as providing a safeguard for the future. President Theodore Roosevelt at the turn of the century said, "The Nation behaves well if it treats the natural resources as assets which it must turn over to the next generation increased and not impaired in value".

Summary

Total U.S. shrimp production in the Gulf of Mexico from 1964 to 1974 has varied annually from a high of over 60,000 metric tons heads-off in 1970 to a low of about 45,000 tons in 1966. The average potential yield for shallow water shrimp is about 55,000 metric tons heads-off, with annual landings fluctuating close to this maximum since 1970. Size at first harvest is important in terms of the total value and weight of shrimp landed. The optimal size is about 20 to 30 shrimp per pounds heads-off.

References

1. Ricker, W.E. (1975). Computation and Interpretation of Biological Statistics of Fish Populations. Bulletin of the Fisheries Research Board of Canada No. 191, pp. 382.

2. Caillouet, C.W. and Patella, F.J. (In press). Relationship between Size, Composition, and Ex-vessel Value of Reported Shrimp Catches from Two Gulf States with Different Harvesting Strategies. *Marine Fisheries Review.*

3. Griffin, W.L., Nichols, J.P. and Smith, J.B. (1975). Economic Analysis of Returns to Gulf of Mexico Shrimp Vessel Owners for the Period 1971-1975. Staff Paper No. 4, Departmental Information Report 75-1, Department of Agricultural Economics, Texas Agricultural Experiment Station, Texas A & M University, College Station, Texas.

CRAYFISH WITH OFFSPRING. (Photo courtesy of Dr. Alan P. Covich, University of Oklahoma.)

Penaeid Shrimp Culture: Current Status And Direction Of Research

Fred S. Conte[1]

Texas Agricultural Extension Service
College Station, Texas

The shrimp fishery is the most valuable fishery in the Gulf of Mexico, accounting for more than half of the 200 million pounds of tails landed annually in the United States . The value of the Gulf shrimp alone is rapidly approaching 200 million dollars per year. Although shrimp populations fluctuate annually, landing statistics and sampling data indicate that the fishery is presently at, or near, maximum sustainable yield.

In 1975, the demand for shrimp in the U.S. resulted in the importation of 230 million pounds, more than the entire U.S. production. Thus, our domestic production which cannot meet the demand, along with sharply rising dockside prices, have combined to stimulate an interest in mariculture as an alternate method of producing shrimp.

Penaeid shrimp culture has been established as a viable and profitable enterprise in Japan, and on limited basis in Central America and in areas of the South Pacific. Labor and operational costs have prevented the establishment of this industry in the continental United States. Although interested investors have access to the same technology that has established shrimp culture in other areas of the world, a greater sophistication of this technology is necessary to reduce the cost of operating a shrimp farm in this country.

Research in penaeid shrimp culture began in the United States in the early nineteen fifties with the work of G. R. Lunz. Working with *Penaeus aztecus, P. duorarum* and *P. setiferus*, Lunz, initiated studies on facility site selection, pond construction, shrimp production and predator management (1-5). Wheeler (6,7), using inorganic fertilizer to initiate phytoplankton blooms in ponds, obtained faster growth among young *P. aztecus*. Broom (8) and Holcomb and Parker (9) noted that at comparable densities *P. setiferus* achieved higher growth rates than *P. aztecus*. Parker

[1] Present address: Cooperative Extension, University of California, Davis, Calfornia, 95616.

and Holcomb (personal communication) in 1972 conducted experiments comparing the production capabilities of hatchery reared non-indigenous species— *P. occidentalis* and *P. vannamei*— with that of *P. aztecus* and *P. setiferus.* They obtained their best production, 816 kg per ha, with *P. vannamei.* Neal and Latapie (10) reported production of *P. setiferus* at 931 kg per ha, while Parker et al. (11) using a tri-level pilot production system with *P. vannamei* and *P. stylirostris* reported harvests of 921 kg and 1065 kg per ha of *P. vannamei* followed by 218 kg per ha of bait size *P. stylirostris.*

Much of the early production work was based on stocking ponds with post-larvae and juvenile shrimp obtained from bays and estuaries. Production figures have increased significantly with the development of hatchery systems capable of using the spawn from egg bearing females obtained from the Gulf of Mexico. Cook and Murphy (12), after reviewing the Japanese hatchery methods, developed a method of rearing penaeid larvae in the laboratory which was later expanded into hatchery systems that could supply the large number of postlarvae necessary for production units (13-16).

Successful reproduction of penaeid shrimp in captivity has been accomplished at several laboratories, but the refined techniques necessary to produce animals on demand and in the numbers necessary to support a commercial operation have yet to be developed. Johnson and Fielding (17) using ponds with limited water exchange reported reproduction of *P. setiferus* in Florida. Moore, Sherry and Montanez (18) using flow-through raceway systems with seven exchanges of water per day reported reproduction of *P. californiensis* in Puerto Peñasco, Mexico. Griessinger et al. (19), using flow-through tanks in Tahiti, reported reproduction of *P. merguiensis, P. semisulcatus, P. aztecus* and *Metapenaeus ensis.* Conte (20,21) using thermal effluent from an electric generating station in Texas reported gonadal development in *P. setiferus* and reproduction in *P. stylirostris.*

Although many dietary studies on penaeid shrimp have been conducted, information on the basic nutritional requirements of shrimp is still seriously lacking (22). Methods of mass algal culture and preservation techniques have been developed to meet the feeding demands of the early stages of penaeids cultured in intensive hatchery systems (23,24). Brine shrimp nauplei used to feed older penaeid larvae have been examined to determine nutritional content, to compare hatchability among different strains, and to develop methods of high density culture (25-30). Nutritional data on shrimp have been collected from studies conducted both in tanks and in grow-out systems (8,31-37). However, in most cases the variations in experimental and environmental conditions complicate meaningful nutritional comparisons (38).

The development of crustacean culture has been hindered by the lack of vaccines and effective chemotherapy, two important weapons used in the prevention of diseases in finfish culture (39). Although chemotherapy is being explored as a method of controlling disease (40-46), most current disease literature relates to description and identification (47-50).

Discussion

In October, 1975, the Oceanic Institute of Hawaii and the Office of Sea Grant of the National Oceanic and Atmospheric Administration hosted a penaeid culture workshop in Galveston, Texas for private, state and federal organizations actively engaged in penaeid research. The workshop was designed to allow exchange of information on the present status of penaeid culture and to define research priorities. Workshop participants met for four days and addressed nine broad categories which included availability of spawners, hatchery systems, grow-out systems, disease, nutrition and feeds, life cycle control, legal implications, economics and future market. This paper will not recapitulate the total results of the 1975 meeting since that information is now available (51). This presentation is a brief overview of penaeid culture in 1977, and includes the current philosophy regarding the areas designated as priority research. Although progress has been made in each of the above categories during the past two years many of the basic techniques of penaeid culture remain the same.

The first six topics listed above will be discussed in detail in this paper. The three remaining topics, legal aspects, economics and future market are summarized as follows: (i) There is a continuing need for research institutions and the industrial community to stay informed of new legislation which will affect aquaculture. A national lobby for aquaculture interests would be beneficial to this effort. (ii) Economic analyses will become more accurate as more information from involved corporations and pilot operations is made available. (iii) Perhaps the most encouraging aspect of penaeid culture is the future market. Seafood processors are willing to pay a premium price for high quality aquaculture products. Quality control is highly desired and is easily applied to aquaculture systems.

Obtaining spawners—Postlarvae used for stocking grow-out systems are obtained from one of the following three sources: i) trapping young shrimp in earthen ponds as the tide receeds; ii) capturing mated female shrimp from coastal waters; and iii) breeding females in captivity. Trapping postlarvae is used in several developing countries where low labor costs are compatible with low density grow-out systems that require labor intensive harvest. The third method, that of obtaining spawn from animals bred in captivity, is a technology in its infancy and will be discussed in greater detail in another section. The majority of postlarvae used in grow-out systems are obtained from animals captured offshore. The disadvantages of this system are the operational and maintenance cost of boats, the seasonality and unpredictability of shrimp, and the limited number of trained personnel with the ability to obtain the necessary animals when they are in demand. Despite these disadvantages, animals are being provided in sufficient numbers for the existing industry. Several commercial operators used their own boats to obtain gravid female shrimp and participate in the traditional shrimp fishery when the vessels are not being used to supply the hatchery. Refinement of techniques continues as researchers explore coastal areas for more favorable spawning grounds and develop better methods of transporting gravid shrimp. Obtaining spawners from the wild is still looked on as a temporary solution, to be replaced by captive reproduction when that technology can support the commercial needs of a hatchery.

Hatchery systems—The approaches to rearing larval penaeid shrimp range from the Japanese method of low density large tank systems to the high density smaller tank system developed by the National Marine Fisheries Service. The fundamental differences between the Japanese and American systems are the tank size, density of larvae and methods of providing feed for the larvae. The Japanese rely on the promotion of natural blooms of algae and zooplankton as a food source, supplemented by the addition of rotifers, oyster eggs and brine shrimp naupleii. In contrast, the NMFS Galveston Laboratory maintains a given density of food with preprepared algae and brine shrimp naupleii from commercially available cysts. Commercial operators throughout the world have adopted both methods along with a wide variety of modifications of each.

Hatchery success is measured not only by larval survival to the postlarval stage, but also by the quality of animals produced. Poor quality spawns are often reflected in the success of a grow-out system. Well-funded hatcheries have the advantage of being able to afford extensive culling of poor quality eggs and larvae before the high cost of hatchery labor and costly food regimes are established. The practice of removing potential problems before they can occur has greatly improved the economics of the larger commercial hatcheries.

Hatchery operators feel that the available technology is adequate for postlarval production, but that research is needed in the supportive elements such as improved nutrition and the prevention of disease.

Grow-out systems—The grow-out systems incorporated in penaeid culture are varied in their size and design. These designs include intensive environmentally self-contained raceways, flow-through raceways, flow-through ponds ranging in size from .25 to 20 acres and larger enclosed bays. Although valuable technology is being developed in all of these systems the most successful system in our hemisphere incorporates small nursery ponds that drain into larger grow-out ponds. This system has the capability of total harvest by draining the water and shrimp through pipes leading to capture nets.

Grow-out technology has shown marked improvement in the past decade and has evolved into workable systems. Acceptable practices in system management have been established in many areas including site selection, system design, water quality maintenance, species selection, stocking densities, predator and competitor control and harvesting. More information is needed on methods of estimating the standing crop and the relation of benthic and planktonic populations to pond conditions and general penaeid well being.

Nutrition and feeds—One of the most intensive areas of research in penaeid nutrition involves the brine shrimp *Artemia salina*. Brine shrimp naupleii are used to feed penaeid shrimp from the mysis stage through early postlarvae and are considered almost essential to the hatchery systems. The high price of brine shrimp cysts and the growing concern about their future availability have resulted in intensive research to improve cyst hatchability and methods of mass culture. Efforts are also being made to find a substitute for brine shrimp either in the form of another invertebrate capable of mass culture or a suitable flake food.

One reason for the increased shrimp production in growout systems has been the availability of commercially prepared supplementary rations. To provide improved diets there is a need for government laboratories and universities to supply information on the nutritional requirements of all penaeid life stages. Until such information is available the full potential of disease control, growth, survival and captive reproduction will not be realized. Nutrition is recognized as an essential foundation for animal husbandry and is considered a major research emphasis in penaeid culture.

Disease—Major diseases that affect penaeid shrimp include protozoans, metazoans, slime molds, fungi, bacteria, and viruses. Our primary defense against penaeid disease is the maintenance of proper nutrition and a healthy environment. Frequently the only available means of controlling disease are as harmful to the shrimp as is the disease itself, and often the only recourse is to drain the system, sterilize and begin again.

Most of the literature on penaeid diseases involve diagnostic and descriptive aspects of the organisms. However, increasing work is now being directed toward developing therapeutics and towards maintaining proper system management in order to prevent disease before it enters the system. The accomplishments already provided by pathologists have been remarkable in light of the short period that disease has been a major concern in penaeid culture. The establishment of several crustacean health workshops is an indication of the increased priority that culturists have given disease research.

Life cycle control—The highest research priority in penaeid culture concerns reproduction of shrimp in captivity. This has been accomplished with a number of species; however, the technology for captive reproduction at a rate necessary to support an industry has not been developed. The successful completion of this aspect of penaeid culture will alleviate the high cost of obtaining wild spawners and can ultimately lead to improved stock for grow-out systems.

Several approaches are now being taken in life cycle control. These include the development of ponds, raceways and large flow-through tank systems, all of which provide the environmental parameters that promote natural reproduction. Pond systems have been used successfully to produce large numbers of sexually active shrimp. This has been accomplished by working with older more mature shrimp that have been cultured from the postlarval stage for approximately fifteen months, or large animals obtained from the wild. In some latitudes in order to maintain the shrimp in ponds through the winter an external heat source is required. This heat has been provided by thermal effluent from electric generating stations and by solar energy.

The advantages of using ponds for life cycle control are the low maintenance required in operating the system and the large number of gravid female shrimp produced. Disadvantages are the inability to make visual observations and the difficulty in sampling the fertilized animals without disturbing the rest of the population. Disturbing female shrimp with developing ovarian tissue often results in gonadal reabsorption. To avoid these problems ponds are now being subdivided with nets so that each area can be sampled separately to reduce disturbance of the total shrimp population.

Successful penaeid reproduction is also being carried out in large flow-through tanks and raceways that allow direct observation and selective capture. These systems do not provide the nutritionally valuable benthic fauna characteristic of earthen ponds, however, they will be enhanced as better nutritional supplements are developed. Disadvantages in small raceways are the increased incidence of chitinolytic bacterial infection and other diseases associated with high density culture. The concept of combining pond systems with a more controlled environment is receiving favorable consideration by several institutions that are carrying on research in penaeid reproduction.

Some success in penaeid maturation has been achieved in tank systems through environmental manipulation of temperature and photoperiod. This method creates artificial seasons and thereby compresses the life cycle of the shrimp. The technique has proven successful with finfish and is currently being employed in several laboratories.

Maturation of shrimp on demand has been accomplished through physiological manipulation of the animals. This is achieved by unilateral eyestalk ablation of females which results in a lower titer of gonadal inhibitory hormone and the release of gonadal stimulating hormone produced in the cephalothorax. This technique, however, is not without its limitations. Eggs obtained after ablation and fertilization, are often less viable than those from nonablated animals. There is some indication that the percentage of viable eggs decreases with each successive generation of ablated animal. Research is now being conducted on the glandular complexes of penaeid shrimp to gain further insights into the endocrine control of reproduction. Such studies are designed to determine the relationship between reproductive success through eyestalk ablation and time of molt. Extensive research is also being conducted on the biochemistry and morphology of the eyestalk's glandular makeup and the biochemistry and morphology of the penaeid sperm and egg.

Studies are also being conducted to identify the biochemical substance in "normal" spawners that initiates disassociation of follicular nurse cells that surround the oocytes prior to fertilization. During *in vitro* fertilization, when eggs and sperm are removed from shrimp and mixed, the follicular nurse cells often do not disassociate from the oocyte. This results in egg adherence and consequently a low incidence of fertilization. When this biochemical release mechanism is identified, *in vitro* fertilization may become another technique to provide eggs for hatcheries.

The highest priority in penaeid culture today is to develop techniques for achieving captive reproduction in shrimp. When this is accomplished the high cost of procuring wild spawners will be eliminated and progress will be made in developing a domesticated stock, a prerequisite for the optimum development of an animal production industry.

Summary

The techniques necessary to culture penaeid shrimp have developed rapidly in recent years. Present techniques are sufficient to maintain commercial operations in areas of the world where labor costs are low enough to allow a margin of profit. In the United States, however, penaeid culture is still considered a high risk venture. Until production costs are decreased and a more constant survival rate is achieved with indigenous species, potential investors will continue to look only at pilot operations.

Penaeid shrimp culture will eventually become a reality. There is a commitment to this means of food production and a realization of its importance as an investment in the future.

References

1. Lunz, G.R. (1951). A Saltwater Fish Pond. *Contr. Bears Bluff Laboratories* **12**, 1

2. *Ibid.* (1956). Harvest from an Experimental One-acre Saltwater Pond at Bears Bluff Laboratories, South Carolina. *Progressive Fish Culturist.* **18**, 92

3. *Ibid.* (1958). Pond Cultivation of Shrimp in South Carolina. *Proc. Gulf Caribbean Fisheries Institute.* **10**, 44.

4. *Ibid.* (1967). Farming the Salt Marshes. *Proc. Marsh and Estuary Management Symposium,* Louisiana State University Press. 172.

5. Lunz, G. R. and Bearden, C. M. (1963). Control of Predacious Fishes in Shrimp Farming in South Carolina. *Contr. Bears Bluff Laboratories.* **36**, 96

6. Wheeler, R. S. (19679. Experimental Rearing of Postlarval Brown Shrimp to Marketable Size in Ponds. *Commercial Fisheries Review.* **29**, 49.

7. *Ibid.* (1968). Culture of Penaeid Shrimp in Brackish Water Ponds, 1966-1967. Proc. 23rd. Annual Conference Southeastern Association Game and Fish Commission. p. 387.

8. Broom, J. G. (1968). Pond Culture of Shrimp on Grand Terre Island, Louisiana, 1962-1968. *Proc. Gulf Caribbean Fisheries Institute.* **21**, 137.

9. Holcomb, H. W., Jr. and Parker, J. C. (1973). Efficiency of Drain and Seine Harvest Techniques in Experimental Penaeid Shrimp Culture Ponds. *Proc. World Mariculture Society.* **4**, 235.

10. Neal, R. A. and Latapie, W. R. (1972). Pond Culture on Grand Terre Island, Louisiana, 1969-1971. *Proc. World Mariculture Society.* **3**, 227.

11. Parker, J. C. *et al.* (1974). An Intensive Culture System for Penaeid Shrimp. *Proc. World Mariculture Society.* **5**, 65.

12. Cook, H. L. and Murphy, M. A. (1966). Rearing Penaeid Shrimp from Eggs to Postlarvae. Proc. 19th Annual Conference Southeast Association Game Fish Commission. 283.

13. Mock, C. and Murphy, A. (1970). Techniques for Raising Penaeid Shrimp. *Proc. World Mariculture Society.* **1**, 143

14. Tabb, D. C., *et al.* (1972). A Manual for Culture of Pink Shrimp *Penaeus duorarum* from Eggs to Postlarvae Suitable for Stocking. University of Miami Sea Grant Special Publication No 7. 59.

15. Mock, C. and Neal, R. A. (1974). Penaeid Shrimp Hatchery Systems. FAO. United Nations. CARPAS 6-74-SE29. 9.

16. Yang, W. T. (1975). A Manual for Large-tank Culture of Penaeid Shrimp to the Postlarval Stages. University of Miami Sea Grant Technical Publication No 31. pp. 94 .

17. Johnson, M. C. and Fielding, J. R. (1956). Propagation of the White Shrimp, *Penaeus setiferus* (Linn.) in Captivity. *Tulane Studies Zoology.* **4**, 175.

18. Moore, D. W., Sherry, R. W. and Montanez, F. (1974). Maturation of *Penaeus californiensis* in Captivity. *Proc. World Mariculture Society.* **5**, 445.

19. Griessinger, J. M. (1975). Maturation and Spawning in Captivity of Penaeid Prawns *Penaeus merguiensis* de Man, *P. japonicus* Bate, *P. Aztecus* Ives and *Metapenaeus ensis* (de Hann). *Proc. World Mariculture Society.* **6**, 123.

20. Conte, F. S. (1975). Penaeid Shrimp Culture and the Utilization of Waste Heat Effluent. Power Plant Waste Heat Utilization in Aquaculture, Workshop 1. Trenton, New Jersey. PSE&G, NSF, FANN, Trenton State College, Rutgers University. 1:23-47.

21. Conte, F. S. *et al.* (In press). Maturation of *Penaeus stylirostris* (Stempson) and *P. setiferus* (Linn.) in Hypersaline Water near Corpus Christi, Texas. *Proc. World Mariculture Society.*

22. New, M. C. (1976). A Review of Shrimp and Prawn Nutrition. *Proc. World Mariculture Society.* **7**, 277.

23. Brown, A., Jr. (1971). Experimental Techniques for Preserving Diatoms Used as Food for Larval *Penaeus aztecus. Proc. National Shellfish Association.* **62**, 21.

24. Griffith, G. W., Kinslow, M. A. and Ross, L.(1973). A Mass Culture Method for *Tetraselmis* sp.: a promising food for larval shrimp. *Proc. World Mariculture Society.* **4**, 289

25. Gallagher, J. and Brown, W. D. (1975). Composition of San Francisco Bay Brine Shrimp (*Artemia salina*). *J. Agricultural and Food Chemistry.* **23**, 630.

26. Sorgeloos, P. (1973). First Report on the Triggering Effect of Light on the Hatching Mechanism of *Artemia salina* Dry Cysts. *Marine Biology* **22**, 75.

27. *Ibid.* (1973). High Density Culturing of the Brine Shrimp, *Artemia salina. Aquaculture* **1**, 385.

28. *Ibid.* (1975). Research on the Culturing of the Brine Shrimp, *Artemia salina* L. at the State University of Ghent (Belgium) . *Proc. World Mariculture Society.* **6**, 441.

29. Sorgeloos, P. and Persoone, G. (1973). A Culture System for *Artemia, Daphnia* and Other Invertebrates, With Continuous Separation of the Larvae. *Arch. Hydrobiol.* **72**, 133.

30. *Ibid.* (1974). Technological Improvements for the Cultivation of Invertebrates as Food for Fish and Crustaceans. *Proc. World Mariculture Society.* **5**, 455.
31. Subrahmanyam. C. B. and Oppenheimer, C. H. (1970). Food Preferences and Growth of Grooved Penaeid Shrimp. In *Proc. Food-Drugs from the Sea.* Marine Technol. Soc., Washington, D.C.
32. *Ibid.* (1970). The Influence of Feed Levels on the Growth of Grooved Penaeid Shrimp in Mariculture. *Proc. World Mariculture Society.* **1**, 91.
33. Venkataramaiah, A., Lakshmi C. J., and Gunter, G. (1972). The Effects of Salinity and Feeding Levels on the Growth Rates and Food Conversion Efficiency of the Shrimp *Penaeus aztecus. Proc. World Mariculture Society.* **3**, 267.
34. Sick, L. V., Andrews, J. W., and White, D. B. (1972). Preliminary Studies of Selected Environmental and Nutritional Requirements for the Culture of Penaeid Shrimp. *Fishery Bulletin* **70**, 101.
35. Meyers, S. P. and Zien-Elden, Z. P.(1972). Binders and Pellet Stability in Development of Crustacean Diets. *Proc. World Mariculture Society.* **3**, 351.
36. Latapie, R., Broom, J. G. and Neal, D. A. (1972). Growth Rates of *Penaeus aztecus* and *Penaeus setiferus* in Artificial Ponds under Varying Conditions. *Proc. World Mariculture Society.* **3**, 241.
37. Broom, J. G. (1970). Shrimp Culture. *Proc. World Mariculture Society.* **1**, 63.
38. Zien-Elden, Z. P. and Meyers, S. P. (1973). General Consideration of Problems in Shrimp Nutrition. *Proc. World Mariculture Society.* **4**, 299.
39. Pauley, G. B. (1975). Introductory Remarks on Diseases of Crustaceans. *Marine Fisheries Review.* **37**, 2.
40. Hanks, K. S. (1976). Toxicity of Some Chemical Therapeutics to the Commercial Shrimp, *Penaeus californiensis. Aquaculture* **7**, 293.
41. Johnson, S. K. (1974). Toxicity of Several Management Chemicals to Penaeid Shrimp. Texas Agricultural Extension Service. FDDL Report S-3, p. 12.
42. *Ibid.* (1974). Use of Guinaldine with Penaeid Shrimp. Texas Agricultural Extension Service. FDDL Report S-4, p. 2.
43. *Ibid.* (1975). Field Application of Several Management Chemicals in Shrimp Rearing Ponds. Texas Agricultural Extension Service. FDDL Report S-5, p. 3.
44. *Ibid.* (1976). Chemical Control of Peritrichous Ciliates on Young Penaeid Shrimp. Texas Agricultural Extension Service. FDDL Report S-7, p. 4.

45. *Ibid.* (1976). Twenty-four Hour Toxicity Tests of Six Chemicals to Mysis Larvae of *Penaeus Setiferus.* Texas Agricultural Extension Service. FDDL Report S-8, p. 2.

46. Lightner and Supplee, V. C. (1976). A Possible Chemical Control Method for Filamentous Gill Disease. *Proc. World Mariculture Society.* **7**, 473.

47. Sindermann, C. J. and Rosenfield, A. (1967). Principal Diseases of Commercially Important Marine Bivalve Molluscs and Crustacea. *Fishery Bulletin* **66**, 335.

48. Sinderman, C. J. (1975). Diagnosis and Control of Mariculture Diseases in the United States. Middle Atlantic Coastal Fisheries Center. Technical Series No 2, p. 306.

49. Johnson, S. K. (1975). Handbook of Shrimp Diseases. Texas Agricultural Extension Service. TAMU-SG-75-603, p. 19.

50. Lightner, D. V. (1975). Some Potentially Serious Disease Problems in the Culture of Penaeid Shrimp in North America. Proceedings Third U.S. Japan Meeting on Aquaculture, Tokyo, Japan. Special Pub. Fisheries Agency. Japan Sea Regional Fisheries Research Laboratory. p. 75

51. Hanson, J. A. and Goodwin, H. L. (1977). Shrimp and Prawn Farming in the Western Hemisphere: State of the art reviews and status assessment. Dowden, Hutchinson and Ross, Inc. Penn. p. 439.

Controlled Environment Aquaculture Of Penaeids

B. Salser, L. Mahler, D. Lightner, J. Ure, D. Danald
C. Brand, N. Stamp, D. Moore and B. Colvin

Environmental Research Laboratory
University of Arizona
Tucson International Airport
Tucson, Arizona

Controlled environment aquaculture (CEA) of crustaceans by the Environmental Research Laboratory of the University of Arizona began in 1972 as an evolutionary product of the controlled environment agriculture technology developed by the laboratory. The research facility, located on the northern Gulf of California near Puerto Peñasco, Sonora, Mexico, is a cooperative project of the Environmental Research Laboratory (ERL) and its counterpart, CICTUS, at the University of Sonora. As a result of progress within the past three years, the project is now moving into a commercial prototype phase.

There are several contrasts between the high density culture possible in controlled environments and other systems most frequently encountered. For example, in open environment culture the animals are in cages or net enclosures. In pond culture, large bodies of water enclose the cultured populations. In the latter system, there is greater human involvement in the construction and maintenance of ponds and some supplemental feeding is required, while in the former intensive feeding may be required.

By contrast, the intensive systems of ERL enclose the complete environment. Water use is programmed, nutrition is almost 100% by supplementation and there is continuous population and biomass monitoring.

Intensive CEA offers several advantages over its counterparts. CEA allows maximal growth rate, survival and stocking densities through optimization of water quality, feeding regimes and disease management. The high densities possible in CEA systems allow higher productivity on less acreage. For example, it has been demonstrated that CEA can produce 40,000 to 60,000 lbs tails/acre (45,000-67,000 kg/ha) compared to a maximum of 2,500 lbs live weight per acre in extensive systems (1). In a

CEA system predation is eliminated and easy visibility of the animals permits rapid recognition and treatment of diseases. In CEA, populations and growth rates can be readily followed, thereby permitting programmable easily anticipated year-round harvest. In addition, the high visibility of CEA uniquely permits manipulation of brood stock to meet the spawning requirements.

However, CEA is not without its disadvantages. Such a system requires a high capital outlay and a subtantial operating budget. There is an elevated feed cost since a more highly defined feed at various stages of the life cycle is necessary. In addition, more feed must be supplied since the primary and secondary productivities cannot keep up with the rapidly growing populations.

There is also a very high technical input. In the engineering aspects there are sophisticated structural requirements and substantial energy needs. Biological aspects require trained specialists to monitor environmental parameters, to conduct routine health maintenance and monitoring, and to produce high quality feed administered in a complex feeding regime.

Production Format

Wild adults are collected from the Gulf of California and are held in the raceways for maturation. Spawnable females are then removed and transferred to the hatchery as needed. Larval culture is an adaptation of the procedures developed at the National Marine Fisheries Service (NMFS) Galveston Laboratory (2-4).

The postlarvae are transferred to a fiberglass, flowthrough nursery system until they reach 10 to 50 mg. The postlarvae may be transferred to a post-nursery system, a miniature raceway, where they are stocked at 500 to 600/m^2 and placed on supplemental feeding. When the animals have reached 0.6 to 1.2 g, they may then be transferred to a growout system where they are stocked at a density of approximately 170/m^2. They will spend 20 to 25 weeks in this growout system and will usually be harvested at approximately 21 g (35CNT).

The first generation of research aquacells consisted of remodeled greenhouses (5). The structures are 7m wide x 30m long with a 0.9m center concrete walkway. Polyvinyl liners were installed to create two 3 x 23m raceways of approximately 0.3m depth, in each inflated plastic structure. The structures were covered with a UV-stabilized 10 mil polyethelene film which was inflated to form a 7 x 30m half cylinder. Inflation is by fans to a pressure of approximately 6 to 12mm water gauge.

Water pumped from a seawater well is introduced into the raceway by headers at the end or along the long axis of each raceway. Both makeup and recirculation water are introduced in this manner and are sprayed directly onto the surface of the raceway to increase efficiency of aeration. Both overflow and bottom drains have been provided in the raceways.

Although certain structural and construction improvements have been made, the second and third generations of this patented design is conceptually the same. Some important changes include an above grade air lock, increased depth to 0.6m, an overall dimension of 4 x 24m, introduction of water through side manifolds along the length of the raceway, and overflow into a common channel to facilitate harvest. In addition, algal production is encouraged in the system. In all cases the feeding program was a phase feeding regime based on the nutrient requirement described previously (6,7).

Production Achieved

Investigations prior to 1975 were devoted largely to development of engineering aspects of controlled environment aquaculture which required primarily short-term studies. The first long-term simulated production experiment (Table I) was conducted with *Penaeus californiensis*. The objectives of this experiment were the primary evaluation of management routines, bio-engineering parameters, e.g., water quality, and the development of diagnostic procedures. A number of problems were encountered, including high mortality due to both high and low oxygen ten-

Table I
Simulated Production Experiment
Aquario 10, 7/75

SPECIES:	*P. Californiensis*
MEAN WEIGHT—INITIAL:	1.20 g
FINAL:	15.15 g
F.C.R. (g Feed/g Gain):	3.17
TIME IN PRODUCTION:	23.1 wks.
GROWTH RATE	0.60 g/wk.
CNT (NO. TAILS/LB)	50
HARVEST DENSITY	0.96 kg/m²

sions and disease losses due to filamentous gill disease. However, in July, 1975, a harvest was made with a mean final weight of 15.2g after 23 weeks in production. Growth rate was approximately 0.6g/wk and the final harvest density was less than 1 kg/m² of surface area (Table I). In February, 1976, the first harvest of the simulated production experiment on *Penaeus stylirostris* was made. This population stocked at 0.74g attained a final weight of 20g (37CNT) in 25 weeks with the survival of 81 percent; however, a significant factor in this experiment was that the harvest density exceeded 2 kg/m² (Fig. 1).

In late 1976, another harvest of long-term growout of *P. californiensis* was conducted. After 20 weeks in production, the population had reached a final weight of 15.9g (Fig. 2), but a severe epizootic due to *Fusarium solani* was encountered in the later stages.

A parallel experiment with *P. stylirostris* (Fig. 3) reached 21g (35CNT) in 21 weeks of production reflecting the slightly higher growth rate of *P. stylirostris*. The lower density due to excessive mortality, resulted from a condition which has been referred to as "Blue Syndrome X" and will be discussed later.

Due to the apparent advantage in growth rate, emphasis was placed primarily on *P. stylirostris* and subsequently a population was harvested which had reached 38 CNT in less than 20 weeks' production with the survival of 90 percent. Significantly, this population reached 2.6 kg/m² of surface area.

In December, 1976, construction was completed on what was called the "preprototype" raceways or a second generation design. These two raceways were 0.6m in depth and contained 99m² of surface area. Due to the extensive check out of engineering parameters, the animals which were intended for stocking in these raceways reached 4.5–4.7g by stocking time; however, in only 14 weeks of production these animals reached 21g (35CNT) with a growth rate greater than 1g/wk and, most importantly, the harvest density was 2.4 kg/m² in one and 2.7 kg/m² in the other raceway (Fig. 4-5).

Problems Encountered

Among the problems manifest in dense and stressed populations are (as expected) diseases. However, not all diseases observed in CEA have been due to pathogens. A significant example is the nutritional disease referred to as "Black Death Syndrome". This syndrome was observed in California brown shrimp *P. californiensis*, reared in tanks and raceways that received no sunlight and contained no plant material. The disease is characterized by blackened lesions in the subcuticular tissues of the general body surface and walls of the esophagus, stomach and hindgut,

SIMULATED PRODUCTION EXPERIMENT

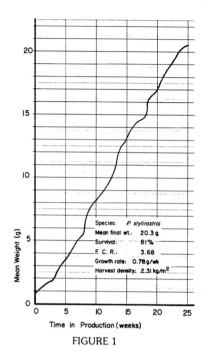

Species: *P. stylirostris*
Mean final wt.: 20.3 g.
Survival: 81%
F. C. R.: 3.68
Growth rate: 0.78 g/wk
Harvest density: 2.31 kg/m²

FIGURE 1

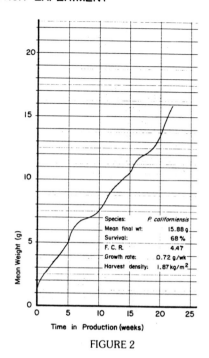

Species: *P. californiensis*
Mean final wt: 15.88 g
Survival: 68%
F. C. R. 4.47
Growth rate: 0.72 g/wk
Harvest density: 1.87 kg/m²

FIGURE 2

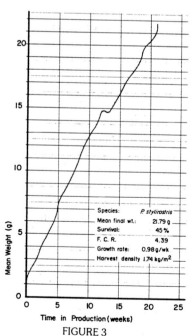

Species: *P. stylirostris*
Mean final wt.: 21.79 g
Survival: 45%
F. C. R. 4.39
Growth rate: 0.98 g/wk
Harvest density 1.74 kg/m²

FIGURE 3

FIGURE 1. Simulated production experiment. Aquario 3. February, 1976.

FIGURE 2. Simulated production experiment. Aquario 4. December, 1976.

FIGURE 3. Simulated production experiment. Aquario 3. January, 1977.

SIMULATED PRODUCTION EXPERIMENT

FIGURE 4

FIGURE 5

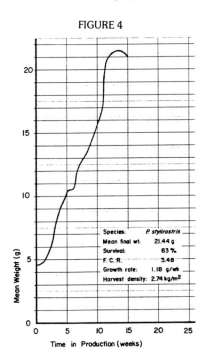

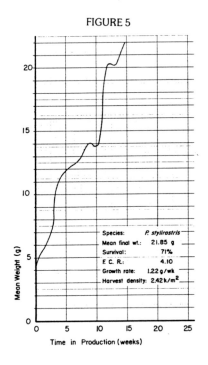

FIGURE 4. Simulated production experiment. Aquario 11. March, 1977.

FIGURE 5. Simulated production experiment. Aquario 12. March, 1977.

and in the gills and gill cavities. This disease has been shown (8) to be related to a dietary deficiency of L-ascorbic acid (Vitamin C), and can be prevented by supplying adequate amounts of the vitamin. The Black Death Syndrome has also been demonstrated recently in *P. stylirostris.*

Another type of nutritional disease is reflected in toxic spirulinosis. The marine blue-green algae *Spirulina* sp. has occasionally bloomed in tanks and raceways in which shrimp are grown in Puerto Penasco. Shrimp which ingest this alga in large quantities develop a disease syndrome characterized by acute suppurative enteritis. The enteritis is often accompanied by secondary bacterial septicemia. This toxicosis usually results in slow growth and elevated mortality rates. The condition may be prevented by maintaining a population of predominately *Enteromorpha* sp. in the raceways.

A unique pathological condition developed as a result of a mechanical condition, and has been referred to as"gas bubble disease" (9). This condition was seen in animals reared in raceways in which the sides and bottoms were lined with a dense growth of predominately *Enteromorpha* sp., although several species of diatoms were also present. In these particular raceways, there was no water flow during the daylight hours or any form of agitation. As a result, the dissolved oxygen was allowed to accumulate, and analyses for oxygen by the Winkler Method, indicated more than 250 percent saturation.

First sign of the onset of "gas bubble disease" in these shrimp was a rapid, erratic swimming behavior. Within one to two minutes the activity subsided and the affected shrimp floated near the surface with the ventral side of the cephalothorax higher than the tail region. Grossly, the gills of the affected shrimp appeared milky white under the carapace. Microscopic examinations of wet mounts revealed bubbles in the gill filaments, in the appendages, and under the cuticle of the entire body surface. The bubbles were assumed to be principally oxygen.

High mortalities were not typical, although in some cases nearly 100 percent of the raceway population was affected. Mortality was typically less than 1 percent of juvenile shrimp but exceeded 27 percent of one group of adults. Reversal of the disease condition was accomplished by vigorously jetting fresh seawater through a high pressure manifold onto the surface of the water. Even the most severely affected shrimp usually recovered and appeared normal within 48 hours.

An important pathological condition in adult and sub-adult populations can be epizootics due to *Fusarium solani. Fusarium* is a ubiquitous imperfect fungus which is a well-known plant pathogen; although it occasionally infects animals including man. The infection occurs as chronic gangrenous-like lesions on the appendages, gills and general body surface, often gaining entry as a result of a wound. One raceway epizootic followed a severe gillburn as a result of an experimental potassium permanganate treatment. All penaeids are probably susceptible, but the brown shrimp (*P. californiensis*) appears to be the most susceptible species. At this point there is no effective therapy for *Fusarium* infections; however, it usually occurs in larger shrimp that molt less frequently. Consequently, it is often possible to harvest before these infections become rampant (10,11).

A consistent problem seen in high density CEA is gill disease (12). Gill disease is due to a complex of several organisms, whose presence on the gills may result in death, either from destruction of the gill, or most often, from the anoxia due to mechanical blockage occurring at molting or other stress periods. The principal organism appears to be a *Leucothrix* sp. This filamentous bacterium attaches itself to the gill surface and can cause physical blockage of water flow across the gills.

Taxonomy of the filamentous forms of this disease continues to be somewhat uncertain. Because of the non-specific nature of the syndrome, chemical control methods, although expensive in terms of labor and materials, offer the most practical therapeutic approach at this time. Experiments in this laboratory suggest that commercial algicides such as the quaternary ammonium salts of copper offer the most suitable management tool for filamentous gill disease in high density crustacean culture. Both flow-through and static methods of application are effective, but the latter is much less often affected by mechanical failures that occasionally occur in flow-through treatments requiring chemical metering devices.

On one recent occasion, a disease condition of unknown origin developed, and has been labelled "Blue Syndrome X". As the name implies, the disease was observed in *P. stylirostris* of harvest size. High mortality was accompanied by high numbers of filamentous gill organisms and protozoans, and in other cases by broad ranges of bacterial infections. The condition was originally thought to be associated with high ammonia levels, and now some evidence has been obtained which would implicate a form of "fatty-liver" degeneration. At present, we have no cure or preventive management which is effective against this infrequent syndrome.

Projections

The growth rate in the production growout phase has progressed from 0.7g/wk in 1975 to the current rate in excess of 1g/wk (Fig. 6). Also, the harvest density has progressed from less than 1 kg/m² to the current 2.8kg/m² which we experienced in the first harvest from the preprototype. In 1978, it is considered possible to achieve 1.25g/wk growth with the harvest density of 3.3kg/m² and feed conversion ratio of less than 3.1.

At commercial levels, there is evidence that the CEA product can demand a premium price due to its very high quality. There is improved visual acceptability of cultured shrimp because of the more intense pigmentation, and there is evidence that the consumer prefers the taste and texture of the cultured animal as seen in the results of a recent "Taste Panel" (Table II).

The Production Facilities

At the time of this writing, a prototype is under construction adjacent to the Research Station at Puerto Penasco, Sonora, Mexico. The one acre facility will contain 18 raceways, enclosing approximately one acre of water, plus a small pond for waste nutrient recovery. In addition, there will be two buildings which will house offices, laboratories, feed storage,

FIGURE 6

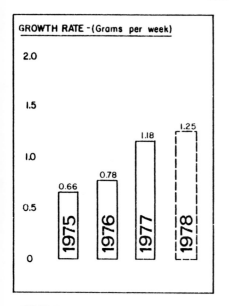
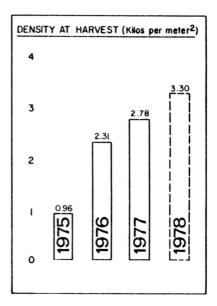

FIGURE 6. Annual Levels of Production Improvement. Controlled Environment Shrimp Culture.

Table II

Sensory Evaluation of Wild versus Cultured Shrimp
Based on a Sliding Hedonic Scale [1,2]

CHARACTERISTIC	*P. californiensis* WILD	CULTURED	*P. stylirostris* WILD	CULTURED
GENERAL ACCEPTANCE	5.6 ± 1.7	7.3 ± 1.5**	5.0 ± 1.8	7.2 ± 1.5**
AROMA	5.4 ± 1.9	6.5 ± 1.8*	5.1 ± 2.0	6.5 ± 1.7**
COLOR	5.5 ± 1.9	7.1 ± 1.6**	5.3 ± 2.1	7.0 ± 2.0**
TEXTURE	6.2 ± 1.8	6.9 ± 1.7	5.9 ± 1.9	6.8 ± 1.8*
FLAVOR	5.2 ± 2.1	7.0 ± 1.8**	4.4 ± 2.1	7.3 ± 1.4**

[1]Values are reported as means ± one standard deviation of all judges on a scale of 1 (undesirable) to 9 (highly desirable).
[2]Statistical significance of preference is indicated by:
* = $p \leq 0.01$
** = $p \leq 0.001$
no asterisk = $p > 0.05$

maintenance and standby power. The total complex is expected to cover approximately three acres of land.

Based on the 3.3kg/m² harvest density and approximate growout time of 21 weeks, it should be possible to complete two and one-half cycles per year. This would result in production of approximately 34,000 kg (75,000 lbs) per year of live shrimp. This would be about 45,000 lbs of 35 count tails. This prototype facility will be completed in about six months and will require five to eight people for operation. Extra temporary staff will be required at the time of harvest, and final processing will be accomplished through existing packing plants.

The University aquaculture staff will understandably concentrate on providing full technical support to the prototype farm, and to other prototype units which are in design for U.S. locations. A much larger commercial facility is planned for the Mexican location following the initial operation of the prototype.

While we anticipate a long-term commitment to the fine-tuning of CEA penaeid systems, we are also looking forward to the transfer of pertinent aspects of this technology to the production of other crustaceans in inland as well as coastal locations.

References

1. Parker, J.C. *et al.* (1974). An Extensive Culture System for Penaeid Shrimp. Proceedings of the Fifth Annual Workshop, World Mariculture Society. p. 65.
2. Mock, C.R. and Murphy, M.A. (1970). Techniques for Raising Penaeid Shrimp. Proceedings of the First Annual Workshop, World Mariculture Society. p. 143.
3. Mock, C.R., and Neal, R.A. (1974). Penaeid Shrimp Hatchery Systems. FAO/CARPAS Symposium on Aquaculture in Latin America.
4. Salser, B.R. and Mock, C.R. (1974). Equipment for the Culture of Larval Penaeid Shrimp at the National Marine Fisheries Service Galveston Laboratory. Proceedings of the V. Congreso Nacional de Oceanografia.
5. Mahler, L.E., Groh, J.E. and Hodges, C.N. (1974). Controlled Environment Aquaculture. Proceedings of the Fifth Annual Workshop, World Mariculture Society. p. 379.
6. Brand, C.W. and Colvin, L.B. (In press). Compounded Diets for Early Postlarval Penaeid Shrimp. Proceedings of the Eighth Annual Workshop, World Mariculture Society.
7. Colvin, L.B. and Brand, C.W. (In press). Protein Requirements of

Penaeid Shrimp at Various Life Stages. Proceedings of the Eight Annual Workshop, World Mariculture Society.

8. Lightner, D.V. *et al.* (In press). Black Death, A Disease Syndrome of Penaeid Shrimp Related to a Dietary Deficiency of Ascorbic Acid. Proceedings of the Eighth Annual Workshop, World Mariculture Society.

9. Supplee, V.C. and Lightner, D.V. (1976). Gas-bubble Disease Due to Oxygen Supersaturation in Raceway-reared California Brown Shrimp. *Prog. Fish-Culturist* **38**, 158.

10. Lightner, D.V. (1974). Some Potentially Serious Disease Problems in the Culture of Penaeid Shrimp in North America. Proceedings of the Third U.S. Japan Meeting on Aquaculture, Tokyo, Japan.

11. Lightner, D.V. (1977). Fungus *Fusarium* Disease of Shrimps in *Disease Diagnosis and Control in North American Marine Aquaculture.* Ed. Carl J. Sindermann. 12. Lightner, D.V., Fontain, C.T. and Hanks, K. (1975). Some Forms of Gill Disease in Penaid Shrimp. Proceedings of Sixth Annual Workshop, World Mariculture Society. p. 347.

SECTION IV

Present Status and Potential Production of Pacific Salmon

Pacific Coast Salmon Industry: Status Of Natural And Artificial Production

Kenneth A. Henry

U.S. Department of Commerce
National Oceanic and Atmospheric Administration
National Marine Fisheries Service
Seattle, Washington

The Pacific coast salmon fishing industry is a rather heterogeneous mixture. The major fisheries are ocean troll fisheries—both commercial and recreational, and extensive net fisheries in the Columbia River, Puget Sound, the inside waters of British Columbia and southeastern Alaska, and some of the coastal rivers of Washington. Of course there are also extensive net fisheries in the more northern part of Alaska, including the extensive Bristol Bay gill net fishery which annually catches millions of salmon.

Of the five species of salmon present (chinook, *Oncorhynchus tshawytscha;* coho, *O. kisutch;* pink, *O. gorbuscha;* chum, *O. keta;* and sockeye, *O. nerka*) only chinook, coho, and pink salmon are caught in any numbers in the ocean troll fisheries, whereas all five species are caught in the net fisheries. Furthermore, a variety of discrete salmon stocks contribute to the various fisheries in varying degrees. Their contributions to the fisheries are somewhat related to the abundance and migration patterns of the various species. For example, chinook salmon tend to migrate generally northward in the ocean after leaving their parent stream, so they contribute primarily to fisheries to the north. Coho salmon, on the other hand, may migrate both north and south from their parent streams; they generally do not migrate as great a distance as do chinook. Therefore, whatever happens to a particular stock of salmon will affect the various fisheries in different ways, depending on how important the stock is to the catch of that fishery.

Following record high natural production from most Pacific Coast salmon stocks in the early part of this century, many stocks experienced rather drastic declines in production and some were even eliminated. These declines were due in large part to industrial development, pollution, urbanization, poor logging practices, overfishing, and, in the Columbia River in particular, to large scale hydroelectric development. The significance of this hydroelectric development to the Columbia River salmon stocks can be better appreciated when it is realized that access to over 500 miles of the upper Columbia River, excluding tributaries, was completely blocked by the construction of Grand Coulee Dam in 1941. Another 52 miles of the Columbia River were lost with the completion in 1955 of Chief Joseph Dam, the farthest upstream barrier to salmon and steelhead migration in the upper Columbia. Finally, over 50 percent of the originally inhabited main stream of the Snake River, a major tributary to the upper Columbia River, is no longer accessible to these fish (1).

These serious declines in natural production can be more clearly seen by looking at the historic salmon catches from some of the major fisheries. Figure 1 shows the catch of pink and sockeye salmon in Puget Sound since 1900. These fish are, in large part, bound for the Fraser River in Canada—although some, particularly pink salmon, are bound for streams in Washington.

Catches of around 15 million sockeye annually were common in Puget Sound in the early 1900's, with a peak catch of almost 22 million fish in 1913. Catches then declined rather drastically, due to a rock slide in the Fraser River that blocked the upstream migration of salmon. This run is now controlled under an International Treaty between the United States and Canada. Production has been increasing in recent years.

Pink salmon catches in Puget Sound also reached record high levels before 1920 of around 15 million fish but, in recent years, catches have been at a lower level with much more variability between yearly catches. These fish also are now under control of the International Pacific Salmon Fisheries Commission.

For the other species of salmon caught in Puget Sound (Fig. 2), the catch of chum salmon has declined rather drastically from a high of almost 2 million caught in 1915-16, and even the peak recent catch in 1972 was less than 800,000 fish. Chinook catches have declined also from a peak of 477,000 fish in 1918 to a low of only 37,000 fish in 1947. Since then there has been a gradual increase in the catches, reaching 230,000 fish in 1975. The coho catch also declined from a peak catch of 1.64 million fish in 1918 to only 104,000 fish in 1960. Since 1960, however, the catch has been increasing rather rapidly and reached 962,000 fish in 1975. Of course, the increased catches of both chinook and coho in recent years are due in large measure to the large increase in hatchery production of these fish.

Looking now at the Columbia River catch (Fig. 3), the overall decline in chinook production is obvious—from catches of over 30 million pounds before 1920 to catches of about 5 million pounds in the last 15 years (historical catches of numbers of salmon were not available). Coho catches in the Columbia River net fishery also declined from almost 8 million

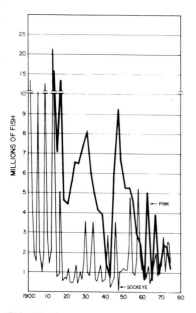

FIGURE 1. Annual catch of sockeye salmon and catch of pink salmon in odd numbered years on Puget Sound, 1900-75.

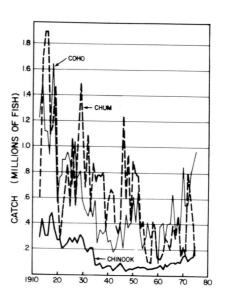

FIGURE 2. Catch of chinook, chum, and coho salmon on Puget Sound, 1913-75.

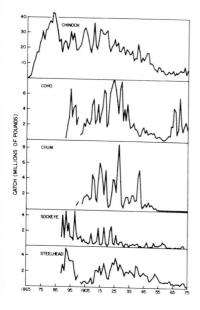

FIGURE 3. Total commercial catch of salmon and steelhead in the Columbia River, 1865-1975.

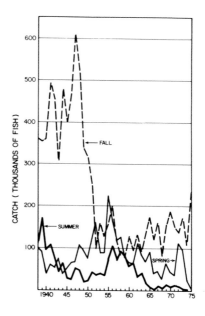

FIGURE 4. Catch of Columbia River, upriver chinook salmon by net fisheries, 1938-75.

pounds annually in the mid-1920's to around 200,000 pounds in the late 1950's. Catches have increased considerably since then, again due in large measure to increased hatchery production. Commercial catches of chum and sockeye salmon and of steelhead trout, *Salmo gairdneri*, have become almost nonexistent on the Columbia River.

The Columbia River chinook stocks are important to the fisheries, contributing over 80% of the chinook catch for the sport and commercial fisheries off the coast of Washington and contributing significantly to the British Columbia and southeast Alaska troll fisheries. The various Columbia River chinook stocks should be, therefore, examined in greater detail to provide a clearer understanding of what has been happening to them.

The chinook stocks that originate above Bonneville Dam— the lowermost dam on the Columbia River, located almost 140 miles above the mouth—are the upriver spring, summer, and fall runs (2). The catch of these stocks in the river net fishery is shown in figure 4.

From a low of only 37,400 fish caught in 1944, the catch of upriver spring chinook increased to a high of 224,000 in 1955 and then again declined to only 29,100 in 1968. The runs were good again in 1972 and 1973 with catches of 112,700 and 94,600 fish, respectively. The runs were disastrously low in 1974 and 1975 with a catch of only 25,900 in 1974 and no fishery permitted in 1975.

Of all the stocks of chinook in the Columbia River, the status of the summer run is most critical. Following a catch of 172,300 fish in 1939, the catch declined steadily to a low of only 20,100 fish in 1949. The catches increased during the 1950's but, following a catch of 103,000 fish in 1956, the landings decreased disastrously. The fishery has been closed since 1964 with only incidental catches being made since that time. No summer chinook were caught in the river in 1974 and 1975.

Fall chinook salmon are the dominant stock in the Columbia River and were even more so during the 1940's. They provide an estimated 70-75% of the troll catch of chinook salmon off the coast of Washington. Following some catches of over 400,000 upper river fall chinook annually during the 1940's and a peak catch of 609,000 fish in 1947, the catch of upper river fall chinook declined sharply. In 1959, it reached a low of only 82,000 fish. Since then the catch appears to be increasing, although there are some rather large annual fluctuations.

Finally, turning to the troll fishery (Fig. 5), here also we see increasing catches of both chinook and coho salmon in recent years, particularly coho, following a period of low production during the early 1960's. This again reflects the significant impact of increased hatchery output for these two species. Fortunately, this increased production in recent years has generally been accompanied by increasing prices for fish. Troll catches of pink salmon have averaged around 1 million fish in recent years. The

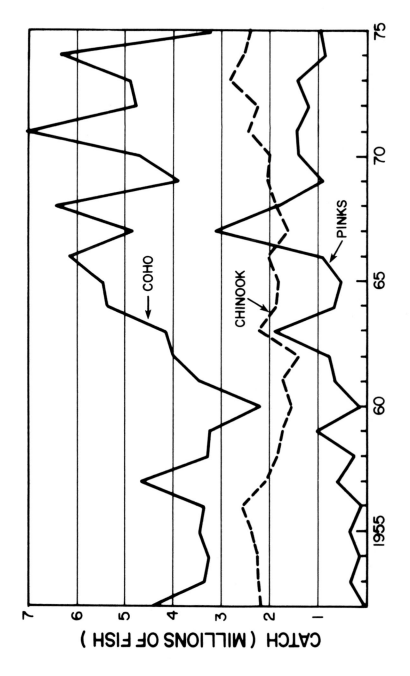

FIGURE 5. Total Pacific Coast troll fishery catch of chinook, coho, and pink salmon, 1952-75.

salmon catches in the ocean sport fishery have been generally increasing in a manner similar to that for the commercial troll fishery.

In summary, many of the natural stocks of Pacific salmon, not only from Puget Sound and the Columbia River, but also from the coastal rivers of Washington, Oregon, and California, are in a depressed condition, both from environmental degradation as well as from very extensive fisheries. Hatchery production, however, has had a significant impact on some stocks—particularly for chinook and coho—and has actually reversed the trend of declining production. Unfortunately, hatchery fish are now such a major proportion of the total production (artificial production amounts to over 50% of all salmon returning to the Columbia River system) that this creates serious problems in the management of the resource. The difficulty arises in trying to harvest hatchery fish (which have a relatively high survival level) that are intermingled with natural stocks that require greater protection. Natural runs will be overfished if the hatchery fish are harvested adequately, whereas hatchery fish will be underutilized if the natural runs are adequately protected. This problem is particularly acute in the troll fishery where the natural and hatchery fish are completely intermingled.

The current balance in the fishery between natural and hatchery stocks of salmon is expected to change even more drastically in the near future, magnifying the management problem mentioned above, in light of all the proposals for increased artificial propagation of salmon. Alaska, which expects natural production to average 13.7 million salmon annually for southeastern Alaska on a short term basis (46.4 million fish statewide) plans to ultimately increase this to 24.4 million salmon naturally produced and 14.7 million supplementally produced, on an annual average (3).

British Columbia has announced a 9 million dollar enhancement program for this year; the State of Washington has announced plans for a 33 million dollar enhancement program, with a major emphasis on chum salmon. Moreover, the International Pacific Salmon Fisheries Commission has had a 14 million dollar enhancement program for Fraser River pink and sockeye salmon proposed for a number of years.

Superimposed on the problem of declining natural production and increased artificial production, with associated management problems and adverse effects on natural stocks, the recent Federal Court ruling (Judge Boldt Decision) permitting certain Treaty Indian tribes the opportunity to catch 50 percent of the salmon returning to their usual and accustomed fishing areas, further complicates the salmon fishery. In 1977, the commercial troll fishery north of Tillamook Head, Oregon (about 30 miles south of the Columbia River), was placed under rather severe new fishing restrictions by the Pacific Fishery Management Council, under the new 200 mile extended fisheries jurisdiction legislation. These restrictions were intended not only to give increased protection to depressed Columbia River chinook stocks, but also to provide more fish to Treaty Indians. Likewise, Puget Sound and Columbia River non-Indian net fishermen have been increasingly restricted in recent years, to provide more fish to the Treaty Indians. Consequently, it appears that this Indian versus non-Indian fishing controversy will stimulate even more effort to provide funds for large scale salmon enhancement in order to ease the economic impact of the court ruling on the non-Indian fisherman.

In light of all these difficulties and the declining natural salmon production, it is apparent that significant increased artificial production of salmon on the Pacific Coast is not only needed but is almost essential. Increased artificial production is particularly needed if the Indian fishing problem is to be resolved without even more serious economic impact on the non-Indian fisherman.

References

1. Status Report, Columbia River Fish Runs and Fisheries, 1957-75, Vol. 2, No. 1. June 1976, 76 p. (Unpubl. Rep.).
2. Season mentioned indicates time of migration of fish into the river.
3. Alaska Salmon Fisheries Plan 157 pp. (Processed).

Pacific Salmon Mariculture—Industry View

Jon M. Lindbergh

Domsea Farms, Inc.
6720 Old Belfair Highway
Bremerton, Washington

The question is frequently asked, "Why did Domsea Farms pick Pacific salmon as a fish for mariculture?""Salmon" is an old and esteemed name, the flesh is good to the palate, and people are willing to pay a handsome price. Rearing salmon fry and fingerling is a well developed technology of many decades' standing, but the fish were formerly released at a small size by public agencies to migrate and forage at sea. Little attempt was made to cultivate them in captivity to a marketable size.

The National Marine Fisheries Service (NMFS) acquired migratory coho salmon, *Oncorhynchus kisutch*, in 1969 and placed them in floating net pens in Clam Bay near Manchester, Washington (Fig. 1), to find out how well the salmon would survive and grow under captive conditions in

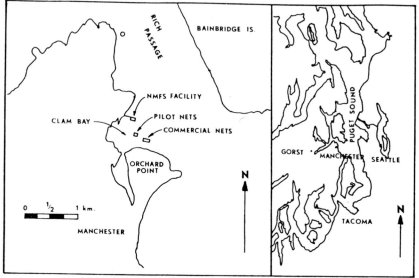

FIGURE 1. Location of NMFS, pilot, and commercial facilities.

salt water (1). Some of us at Domsea Farms had the opportunity to follow the experiment. We concluded that the results were promising enough that if the project could be scaled up from a few hundred fish to a million or more, a viable business might be possible.

In the Fall of 1970, Domsea worked with NMFS to establish a joint industry-government Pilot Program (2). The Pilot Program was subsequently awarded a grant of $100,000 from the Sea Grant Office of the U.S. Department of Commerce. A small hatchery was constructed, and coho salmon eggs were procured from the State of Washington.

In spite of various problems, the coho grew from 15 grams in July to a marketable size of approximately 300 grams by the following January. Density in the most crowded net reached more than 20 kg per cubic meter. A harvest weight of about 300 grams was selected. The basic objective of cultivating large numbers of Pacific salmon in high concentrations in floating net pens was achieved. Growth, survival and conversion rates of feed to flesh were good. Acceptance in the market place was quite good, the only complaint being that the reddish flesh color was not as pronounced as the color in large, wild salmon.

First Approach To A Commercial Program

In the late Summer of 1971, Domsea faced the decision to proceed with a full-scale production program beginning with Fall 1971 brood eggs. Analysis of data from the Pilot Program was incomplete, but to wait would mean a full year's delay, as salmon eggs are available only once a year. We elected to proceed(3).

Engineering the net complex—In an attempt to gain economy of size, the first generation of commercial grower nets were 20 m square, 10 m deep, and had a theoretical capacity of 250,000 salmon weighing 250 grams apiece, double that of the Pilot Program nets. Net strength was reinforced by adding more and stronger criss-crossing rib lines. Each pair of grower nets was enclosed by a predator net 45 m long, 23 m wide and 11.5 m deep. Both nets were treated with a thick protective coating, and the predator net was weighted along the foot line with 30 kg weights. The top perimeter of both nets was supported by a continuous chain of polystyrene billets.

One set of nets within a confining grid of cables was secured to each side of a central walkway. The walkway and grids were moored with wire cables terminating in 1360 kg danforth-type anchors. The entire complex was maintained in tension by 200 kg weights secured partway down the mooring cables. We fabricated two such net complexes and later added two nets to each complex for a total of twelve nets (Fig. 2).

The first net complex was installed in 1972. Tidal currents with water velocities up to 1.5 m per second dragged and twisted the vast expanse of netting. Tears appeared, usually at the intersections of rib lines or where weights were attached. The rib lines loosened several times and whole panels of netting tore free, releasing the fish into Puget Sound. Floating debris damaged the top sections of mesh. We replaced the large predator nets with stronger, individual nets enclosing only one grower net apiece. For the next year these nets, reduced in size and greatly reinforced in strength, held together.

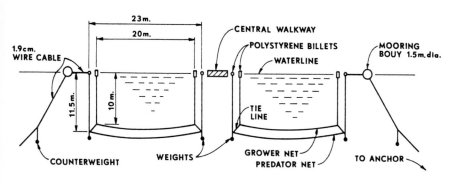

FIGURE 2. Elevation view of first commercial floating net complex.

Captive brood stock—The largest and fastest growing specimens from the Pilot crop were selected for brood stock. They were held in a separate net and fed dry pellets with the carotenoid pigment canthaxanthin added. Maturation occurred at two years of age and an average weight of 2.7 kg, about half the weight of their wild parents at 3 to 4 years of age. The average number of eggs per female coho was about equal to that of wild females, but were smaller in size and had less carotenoid pigments. Fertility was about 60%, as compared to 70% in a parallel group of wild eggs. The resulting progeny were smaller than wild fish and early fry losses were higher. After reaching a weight of one gram, however, they grew about 10% faster than fry from wild parents.

The first significant harvest of coho began in November 1973. A total of 655,000 fish, with a total round weight of 213,000 kg, were harvested. As each net was emptied, we invariably found that there were fewer fish than estimated in our inventory.

Problems with the new complexes—Engineering failures in the modified net complexes began to appear in late 1973. Mooring systems were not sufficiently stable, and the whole complex continuously racked and skewed in the current. Accumulated stress resulted in tears in nets and increasing mechanical damage to the walkways and moorings.

Biological fouling, particularly the mussel, *Mytilus edulis,* became heavy. Various schemes to remove fouling were only marginally successful, and the weight of fouling organisms and resulting increase in current drag on the nets steadily mounted. In June 1974, an extra strong Spring tide caused the mooring cables to part, causing almost complete destruction of both complexes. All remaining fish escaped or were killed in collapsing nets.

A Redesigned Net Complex

Engineering—Previous reasoning had been that economy lay in size and that small nets, although more workable, would be too costly. Experience began to indicate that the reverse might be true. A large part of the cost of large nets lay in the labor of sewing in rib lines. Almost all of our net failures, though, happened at stress points near the interface of netting and lines.

We have designed a simple net with dimensions of approximately 15 m long, 6 m wide, and 5 m deep. It is made of 57 kg nylon twine with approximately 2 cm stretch mesh. All seams are stitched, and there are no head, foot, or rib lines. Weights are suspended on the inside. Cost is about one-third of a similar sized net reinforced with rib lines.

Nets are installed within a lattice work of perimeter walkways secured on each side of a 4 m wide center walkway (Fig. 3). All walkways are tied together with cables and held in tension by moorings. Moorings are comprised of a 3.8 cm chain terminating in 1360 kg danforth-type anchors. The articulated system undulates on the water surface as waves pass through the complex. Each net well is bordered by a wooden railing with pegs on the top which hold up the net, weights, and a tightly stretched bird predator net.

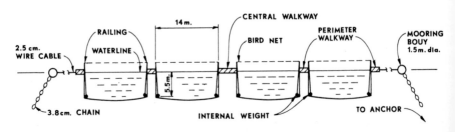

FIGURE 3. Elevation view of second commercial floating net complex.

Performance of the redesigned system—The new nets are easy to install and remove by two persons with no requirement for diver assistance. Fish mortalities are picked by an attendant on the perimeter walkway with a long-handled dip net. Fish are harvested by lifting one end of the net to confine the fish to a pocket whence they are pumped out. Marine fouling is reasonably easily controlled by lifting the net, or one end of it, out of the water and cleaning off the fouling organisms. The greatly increased strength and stability of the new system plus the reduced drag of shallower nets has resulted in reduced stresses and few failures. Capital costs are about the same as the previous system in terms of fish produced, but labor costs are reduced to about half.

Disease control—Dr. John Fryer of Oregon State University was the first to show success in immunizing salmon against Vibrio by using a killed Vibrio bacterin in their feed (4). Anthony Novotny of NMFS had subsequently experimented with injecting salmon with Vibrio bacterins before introducing them to salt water. Working with both Fryer and Novotny, Domsea developed a program to immunize grown salmon against *Vibrio* commercially. Results with injected bacterins have been very successful, with reduction in *Vibrio* related mortality of less than 10%. Costs to vaccinate are about $0.01 per fish, but the logistics of injecting hundreds of thousands of fish, with the inevitable stress, is of significant concern. The use of oral bacterin costs about the same, but is logistically simpler and involves far less stress to the fish. However, Domsea's results with orally immunized fish have not shown consistent protection. More recently experiments have been conducted with two new methods of administering *Vibrio* bacterins: immersion in a highly saline solution followed by immersion in a bacterin solution, and a high-pressure spray technique. Preliminary results show that both systems provide definite protection, but still are not as effective as injection.

Present Status

Commercial mariculture of Pacific salmon is now an ongoing business which provides an annual harvest in excess of 250,000 kg. Most of the major problems have been controlled, but there are still areas in the field of Pacific salmon mariculture where improvement would greatly increase its economic well-being.

Species in agriculture have been selected for thousands of years for efficiency in terms of man's needs. Salmon mariculture is very new and salmon farmers still rear most of their stock from eggs taken from wild parents. Those parents have been selected by nature for survival at sea. Their offspring are not necessarily adapted to high density culture in salt water net pens and do not attain optimum growth, survival and feed conversion of a domesticated, totally cultured strain.

A start has been made towards the development of domesticated strains of Pacific salmon. The fastest growing and best looking fish are generally segregated out for this purpose. So far, this rather crude approach has worked quite well. Very roughly, each succeeding generation (Domsea is now culturing on F2 generation) has grown about 10% faster than their parent's year class. However, visual selection can be expected to introduce difficulties. When will the in-breeding begin to adversely affect the strain? In selecting the largest fish, are we perhaps selecting for aggressiveness rather than efficiency? How much potential efficiency are we losing by a lack of a scientific approach to genetics?

A number of nutritionally-related problems also need to be solved for rearing brood Pacific salmon. Net pen reared brood fish do not become as large as wild mature salmon. Their eggs have not become as large as wild eggs, and the resultant fry are smaller and frailer. The use of canthaxanthin and other carotenoid pigments in brood diets has greatly improved egg color and also survival. It is believed by some researchers that pigmentation may also be important in the maturation process. Domesticated coho brood fish mature and ripen more than a month later than their parent strains. The delay causes difficulty when one attempts to rear fingerlings which will smolt in their first summer. This delay in maturation, especially in the females, is almost certainly related to nutritional deficiencies, and continued research is greatly needed.

Growout feed—Feed is the largest production cost in salmon mariculture. With present feed costs and at typical conversion rates, feed is about 50% of the total cost. Obviously, small changes in the price of feed and in the efficiency of food conversion will have large effects on the profitability and competitiveness of the product. Salmon feeds rely on animal proteins, grains, and soybean products as major components and fluctuations in the commodity markets in these items can, and do, cause serious dislocations. The rise in the price of fish meal after the recent Peruvian anchovy failure is an example. Furthermore, the use of animal and grain protein for aquaculture competes with agricultural programs and increasingly will compete with direct human consumption. The development of feeds which are nutritious but use components which are relatively inexpensive and do not compete with direct human consumption will be very important in the future.

With market-size fish the diets are adequate, but almost certainly not equal to wild diets. The fine points of salmon nutrition are subtle and will take dedicated and ingenious people working for an extended period of time. We hope that governmental and private groups will continue and expand work in this vital area.

Disease problem—The economics of salmon mariculture generally requires that the fish be reared under relatively high density, and high density encourages the transmission of disease. One important approach to disease control lies in the selection of strains genetically resistant to disease organisms. A comprehensive disease control program, however, must also have methods of immunization to forestall infection and methods of treating infection when it occurs. The development of efficacious vaccines and bacterins by government and industry is proceeding expeditiously.

Unfortunately, the licensing of drugs and medications for use in aquaculture is not so promising. Drugs and medications come under the jurisdiction of the Food and Drug Administration and must pass rigid and highly specific certification requirements. A medication must not only be cleared as safe in general, but must be separately certified as safe and effective for use with each species and for each disease in that species. Certification is very expensive and time consuming. Cost for each specific certification can now be expected to be in the range of $250,000, far too much for aquaculturists to afford at the present stage of development. Manufacturers of drugs and medications for aquaculture are reluctant to initiate costly certification procedures when the immediate market is quite small. Conversely, the market is constrained from growing by the lack of an adequate battery of effective and certified drugs and medications.

At the present time, there are only a few drugs and medications which have been certified by the FDA (and in some cases, the Environmental Protection Agency) for commercial use in aquaculture. There are others which have been used extensively in the past, but have not been certified. Many of these continue to be utilized in a quasi-legal status. Furthermore, some agents which have been certified may now require re-certification in the near future. Existing salmon mariculturists and potential investors are seriously concerned about the situation for several reasons: (i) They feel vulnerable to a disease pathogen which develops resistance to one of the few certified medications. (ii) They feel uncomfortable with a situation where both governmental and private groups routinely use materials which are not properly certified for aquaculture use. However, they are also concerned about the stock losses to be expected if regulatory agencies enforce strict certification, which now appears probable (iii). They are apprehensive that even those few certified materials will be decertified, leaving growers completely vulnerable to the known effects of existing diseases.

Salmon mariculturists and other aquaculturists recognize the potential dangers of uncontrolled use of drugs and medications. They are not asking to be exempted from all controls. However, drugs and medication are a vital part of disease control in all animal husbandry, and disease control is vital to the survival of salmon mariculture. Salmon mariculturists do ask that in cases where there is no threatened danger to human health, regulatory agencies do not take abrupt and arbitrary actions. They ask that the agencies work with the aquaculture industry to phase in policies and actions in such a way as to avoid catastrophic dislocations.

Health certification of eggs, live fish, and harvested product— Salmon mariculturists must transport their harvested fish to market and often need to ship live salmon eggs and fingerlings. If the shipment crosses state or international boundaries, health certification is almost always a legal requirement. At the present time, it is often very difficult to locate an available certification agency. For example, in the Pacific Northwest there is no private certifying body, and governmental agencies consider certification for private activities something beyond their normal duties. Northwest salmon growers have been able to carry out necessary shipment only because various government agencies took time out from their own schedules to oblige unofficial requests. We feel that the federal government should take over health certification of fish and fish products. Few private companies appear to wish to engage in the business of fish health certification. Furthermore, federal standards would be uniform and would be uniformly respected. This would be particularly true with international shipments, where a health certificate with a private letterhead is often questioned.

Institutional problems— A diverse list of regulations, restrictions, and permit requirements often act as strong deterrents to new aquaculture ventures. New industries should have some control and overall management to assure that they develop in an orderly manner compatible to society in general. The control of aquaculture, however, tends to be fragmented and disorganized. Dozens of regulatory bodies are involved from the local to the federal level. They often do not coordinate with each other, and at times their demands conflict. It is costly to meet and remain in compliance with the requirements of such a multiplicity of regulatory bodies. It may take months, often years, of costly effort to obtain the permits necessary to initiate aquacultural production.

Summary

Pacific salmon mariculture, like most of aquaculture, is relatively new. The industry is in commercial production and has great promise, but it does still have teething problems. We expect and accept higher costs and frustrations during the learning period. We strongly desire, however, that governmental bodies and the public would recognize aquaculture as a growing industry with the potential of a significant contribution to society.

Presently it is considered an orphan worthy of kindly lip service, but otherwise a nuisance. Hopefully, legislation being developed in Congress will help bring about better understanding of and a more adequate level of governmental support for the aquaculturists, and public agencies supporting their activities.

References

1. Mahnken, C.V.W., Novotny, A.J. and Joyner, T. (1970). Salmon Mariculture Potential Assessed. *American Fish Farmer World Aquaculture News* **2**,12.
2. Lindbergh, J.M. (1972). Pacific Salmon Aquaculture Program. Sea Grant Final Report, Ocean Systems, Inc. Domsea Farms, Inc., Reston, VA, pp.52.; App. A-C (processed).
3. Lindbergh, J.M. (1976). The Development of a Commercial Pacific Salmon Culture Business. FAO Technical Conference on Aquaculture, Kyoto, Japan.
4. Novotny, A.J.(in press).Epizootics of Vibriosis and Furunculosis in Marine Cultured Salmonids. Symposium on Health, Disease, and Disease Prevention in Fish. Veterinary Practice Publishing Company.
5. Fryer, J.L., Nelson, J.S. and Garrison, R.L. (1972). Vibriosis in Fish. *Progress in Fishery and Food Science* (University of Washington) **5**, 129.

Current Status Of Ocean Ranching Of Salmon

Brian J. Allee
Aquaculture Research
Weyerhaeuser Company
Tacoma, Washington

The use of salmon hatcheries to produce juvenile salmon which mature in the ocean is a traditional method of salmon enhancement. These publicly funded programs contribute adult fish to the commercial and sports fisheries.

Ocean ranching is the term more recently applied to privately operated hatcheries which contribute fish to the commercial and sport fisheries and eventually capture fish in land-based facilities. The land-based facilities are within or in close proximity to saltwater so as to maintain a high quality salmon.

Ocean ranching is the application of i) publicly developed technology relative to fish culture, and ii) the unique "homing" behavior of salmon which causes them to return as adults to the point of release as juveniles. This behavior is a result of natural selection and therefore genetically preprogrammed.

Since the concept, whether public or private, shares a common ocean environment, it is truly an international resource consideration. In this connection, massive pink and chum salmon hatchery programs from Japan and Russia are four times the size of all hatchery programs combined on the North American continent (1).

In an effort to ameliorate declining salmon runs, large scale publicly funded enhancement programs are planned for Washington (200 million dollars), Alaska (250 million dollars) and British Columbia (300 million dollars).

In addition, the states of Alaska, Oregon, and California have adopted legislation legalizing private ocean ranching. The State of Washington has no legislation currently, but several Indian tribes are actively pursuing programs.

Alaska

The Alaskan non-profit hatchery program involves 7 organizations which have been given permits by the Alaskan Department of Fish and Game, plus the Annette Island Indian Reserve. Three of these organizations are regional associations of commercial fishermen with a fourth one proposed. One permit holder is the Sheldon Jackson Community College in Sitka.

The magnitude of this program varies from a design capacity of 2 million pink fry for the Douglas Island group to a plan to create capacity for 300 million pink or chum eggs at the Prince William Sound Association (2).

The potential success of these programs is evidenced by the adult returns this year from two operations.

The Sheldon Jackson College program has received, to date, approximately 80,000 adult pink salmon of which 65,000 are being harvested and sold. This represents a 5% return. (McNeil personal communication).

The Prince William Sound Association has received, to date, 50,000 adult pink salmon and the returns are not yet complete (McNeil personal communication).

Washington

There is currently no legislation allowing private ocean ranching in Washington State. A number of Indian tribes which are not under state jurisdiction are actively involved, however. Two of these tribes, the Lummi in the Northern Puget Sound and the Quinault on the coast of Washington have the most advanced programs.

The Lummi program began in 1971 and has accumulated since that time roughly 12 million released salmon. Coho salmon represent half the releases, with chum as the next in the bulk, followed by chinook salmon. A smaller number of steelhead trout are also released. The annual capacity of their hatchery is 3-10 million smolts.

The Quinault tribe began its program in 1970 and has an unusually diverse salmon program with sockeye, chinook, coho, chum salmon, and steelhead trout. The facilities available to this tribe include a federal hatchery and three tribal hatcheries, one of which employes a floating nylon net concept. The tribe's accumulated releases to date exceed 12 million smolts. The design capacity of its combined hatchery could eventually double this number.

Oregon

The ocean ranching legislation in Oregon has adopted the private-profit institutional arrangement. The first legislation in 1971 allowed for the propagation of chum salmon. Subsequent legislation in 1973 permitted the same for coho and chinook salmon (3).

The Oregon legislation has produced an active industry composed of 11 chum salmon permitees, 4 coho salmon permitees, and 4 chinook salmon permitees. These operations vary from low capital gravel box incubator facilities in freshwater for chum salmon only, to large capital facilities in both freshwater and saltwater for all three species.

As an example of the potential magnitude of the program in Oregon, both Oregon Aqua Foods, (Weyerhaeuser subsidiary) and Domsea (Union Carbide subsidiary), are planning releases of coho, chinook, and chum totaling 180 million smolts. The Weyerhaeuser program alone represents an investment of 10 million dollars in Oregon State. Moreover, as an example of the expansion of public technology in an industrial application, this ocean ranching business is composed of a freshwater hatchery and two saltwater release-recapture facilities. The former will temper river water with non-process cooling water from a pulp mill and disinfect this water to achieve a"disease free" hatchery. The latter facility will pump saltwater to attract adult salmon into the fish ladder in the Fall and create a rearing pond for post smolt salmon during a period of osmotic acclimation to saltwater in the Spring. Salmon smolts will be vaccinated in the Freshwater hatchery and transported by truck to the Oregon coastal saltwater release site.

It is premature to evaluate the success of the Oregon ocean ranchers to date because of the following reasons:

(i)   Adult salmon have not yet completed maturation in the ocean;

(ii) availability of egg supply is critically short which limits the number of smolts perhaps below the critical threshold to survive the ocean mortality; and

(iii) because of ii, transplanted stocks must be used and the biological risk is higher.

Some indication of success from ocean ranching programs comes from marked fish contributing to the sport and commercial fisheries. Table I summarizes tagged coho and chinook salmon caught in the sport and commercial fisheries off the Oregon coast as of September 1, 1977. (Oregon Department of Fish and Wildlife). These data suggest that 4.6% of the total tagged coho salmon caught and 0.3% of the total chinook salmon originated from salmon released from the Oregon Aqua Foods facilities. This comparison, without supporting data on release number, average size, time of release, is, of course, only suggestive of a relative contribution to the Oregon fishery.

Table I[1]

Combined Sport and Commercial Catch of Coho and Chinook Salmon from the Oregon Coast

AGENCY	COHO	CHINOOK	TOTAL
California	3	119	122
Oregon Department of Fish and Wildlife	142	419	561
Oregon Aqua Foods	62	2	64
United States Fish and Wildlife Service	442	193	635
Washington Departments of Fisheries	664	30	694
University of Washington	14	5	19
Canada	14	0	14
TOTALS	1341	768	2109

[1] Oregon Department of Fish and Wildlife unpublished report, as of September 1, 1977

California

Under California law, only one company, Silver King, has been granted an ocean ranching permit. This permit is experimental in nature, allowing the release of coho, chinook salmon, and steelhead trout until 1981. 800,000 coho smolts have been released to date and the first return of coho "jacks" is expected during the Fall of 1977.

Summary

The success of private ocean ranching will be measured, in the short run, as a function of egg availability from approved state salmon stocks.

Specifically adapted brood stock are critical in order for private ocean ranchers to be self sufficient.

The technology which will ignite the ocean ranching industry into a successful enterprise, in the near term, has been developed in the public sector exclusively, so that technology is not a limiting factor at this time.

Private ocean ranching represents a significant new contribution to the salmon industry by producing fish to enhance the established fishery together with public programs and providing salmon to the consumer.

References

1. McNeil, W.J. (1976). Artifical Recruitment of Pink and Chum Salmon in Japan and Eastern USSR. Northwest and Alaska Fisheries Center Processed Report.
2. Orth, F.L. (1977). The Economic Feasibility of Private Non Profit Ocean Ranching Ventures. University of Alaska—Sea Grant Programs.
3. Cummings, T. Edward and Korn, Lawrence. (1975). Status of Private Salmon Hatcheries in Oregon, 1973-74. Coastal Rivers information Report 75-1, Management and Research Division, Fish Commission of Oregon.

SECTION V

Diversified Aquaculture

The Polyculture Alternative In Aquatic Food Production

Robert R. Stickney
Department of Wildlife and Fisheries Sciences
Texas A&M University
College Station, Texas

Traditionally, United States aquaculture with respect to human food production has involved the stocking of a single species within individual ponds, cages, tanks or raceways. Largely overlooked by monoculturists is the fact that the pond environment is a three-dimensional space which incorporates several habitats, while the species produced are often rather restricted in terms of habitat preference. Thus, much of the space available in a pond may be left empty when only one species is stocked. Polyculture, the stocking of two or more species in combination, is normally undertaken with the intent of filling as many of the available niches as possible with non-competitive species. When properly conducted, polyculture can result in significant increases in total production as compared with monoculture.

Freshwater fish culture probably began in China, with the earliest records dating back to about 11,000 B.C. (1), and it is in China and other parts of Asia that polyculture is best developed and most widely practiced. Other regions of the world which are turning to polyculture include parts of Europe, Africa, the Middle East, and the Americas (2). Polyculture is currently being practiced by both freshwater aquaculturists and mariculturists.

The typical aquaculture pond ranges from about 1 to 2 m in depth, with sides having a slope of 2:1 or 3:1. The relative percentage of pond bottom covered by shallow water will vary as a function of total pond area, with the range of surface area commonly between 0.1 to 10 hectares (ha). A pond has three relatively distinct environments associated with it: (i) a pelagic zone which includes all the water except that overlying the pond banks, (ii) the water above the banks of the pond, and (iii) the pond bottom (Fig. 1). In general, the natural production in the pelagic zone is characterized by phytoplankton and zooplankton, though these organisms also occur in the shallow water over the pond banks. If rooted aquatic macrophytes are found, they will predominate in the shallow water. The bottom is characterized by a variety of benthic animals including, but not limited to, polychaetes, oligochaetes, mollusks and crustaceans. Aquatic insects often dominate the benthos of freshwater ponds. Various species of benthic algae may also occur in conjunction with the bottom. Exceptions to this general pattern can be found, but in most instances the habitats and natural inhabitants described are typical.

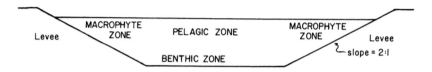

FIGURE 1. Cross-section of culture pond showing habitat locations.

The polyculturist can take advantage of all available water volume through proper species selection. For example, in China, polyculturists often stock four types of fish (2). Grass carp (*Ctenopharyngodon idella*) may be utilized to feed on the rooted aquatic vegetation of the shallow water, while silver carp (*Hypophthalmichthys molitrix*) and big head carp (*Aristichthys nobilis*) inhabit the pelagic zone and feed on phytoplankton and zooplankton, respectively. The omnivorous common carp (*Cyprinus carpio*) may be selected to feed on the benthic community. Similar techniques are utilized in India with the major carps, although the food habits of Indian carps are not as distinct as those of the Chinese species.

United States aquaculture, unlike subsistence culture in many parts of the world, depends upon the production of high quality, even gourmet food. Thus, fishes such as the carps, which are widely accepted in other parts of the world, cannot be economically produced in this country. Trout and catfish presently dominate United States aquaculture. Trout culturists rarely practice polyculture, and to date, most of the polyculture practiced by catfish farmers has involved one or more species of buffalo fish (*Ictiobus* spp.). Few other native fresh-water fishes, or invertebrates in the United States appear to be suited to the type of polyculture scheme which is practiced in Asia.

Polyculture in the marine environment appears to hold a certain amount of potential. However, at present, mariculture is not well developed in the United States. Those persons who engage in marine aquaculture are generally not ready to attempt polyculture until satisfactory monoculture techniques are perfected. In the future, however, such combinations as shrimp (*Penaeus* spp.) with oysters, *Crassostrea virginica*, and a non-carnivorous fish like the striped mullet (*Mugil cephalus*) may be found in marine polyculture systems. The filter feeding oysters could be hung on strings from rafts. The shrimp would browse on the sediments, while the mullet would consume *Aufwuchs* and plankton.

Some dislocation of marine fishes to freshwater and freshwater fishes to estuarine aquaculture sites is possible. For example, mullet, red drum (*Sciaenops ocellata*) and flounder (*Paralichthys* spp.) all adapt well to fresh-water. Of these, only the mullet is a non-piscivore; so the potential for utilizing the others in polyculture is somewhat limited. Many species of freshwater fishes can survive, grow and even reproduce in low salinity water. Perry and Avault (3,4) demonstrated that channel catfish, as well as blue catfish (*Ictalurus furcatus*) and white catfish (*I. catus*) can survive in salinities ranging from 2 to 11 parts per thousand. The same authors (5) conducted a polyculture experiment in brackish water and determined that of the three species the channel catfish demonstrated the best growth, survival, food conversion and condition. In another experiment (6), bigmouth buffalo (*Ictiobus cyprinellus*), black buffalo (*I. niger*) and the hybrid of the two buffalo species were stocked at a density of 250/ha, with channel catfish at 4,000 to 5,000/ha and fed an artificial diet. These authors reported no competition for feed between the catfish and the buffalo fish, and found that catfish production was not decreased from that of fish in ponds without the buffalo. In the polyculture ponds about 340 kg/ha of buffalo was produced.

In other polyculture experiments, Williamson and Smitherman (7) reported that hybrid buffalo, tilapia (*Tilapia aurea*), the Israeli strain of the common carp and channel catfish all competed for the artificial diet and that the yield of channel catfish was significantly reduced by the presence of the other species. More recent experiments with these fishes have led to more encouraging results (R. O. Smitherman, personal communication), and while some competition may occur, the additional production obtained will often compensate for this problem.

Various investigators have attempted to raise rainbow trout (*Salmo gairdneri*) and other species of salmonids in the southern United States during the winter. Reagan and Robinette (8) stocked rainbow trout in catfish ponds and demonstrated that both species grew significantly when fed each day at 3% of the body weight of the trout. Trout stocked without catfish grew somewhat larger (because of lack of competition for food).

Exotic Species in United States Polyculture

United States aquaculturists have begun to turn increasingly toward exotic species to augment channel catfish in warmwater polyculture. Grass carp was introduced into the United States several years ago, primarily for aquatic vegetation control. However, it appears to hold some potential for aquaculture. Many consumers appear to accept grass carp when they would avoid the consumption of common carp. Because of fears that the grass carp might reproduce in nature and compete to the disadvantage of native species, destroy marshlands by consuming the vegetation which presently is valuable wildlife habitat, and for a variety of other reasons, these fish have been outlawed in over 30 states. At present, Arkansas appears to be the only state actively promoting grass carp culture, for either food or aquatic vegetation control.

Various species of tilapia have been introduced to the United States, and have since been widely distributed. Although touted for their potential role in aquatic vegetation control, many species of tilapia prefer phytoplankton or filamentous algae to macrophytic vegetation. Thus, *Tilapia* represent a genus which has attributes that no native aquaculture species can claim; it is an almost exclusive herbivore. Drawbacks to tilapia culture include their intolerance to cold temperature (most species will die when the water gets below 10 to 12° C), and the problem of overpopulation and stunting if reproduction is not controlled (9). In much of the southern United States the growing season is sufficiently long to rear tilapia from egg to market before cold weather limits growth, and a small population overwintered indoors will supply adequate stock for the following year. Significant tilapia growth can also be obtained by summer polyculture in the northern states (10). The overpopulation problem can be controlled through the stocking of monosex (usually all-male) populations.

Tilapia have been successfully reared with channel catfish in the southern United States, and producers indicate that a good market exists for both species. Tilapia will consume artificial feeds (7, 11, 12), so some competition will occur for food even if a good phytoplankton bloom is maintained in the culture pond. Smith (12) reported that after reaching sufficient size, channel catfish will prey on juvenile *Tilapia aurea*, and will remove up to 80% of the young tilapia. Thus, the artificial feed lost to tilapia can be offset, in part, by predation on the part of the catfish. Since most aquaculturists attempt to avoid tilapia reproduction, it may be necessary to feed the catfish at a higher rate to compensate for artificial diet consumption by tilapia. It appears as though the price of tilapia will compare favorably with that of channel catfish; so no exceptional financial loss will be incurred through provision of a higher than normal feeding rate, and total production may greatly exceed the biomass which could be produced in the same pond through monoculture.

Silver carp, big-head carp and other species have been brought into the United States and are presently being studied on an experimental basis. The spread of exotic fishes in the United States is generally being discouraged at the present time, so the future of such organisms in aquaculture remains somewhat doubtful. Careful study of their potential impact on natural aquatic communities must be made before they are promoted for general use in fish culture or as recreational species. In general, it is better to attempt the utilization of native species in polyculture when suitable organisms are available than to bring in the exotics. One advantage of tilapia is that if they are released, they will be unable to survive the winter, except in the southernmost parts of the United States and in the heated water of power plant cooling reservoirs.

Other Polyculture Schemes

Thus far the discussion of polyculture has centered on the stocking of two or more species of aquatic animals within a pond, but other alternatives exist. For example, plants (aquatic or terrestrial) may be a final product of polyculture, or terrestrial animals may be involved in a polyculture system as both a source of nutrients and an additional crop. The use of livestock in conjunction with fish rearing has been practiced for generations in Asia, but has only recently aroused the interest of aquaculturists in the rest of the world. Cattle wastes have been used in Israel to produce fish (13) and studies on the rearing of *T. aurea* in ponds receiving swine and poultry wastes have been initiated in the United States (14). Such systems may produce vast amounts of phytoplankton, duckweed or other types of plant material, but also encourage the production of large concentrations of aquatic insects and zooplankton. Tilapia are able to tolerate the very poor water quality which often occurs in a pond receiving large quantities of raw manure, while many other species will not survive under the same conditions. One alternative is to stock the herbivorous tilapia into a pond receiving concentrated waste or in a secondary pond, and flow water into additional ponds containing channel catfish or some other species which will consume the secondary production (Fig. 2). Supplemental feeding may be unnecessary. Further research on such systems is required to determine the proper loading rates of livestock waste and the proper stocking densities of the various fishes which might be placed in the system. Even more complex systems can and have been developed. The best marine example is the system at the Woods Hole Oceanographic Institution which employs the effluent from a sewage plant as the nutrient source for the rearing of algae and a variety of marine animals (15). Many of the aesthetic and public health objections to such systems can be overcome if the organic wastes are not directly available to the aquaculture animals, but can only provide nutrients to algae which are then incorporated into animal diets.

The energy crisis is forcing aquaculturists to turn away from intensive running water systems (closed recirculating systems, flow-through

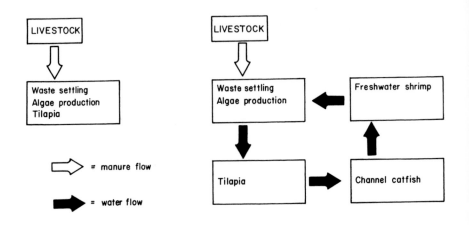

FIGURE 2. Polyculture systems employing terrestrial livestock as a primary nutrient source.

raceways and semi-closed systems) and back to the more traditional extensive pond culture techniques. Pond culture still requires significant investments in land and energy, especially in the form of water pumping. In order to maximize production and efficiency, it is vital that all of the available space in each pond be utilized. Polyculture holds excellent promise with respect to meeting this goal.

Management of Polyculture Systems

Certain management problems may arise as a result of polyculture. For example, the roles of disease transmission and treatment may have to be re-examined relative to each new polyculture combination that is attempted. Further, each species within a polyculture system may reach market size at a different time, thus methods of differential harvest may have to be devised, especially if two or more species occupy the same pond.

Polyculture usually depends upon one primary species which has the highest market value. The growth of that species and its annual production should not suffer as a result of the addition of secondary culture species. For instance, the annual production of channel catfish in ponds is generally in the vicinity of 3,000 kg/ha under well managed monoculture conditions. The addition of secondary species by way of polyculture should not result in a significant change in catfish production; however, the total production within the pond should increase appreciably. Since many catfish culturists presently experience degraded water quality conditions, especially in the summer, it is anticipated that the added stress placed upon water quality by increasing the total stocking rate within polyculture ponds will call for careful monitoring and for the presence of aeration devices and chemicals for immediate use when water quality problems arise.

Polyculture does appear to hold significant promise for the future of the United States aquaculture. The problems which can be expected as a result of polyculture offer new challenges, as well as new opportunities for both the researcher and the commercial aquaculturist. As polyculture develops, an ever increasing diversity of products can be expected to flow, both from freshwater aquaculture and from mariculture.

Summary

Polyculture, the rearing of two or more non-competitive species in combination, is well developed in some parts of the world, but relatively new to the United States. Aquaculturists will undoubtedly turn to polyculture in increasing numbers as a means of obtaining more biomass and greater culture system efficiency without adding to facilities or increasing energy requirements. Polyculturists may employ several aquatic species within the same pond or flow water through interconnected ponds. Nutrient inputs from terrestrial animal wastes appear to be readily adaptable to polyculture systems. Innovative polyculturists may employ exotic as well as native species and will be called upon to develop new management strategies as various combinations of species are utilized in both fresh and marine systems.

References

1. San-Dun, G. (1975). Fish Biology in China. Copeia, p. 404.
2. Bardach, J.E., Ryther, J.H. and McLarney, W.O. (1972). *Aquaculture.* John Wiley and Sons, New York, p. 868.
3. Perry, W.G., Jr. and Avault, J.W. Jr., (1968). Preliminary Experiment on the Culture of Blue, Channel and White Catfish in Brackish Water Ponds. *Proc. S.E. Assoc. Game and Fish Comm.* **22**, 397.
4. *ibid.* (1969). Culture of Blue, Channel and White Catfish in Brackish Water Ponds. *Proc. S.E. Assoc. Game and Fish Comm.* **23**, 592.
5. *ibid.* (1971). Polyculture Studies with Blue, White and Channel Catfish in Brackish Water Ponds. *Proc. S.E. Assoc. Game and Fish Comm.* **25**, 466.
6. *ibid.* (1975). Polyculture Studies with Channel Catfish and Buffalo. *Proc. S.E. Assoc. Game and Fish Comm.* **29**, 92.
7. Williamson, J. and Smitherman, R.O. (1975). Food habits of Hybrid

Buffalo Fish, Tilapia, Israeli Carp and Channel Catfish in Polyculture. *Proc. S.E. Assoc. Game and Fish Comm.* **28**, 86.

8. Reagan, R.E., Jr. and Robinette, H.R. (1975). Culture of Rainbow Trout in Combination with Over-wintering Channel Catfish in Mississippi. *Proc. S.E. Assoc. Game and Fish Comm.* **28**, 99.

9. Stickney, R.R. (1976). Tilapia Culture. Proceedings of the 1976 Fish Farming Conference and Annual Convention Catfish Farmers of Texas, Texas A&M University, College Station, p. 5.

10. Buck, D.H. *et al.* (1972). Combined Culture of Channel Catfish and Golden Shiners in Wading Pools. Illinois Natural History Survey, Biological Notes No. 79, pp. 12.

11. Miller, J.W. (1972). Culture of Channel Catfish, *Ictalurus punctatus* (Rafinesque), *Tilapia aurea* and Israeli Carp, *Cyprinus carpio*, in Separate and Continuous Pens. M.S. Thesis, Auburn University, Auburn, Alabama.

12. Smith, P.L. (1973). Effects of *Tilapia aurea* (Steindachner), Cage Culture, and Aeration on Channel Catfish, *Ictalurus punctatus* (Rafinesque), Production in Ponds. Ph.D. Dissertation, Auburn University, Auburn, Alabama.

13. Schroeder, G. (1974). Use of Fluid Cowshed Manure in Fish Ponds. *Bamidgeh* **26**, 84.

14. Stickney, R.R., Rowland, L.O. and Hesby, J.H. (In press). Water Quality— *Tilapia aurea* Interactions in Ponds Receiving Swine and Poultry Wastes. *Proc. World Maricult. Soc.* **8**.

15. Huguenin, J.E. (1975). Development of a Marine Aquaculture Research Complex. *Aquaculture* **5**, 135.

Aquaculture Potentials In The Great Lakes

George F. Greene Jr. [1]

The Applied Research Center
On Little Traverse Bay
Petoskey, Michigan

When the subject of fisheries comes up, our great inland seas are a dismal failure and a great success story at one and the same time. It depends on your interests as to which category fits your belief.

If you are a sports fisherman, boat owner, boat dealer, fishing tackle manufacturer or a resort owner, the Great Lakes are a huge bonanza that has seen business rise into the billions of dollars spent for recreational vehicles and equipment. The introduction into the lakes of coho salmon *(Oncorphynchus kisutch)*, and chinook salmon *(Oncorhynchus tshawyscha)*, and the return of the lake trout *(Salvelinus namaycush)*, have been one of the greatest achievements in sports fishing history. In cities like Waukegan, Illinois; Kenosha, Wisconsin and all along the eastern shore in Michigan, "Coho Fever" has struck and rejuvenated many a dying town. Where 14 foot outboards were the normal boat sale previously, flying bridge sports fishermen are now common, and a thriving charter boat industry has sprung up on both sides of Lake Michigan. Similar development, but to a lesser extent, has occurred in the other lakes. At present Lake Michigan is the center of the fishing bonanza. "Coho Derbys" , " Cohoramas" and the like are now big annual attractions of many a Great Lakes town. Waukegan, Illinois is now famous for Coho as well as for Jack Benny, and bills itself as the"Coho capital of the Great Lakes." People come from all over the country to fish for salmon and the annual contest draws tens of thousands of entrants and pays off in prizes exceeding $20,000 in goods and services.

Twenty years ago this same water was declared a sports fishing desert. The lake trout were decimated by the accidentally introduced sea lamprey *(Petromyzon marinus)*, and the alewife *(Alosa pseudoharengus)*had driven the local minnows to near extinction by successfully winning the race for the available food. Alewife die-offs covered the beaches feet thick with rotting carcasses and the odor was overwhelming. Then the problem

[1]Address: 14175 Oak Knoll Road, Wadsworth, Illinois

of lamprey control was solved, the infestation of large fish was cut from 95% to less than 10%, and the lake trout started back up the population ladder. Tougher pollution laws started the reclamation of the lakes and, particularly in Lake Erie, allowed the native populations, to rebound and flourish. With the introduction of the salmon and their enthusiastic acceptance of their new home, happy days were here again for the mid-west fisherman.

Meanwhile, back on the other side of the picture, the original depressed conditions had played havoc with the commercial Great Lakes fishing fleets. Yellow perch *(Perca flavescens)* populations were heavily overfished while natural factors and increased pollution were militating against them. The result was the end of an era. While yearly tonnage stayed about the same, its makeup tended heavily towards "trash" fish. The present picture (1) is improved somewhat, but the species composition still leaves much to be desired (Tables 1-3). The commercial fishery in the lakes was then, and remains now, at a low ebb as far as desirable eating fish are concerned. Lake Erie still supports a modest fishery with a few firms spread out over the rest of the system.

The heart-felt love of the Wisconsinite for his Friday night perch fry is legendary. Nearly every tap and restaurant in the state has honored this weekly ritual since time immemorial. Now much of the raw material for this feast is "ocean perch", flown in from the coasts frozen. While this is tolerated, the locals bemoan the loss of taste compared with "our" lake perch. Paradoxically, the demand has risen greatly as the supply has diminished drastically.

Market projections in the mid-west are highly encouraging. Demand far exceeds supply and present stocks of "real" perch are contracted for well in advance and moved out as fast as they arrive. In addition this demand exists in a climate of little or no exploitation. Naturally dealers are loath to promote what they cannot supply. Conservative estimates put the mid-west demand at 6-10 times the available supply with a great expansion possible nationwide if supplies were adequate. This is a very promising market position.

Other problems are endemic to other areas. In upper and lower Michigan and in Minnesota, the Indians have resorted to gill netting to increase their catches. This has infuriated local sports fishermen and the situation has heated up to the point that tempers are boiling and shots have been fired in the night. Into all this have come a few visionaries with some possible solutions. Aquaculture is one of them.

In a situation where demand is high and supply is nearly absent, our economics professor always said that entrepreneurs would rise and thrive, entering the market to meet the demand. In our case the demand is for large quantities of *Perca flavescens.*

In Wisconsin, a concomitant problem has occurred that may well play

Table I

U. S. Great Lakes Commercial Fish Production, 1976

LAKE MICHIGAN 1976

Species	Illinois		Indiana		Michigan		Wisconsin		Total	
	Pounds	Value	Pounds	Value	Pounds	Value	Pounds	Value	Pounds	Value
Alewives	--	--	1,547	--	4,620,782	56,770	34,589,768	419,124	39,212,097	475,894
Bowfin	--	--	--	--	--	--	25	--	25	--
Buffalofish	--	--	--	--	--	--	6	--	6	--
Bullheads	--	--	--	--	--	--	119,875	15,633	119,875	15,633
Burbot	--	--	10	--	30,328	62	130,254	5,507	160,592	5,569
Carp	--	--	112	--	181	3	748,407	25,697	748,700	25,700
Catfish	28,530	29,226	357	--	--	--	353	129	710	129
Chubs	--	--	1,642	591	176,649	185,033	214,859	218,123	421,680	432,973
Gizzard shad	--	--	--	67	--	--	11	--	78	--
Lake herring	--	--	--	--	9	--	1,599	938	1,608	938
Brown trout	--	--	29	--	--	--	--	--	29	--
Lake trout	--	--	5,741	4,048	138	93	3,690	1,669	9,569	5,810
Northern pike	--	--	--	--	--	--	15,659	2,803	15,659	2,803
Salmon coho	--	--	103	--	--	--	--	--	103	--
Sheepshead	--	--	--	--	4	--	1,292	111	1,296	111
Smelt	11,696	3,366	5,613	1,278	1,964,416	67,412	204,333	32,345	2,186,058	104,401
Suckers	--	--	4,015	491	140,744	1,251	281,097	6,994	425,856	8,736
Walleye	--	--	--	--	7	--	5,913	4,910	5,920	4,910
White bass	--	--	--	--	--	--	4,165	1,648	4,165	1,648
Whitefish	--	--	175	--	2,457,459	1,732,204	1,612,491	1,445,577	4,070,125	3,177,781
Menominee	--	--	--	--	112,306	40,200	19,655	9,486	131,961	49,686
Yellow perch	224,089	186,464	180,786	111,116	82	--	448,688	446,866	853,645	744,446
Total	264,315	219,056	200,197	117,524	9,503,105	2,083,028	38,402,140	2,637,560	48,369,757	5,057,168

Table II
U. S. Great Lakes Commercial Fish Production, 1976

LAKE ERIE 1976

Species	GREAT LAKES TOTAL Pounds	Value	New York Pounds	Value	Pennsylvania Pounds	Value	Ohio Pounds	Value	Michigan Pounds	Value	Total Pounds	Value
Alewives	39,212,101	475,894	--	--	--	--	--	--	--	--	--	--
Bowfin	914	69	--	--	--	--	--	--	--	--	--	--
Buffalofish	93,540	29,146	--	--	--	--	29,576	8,692	63,958	20,454	93,534	29,146
Bullheads	212,749	35,992	77	--	268	--	42,851	7,008	1,048	234	44,244	7,242
Burbot	233,584	5,577	8	--	130	7	--	--	--	--	138	7
Carp	4,611,977	292,600	19,707	1,865	6	1	2,634,551	160,250	487,408	41,444	3,141,672	203,560
Catfish	643,488	288,453	318	110	945	28	223,160	118,784	36,714	18,163	261,137	137,085
Chubs	1,657,308	1,185,847	--	--	--	--	--	--	--	--	--	--
Crappie	58,705	43,634	6	--	--	--	--	--	--	--	6	--
Eels	35,461	27,967	--	--	--	--	--	--	--	--	--	--
Gizzard shad	626,490	27,273	4,980	--	1,820	--	604,204	26,497	10,000	150	621,004	26,647
Goldfish	133,522	6,830	--	--	--	--	133,522	6,830	--	--	133,522	6,830
Lake herring	448,711	118,366	--	--	--	--	--	--	--	--	--	--
Lake trout	325,510	209,016	--	--	268	176	--	--	--	--	268	176
Brown trout	1	--	--	--	--	--	--	--	--	--	--	--
Rainbow trout	29	--	--	--	--	--	--	--	--	--	--	--
Northern pike	15,659	2,803	--	--	--	--	127,195	7,027	--	--	127,195	7,027
Quillback	134,687	8,694	238	--	--	--	--	--	--	--	241	--
Rock bass	7,395	1,543	--	--	3	--	--	--	--	--	241	--
Salmon coho	103	--	--	--	--	--	--	--	--	--	--	--
Sheepshead	1,049,665	45,324	70,329	1,871	8,102	103	952,261	41,380	3,985	225	1,034,677	43,579
Shiner	6,519	7,600	--	--	6,519	7,600	--	--	--	--	6,519	7,600
Smelt	5,345,388	204,954	819	--	3,049	442	34,767	924	--	--	38,635	1,366
Suckers	668,082	25,778	15,950	17	638	10	62,701	3,544	772	54	80,061	3,625
Sunfish	6,816	2,015	--	--	--	--	--	--	--	--	--	--
Walleye	75,403	55,691	65,290	47,909	3,742	2,699	--	--	--	--	69,032	50,608
White bass	1,528,453	676,002	7,343	1,641	3,271	518	1,499,450	666,965	13,515	4,876	1,523,579	674,000
Whitefish	5,297,519	4,099,590	--	--	28	21	--	--	--	--	28	21
Menominee	147,353	53,963	--	--	--	--	--	--	--	--	--	--
White perch	45,236	13,682	25	--	--	--	--	--	921	493	25	--
Yellow perch	3,113,432	2,477,519	138,893	105,939	306,902	239,118	1,438,490	1,187,074	618,321	86,093	1,885,206	1,532,624
Total	65,735,800	10,421,852	323,983	159,352	335,691	250,723	7,782,728	2,234,975	618,321	86,093	9,060,723	2,731,143

Source: Great Lakes Fishery Laboratory
U.S. Fish and Wildlife Service
Ann Arbor, Michigan

Table III
U. S. Great Lakes Commercial Fish Production, 1976

| | LAKE SUPERIOR 1976 | | | | | | | | LAKE HURON 1976 | | LAKE ONTARIO 1976 | |
| | Michigan | | Minnesota | | Wisconsin | | Total | | Michigan | | New York | |
Species	Pounds	Value	Pounds	Value	Pounds	Value	Pounds	Value	Pounds	Value	Pounds	Value
Alewives	4	--	--	--	--	--	4	--	--	--	--	--
Bowfin	--	--	--	--	--	--	--	--	--	--	5	--
Buffalofish												
Bullheads	--	--	--	--	--	--	--	--	884	69	18,662	8,223
Burbot	71,884	--	943	--	18	1	72,845	1	29,996	4,894	--	--
Carp	15	--	--	--	530	--	545	--	716,024	63,157	5,036	183
Catfish	--	--	--	--	--	--	--	--	378,892	150,648	2,749	591
Chubs	894,582	547,468	64,388	38,082	276,658	167,324	1,235,628	752,874	55,575	42,324	3,124	1,310
Crappie	--	--	--	--	--	--	--	--	--	--	35,461	27,967
Eels	--	--	--	--	--	--	--	--	--	--	--	--
Gizzard shad	--	--	--	--	--	--	--	--	5,408	626	--	--
Goldfish												
Lake herring	108,465	32,432	179,711	63,196	158,766	21,788	446,942	117,416	130	--	31	12
Lake trout	127,991	74,387	32,262	26,133	155,420	102,510	315,673	203,030	--	--	--	--
Brown trout	--	--	--	--	--	--	--	--	--	--	--	--
Rainbow trout	--	--	--	--	--	--	--	--	1	--	--	--
Northern pike	--	--	--	--	--	--	--	--	--	--	--	--
Quillback	--	--	--	--	--	--	--	--	7,492	1,667	--	--
Rock bass	--	--	--	--	--	--	--	--	--	--	--	--
Salmon coho	--	--	--	--	--	--	--	--	--	--	7,154	1,543
Sheepshead	--	--	--	--	--	--	--	--	13,423	1,620	269	14
Shiner	--	--	--	--	--	--	--	--	--	--	--	--
Smelt	655	313	2,881,487	75,494	210,268	15,637	3,092,410	91,444	16,000	1,600	12,285	6,143
Suckers	12,347	337	721	--	18,233	1,754	31,301	2,091	126,788	11,195	4,076	131
Sunfish	--	--	--	--	--	--	--	--	--	--	6,816	2,015
Walleye	--	--	--	--	3	2	3	2	--	--	348	171
White bass	--	--	--	--	--	--	--	--	100	--	169	32
Whitefish	505,489	409,810	794	398	234,786	189,690	741,069	599,898	540	322	--	--
Menominee	201	49	1,445	440	13,731	3,785	15,377	4,274	486,297	321,920	--	--
White perch	--	--	--	--	--	--	--	--	15	3	45,211	13,682
Yellow perch	3	3	--	--	--	--	3	3	322,065	170,978	52,513	29,471
Total	1,721,636	1,064,796	3,161,751	203,743	1,068,413	502,491	5,951,800	1,771,030	2,159,611	771,023	193,909	91,488

into the hands of these same entrepreneurs. The Dairy State has seen hard times hit the family dairy farm. Competition plus the high cost of doing business has driven many dairies out of business. As a result, the state has a surplus of large, heated structures with running water and, in many cases, waste treatment facilities. These are, of course, the empty dairy barns.

Our entrepreneur now has a partial solution to the problem of where to set up shop for year round operation. The weather in the mid-west is never too pleasant in the winter. The winter of 1976-1977 was downright ridiculous, anything done outdoors other than skiing, ice skating, or snowmobiling was brought to a complete standstill. Ponds were frozen to their bottoms at depths of six feet. Fish kills in shallow ponds were substantial.

Let's look then at the situation that our entrepreneur has before him: (i) A short term unlimited demand for his product, (ii) a depressed natural fishery, (iii) available buildings suitable for production, (iv) a reasonably good water supply, (v) state universities with Sea Grant services and an interest in helping. (University of Wisconsin, University of Michigan), and (vi) excellent public interest.

Now let's look at what is happening. On April 16, 1975, a conference on the aquaculture of yellow perch *(Perca flavescens)* was held at the University of Wisconsin in Madison. Five hundred people attended and others were turned away for lack of room. It was a great success as members of the Wisconsin Sea Grant Program discussed their perch aquaculture project, underway since 1973. Food wholesalers and processors told of the large unfulfilled market in the mid-west and even larger markets that would be available in the rest of the nation if a reliable supply could be produced (2).

The basic idea of the demonstration project is to build tanks of roughly 4,500 gallons each, with a production facility having ten growing tanks and a fingerling tank, (2,000 gals.). Water would be supplied from a well and would be heated to 55-60 degrees F by a standard large water heater. Low intensity light is maintained in the growing area as experience has shown that the fish preferred it. The water would be recycled to a large extent with a fixed amount of new water added daily to maintain water quality.

Tanks in the prototype system were constructed of 1 inch plywood with plastic liners. Considerable variation can exist in tank size and make-up. Readily available aboveground swimming pools of the type found in backyards all over the country have been suggested as inexpensive off-the-shelf items for indoor aquaculture. Certainly they have been used extensively in outdoor projects. The cost savings can be considerable. A 4,500 gallon plastic lined plywood tank runs in the neighborhood of $1,500. A swimming pool of the same size will sell for one-fourth of that price or less. End-of-season bargains can even reduce that price. These pools are available from hundreds of gallons to well over 10,000 gallons.

The heart of the system, as in any aquarium from 1 gallon to thousands of gallons, is the filtration system. Various types are available, but in general, the system will be put together by the entrepreneur himself from parts collected in his locality until such time as commercial units are available.

Biological filter systems have proved to be most effective. A major drawback to date has been the relatively large size and the heavy consumption of energy of these units. On October 25, 1977, the University of Wisconsin Sea Grant Advisory Service will hold a Conference on the Technology of Perch Aquaculture to discuss alternate and less energy consuming filtration methods.

EPA requirements will play a large part in the final design of these units and in their resultant efficiency. At present such regulations are not formulated, and represent an unknown quantity for the new enterprise.

Serious entrants to the field will need to busy themselves politically to assure favorable legislation. Certain state game laws may need amending to cover the raising and selling of what are now considered "game" fish. Other aquaculturists have run afoul of these laws in the past. I am thinking of the net-pen growers of salmon in the Northwest and Maine.

The demonstration unit in Madison is now utilizing trout chow as a standard feed. Perch do well on the diet but as in all aquaculture, the cost is too high. Investigators feel that the fish could be raised as well on a lower protein diet. Alternate feed sources are being investigated.

Presented with the above facts, a logical question might be: "What's holding up the parade?" For one thing, neither our animal, *Perca flavescens*, nor his cousin *Stizostedion vitreum vitreum*, the wall-eyed pike, (another taste delight being considered as a companion product), is available economically in large quantities from hatcheries, though artificial spawning has been carried out successfully in ponds. Egg sources exist, but the hatchery methods and volume to alleviate the economic situation are still being developed. Present prices for fingerlings are seven cents each. More difficult problems have been solved in the past, and time should see this one beaten as more time and money is spent on it. At present, this is an obstruction to expansion of private commercial ventures.

Another problem is the large energy consumption of the present filtration systems, plus the large size of these units. Intensive work is being done in this area, and cost reductions and increased efficiency should result.

In spite of the difficulties, at last count, six brave new enterprises have started in Wisconsin. At this time none are showing a profit. Fingerling losses are running as high as 15-30%. However, as experience grows, this should drop to near zero. The demonstration unit has had no significant fingerling mortality.

What other areas of aquaculture could be carried out in the Great Lakes? What do the visionaries think?

This one thinks, for one, that the "ocean ranching" of salmon is feasible in the lakes. Fish released in rivers and streams on both sides of Lake Michigan return to these areas to spawn. In many cases the streams cannot accommodate the adult fish when they return and they dash themselves to death trying to ascend a waterway that does not contain enough water to provide bouyancy. The Applied Research Center On Little Traverse Bay (ARC), proposes to set up a pilot project, possibly with the local Indians, during 1978-81 to test the feasibility of such a scheme (3). This could also go a long way in reducing the sportsman/Indian tensions. A potential fly in the ointment in Lake Michigan is the PCB content of the water. This is not a problem in Lake Superior which still has the purest water of all the Great Lakes. PCB's are expected to be a problem in Lake Michigan for the next ten years, after which levels should drop considerably.

Net-pen culture of salmon, perch, walleye and catfish is also a possibility. Protected waters exist in Lake Michigan at Green Bay, Grand Traverse and Little Traverse Bays. Lake Huron contains many such areas as do the other lakes in the system. The heavy use of the lakes for recreation will produce some problems, since vacationers and permanent residents may object to their view being marred by a large net-pen rafting system. Feed sources may be a major problem as they are in all aquaculture. A possible source of feed could be the alewife which now supports a 40 million pound/year fish meal industry. Its product is now used mainly in pet food. More work should be done to try to fully utilize this species. ARC has planned some projects in this area as has the University of Wisconsin.

An interesting and intriguing area of study is the use of power plant waste heat to foster aquaculture. Throughout the mid-west, many large cooling lakes have been constructed that could be used for fish culture year-round. Many have been stocked and opened to the public for sport fishing. Cage culture is one possibility, as is the use of this water in standard raceway systems. If present restrictions on the use of waste heat from atomic units were lifted, another source of heated water could be utilized.

With the advent of the big salmon sportsfishing industry has come a heavy demand for bait and an increase in the total number of fishermen in all local waters. Most of the states and Canadian provinces around the Great Lakes have a reputation for good fishing. This is especially true of Michigan, Wisconsin, Minnesota and Ontario, all of whom depend heavily on the fisherman-tourist.

These fishermen support a large bait minnow industry nationally. Minnesota has over 14,000 acres of ponds in the production of bait minnows, making it the second largest bait minnow state in the country. Still, it is far below the state of Arkansas with its 25,000 acres. Bait minnows constitute a national industry estimated at some $175 million per year, making it the largest single aquaculture industry in the country. It sells more product than the trout, catfish and crawfish producers combined. Little fish are big business.

Other Great Lakes states could support a minnow industry and indeed do on a small scale. ARC is also planning projects in this area, hopefully in conjunction with the Department of Natural Resources of Michigan.

In summary then, the outlook for Great Lake aquaculture is bright. The market is present, the interest is present, and the facilities are present. Our knowledge needs bolstering and a cadre of risk-takers is needed. At this stage, the ocean ranching of salmon in Lake Superior would seem to be a good gamble to deliver dividends in the near term. Indoor, controlled environment, perch culture would be second, with minnow culture a concomitant venture.

Our inland seas should be able to provide the mid-west first, and later the whole nation, with a steady supply of excellent and nutritious seafood. The Wisconsin Friday Night Perch Fry may again feature the "Real McCoy" instead of a pale imitation from blue water that has been thawed out and prepared. Those who are lucky enough to get the real article know the difference well. Perhaps by the time of the next Food—Drugs Conference, we will be able to report some real progress in the establishment of a new industry.

References

1. Tables courtesy of the Great Lakes Fishery Laboratory, U.S. Fish and Wildlife Service, Ann Arbor, Michigan. 1977 and the Great Lakes Commission, Ann Arbor, Michigan.
2. Aquaculture: Raising Perch for the Midwest Market, University of Wisconsin Seagrant College Program. Advisory Report No. 13 June, 1975.
3. A Plan of Action. The Applied Research Center On Little Traverse Bay. (ARC) Petoskey, Michigan/Wadsworth, Illinois. 1977.

SECTION VI

Constraints on Food Production from the Sea

Food From The Sea: Myth Or Reality?

John P. Wise

U.S. Department of Commerce
National Oceanic and Atmospheric Administration
National Marine Fisheries Service
Washington, D.C

Food from the sea differs from nearly all other food sources in that 95 or more percent of the supply comes from wild stocks. Wild marine organisms have traditionally been considered a common property resource, belonging to no one until they have been harvested. The only significant variation in this policy in the past has been the declaration by various political divisions from the level of nations to the level of townships that marine food resources within certain boundaries belong to the inhabitants of that political division, and that harvest rights are vested in those inhabitants. In general, this policy has not contributed significantly to ameliorating the "tragedy of the commons," since the total harvest has rarely been effectively limited.

These problems have been recognized by the United Nations Law of the Sea Conferences, but after several years the LOS Conferences have not been able to agree on an effective treaty including the protection of living aquatic resources. As a result, many major fishing nations, including the United States, have recently declared unilateral jurisdiction over marine fishery resources off their shores and now manage those resources.

The Food and Agriculture Organization of the United Nations has estimated that the potential annual yield of conventional species of marine fish, crustaceans, and molluscs from the world ocean is well over 100 million metric tons[2]. By 1975, catches had increased to the point at which about 60 million metric tons was being harvested (Table I).

Increases in catches from 1938 to 1975 have been 380 percent for freshwater species and 215 percent for marine species. These increases progressed in a reasonable orderly fashion until the 1970's, but a sharp

---

[1]Opinions expressed in this paper are those of the author, and not necessarily those of the National Marine Fisheries Service or NOAA.
[2]Weights referred to throughout this paper are live (round fresh).

Table I-World Fishery Landings, 1938-75.
million metric tons

Year	Freshwater[1]	Marine	Peruvian[2] anchovy	Total
1938	2.0	19.1	—	21.1
1948	1.6	18.0	—	19.6
1952	1.2	22.9	—	24.1
1953	2.6	22.4	—	25.0
1954	2.8	24.2	—	27.0
1955	3.0	25.9	—	28.9
1956	3.1	27.7	0.1	30.8
1957	3.7	28.0	0.3	31.7
1958	4.2	29.1	0.8	33.3
1959	4.3	32.6	2.0	36.9
1960	4.4	35.8	3.5	40.2
1961	5.5	38.1	5.3	43.6
1962	5.6	39.2	7.1	44.8
1963	5.7	40.9	7.2	46.6
1964	5.8	46.1	9.8	51.9
1965	7.0	46.2	7.7	53.2
1966	7.3	50.0	9.6	57.3
1967	7.2	53.2	10.5	60.4
1968	7.4	56.5	11.3	63.9
1969	7.6	55.1	9.7	62.7
1970	8.5	61.9	13.1	70.4
1971	9.0	61.9	11.2	70.9
1972	9.2	57.0	4.8	66.2
1973	9.3	57.5	2.0	66.8
1974	9.3	61.2	4.0	70.5
1975	9.6	60.1	3.5	69.7

[1]Excludes diadromous.
[2]Also included in both Marine and Total.
Source: Yearbooks of Fishery Statistics, Food and Agriculture Organization of the United Nations.

decrease occurred in 1972 when the Peruvian anchovy catch dropped to 4.8 million tons from its 1970 high of 13.1 million tons. The anchovy catch dropped even further in 1973 to 2 million tons, and it is expected to continue low for at least a few more years, although it increased in 1974 and 1975 to 3-4 million tons. The decline in Peruvian anchovy catches is attributable to a combination of oceanographic factors and overfishing. This single species, whose catch was over 20 percent of the world marine catch in 1970, will undoubtedly cause further perturbations in world catch statistics for some years to come.

The anchovy phenomenon points out that the implication that world catches of conventional species can be roughly doubled over their present level has to be qualified. An increasing number of species are now fully exploited or overexploited, and it is clear that management is needed to assure realization of the full potential of the conventional species.

Recent extensions of national jurisdiction offer real hope that effective management will now be undertaken.

A total yield several times in excess of 100 million tons may be possible if harvesting turns to less familiar types of marine animals. An example is squid and other cephalopods, heavily fished in a few areas, but almost unexploited in others. Other examples are the krill of the Antarctic and the lantern fish of warmer oceans. Harvesting and marketing of these less familiar species on a large scale present serious technological problems. Nonetheless, some experts have estimated that the total sustainable harvest of all species from the world ocean might be in the order of at least 150 million to 300 million tons, and there are a few considerably higher estimates.

The long-term increase in production of marine species will be interrupted in 1977 and probably for some following years by recent extensions of jurisdiction and imposition of quotas reducing catches to reduce over-fishing. For example, about 3 million metric tons a year were caught by foreign ships in 1974 and 1975 in what is now the U.S. Fishery Conservation Zone. Total 1977 quotas for foreigners in the Zone are just 2 million tons, a potential reduction of a million tons in world catches by U.S. conservation action alone.

The countries hardest hit by quotas in national zones are those that since about 1960 have increased their production by means of distant-water fleets. The most outstanding of these are the U.S.S.R. and Japan. It would not be surprising if catches by each of these countries decreased in 1977 by a million tons or more, or if the total decline in world production in 1977 were 3-4 million tons. Of course these declines should be only temporary, and, as overfished stocks rebuild, catches should once again increase.

There are other ways beside increasing harvests in which the production of food from the sea could be increased. One is the diversion to the direct food market of large amounts of herring-like species now used for fish meal and oil, such as menhaden, South African pilchard, and Peruvian anchovy. While most of the fish meal eventually finds its way to the world's table as feedstuffs for poultry and other animals, a good deal of the food potential is lost in conversion. The long-term trend has been for the percentage of fish used for meal and oil to increase, but since the mid 1960's it has leveled off at about one-third of total production (Table II).

It has also been estimated that the total useful fish production could be increased by some millions of tons by elimination of waste. A great deal of fish is thrown back into the sea by vessels fishing for other species, especially by shrimp fleets. Other large amounts are lost after catching by improper handling, preservation, and storage. Reduction of losses in processing could also increase yields substantially.

It has often been said that worldwide marine harvests are leveling off or

Table II

Percentage of World Fishery Landings
Used for Various Purposes, 1938-75.

| | For Human Consumption | | | |
| | | | | For Meal |
Year	Fresh	Other	Total	and Oil
1938	53	34	87	8
1948	49	38	87	8
1952	45	40	85	11
1953	45	40	85	11
1954	44	40	84	12
1955	43	41	84	12
1956	42	41	83	13
1957	44	40	84	13
1958	45	39	84	13
1959	43	37	80	17
1960	42	37	79	19
1961	39	36	75	22
1962	37	35	72	26
1963	37	36	73	25
1964	34	35	69	29
1965	34	36	70	29
1966	32	35	67	31
1967	30	34	64	34
1968	28	34	62	36
1969	28	36	64	34
1970	28	34	62	37
1971	28	36	64	35
1972	30	39	69	29
1973	31	41	72	26
1974	30	40	70	28
1975	30	40	70	29

Note:Will not add to 100 percent because a small amount goes to other uses.
Source: Yearbooks of Fishery Statistics, Food and Agriculture Organization of
the United Nations.

falling because traditional waters have been overfished and polluted. Gross catch figures must be interpreted carefully, however, in light of the facts that freshwater fisheries, high seas (as opposed to coastal) fisheries, fisheries for shellfish, and fisheries in warmer ocean waters have been increasing over the past several years.

The answer to these apparent contradictions is that the recent changes in total catch were caused almost solely by the precipitous decline in catches of Peruvian anchovies. Examination of world marine fish and shellfish catches, excluding the Peruvian anchovy, shows a reasonably uniform rate of increase of about 5 percent per year from 1955 to 1975, about double the rate of growth of the world human population.

Popular opinion to the contrary, pollution and most other man-induced alterations of the environment have had little or no measurable effect overall on large-scale marine fisheries. (Exceptions are the effects of building of dams on salmon stocks, and the effects of fishing itself.) Of course some local effects have been severe, but they have been limited to small areas. Recent studies have shown that predictions of the supposedly disastrous effects of oil spills may have been overdramatized. All of this does not mean however, that a close watch should not be kept on the possible effects of pollution and man-induced changes in the future.

World catches have not been equally distributed among countries, nor have the increases of recent years been equally distributed among the

Table III

World Fishery Landings by Major Fishing Countries, 1955-1975.
million metric tons

Country	1955	1960	1965	1970	1975
Japan	4.9	6.2	6.9	10.8	10.5
U.S.S.R.	2.5	3.1	5.1	7.3	9.9
China	2.5	5.8	—	6.3	6.9
Peru	0.2	3.6	7.5	1.3	3.4
U.S.A.	2.8	2.8	2.7	2.8	2.8
Norway	1.8	1.5	2.3	3.0	2.6
India	0.8	1.2	1.3	1.8	2.3
S. Korea	0.3	0.5	0.6	0.8	2.1
Denmark	0.4	0.6	0.8	1.2	1.8
Spain	0.8	1.0	1.3	1.5	1.5
Indonesia	0.7	0.8	0.9	1.2	1.4
Thailand	0.2	0.2	0.6	1.4	1.4
S. Africa	0.4	0.6	0.7	1.2	1.3
Phillipines	0.4	0.5	0.7	1.0	1.3
Chile	0.2	0.3	0.7	1.2	1.1
Canada	1.0	1.0	1.3	1.4	1.0
N. Vietnam	0.1	0.2	—	0.3	1.0
Iceland	0.5	0.6	1.2	0.7	1.0
Other	8.4	9.7	18.6	25.2	16.4
Total	28.9	40.2	53.2	70.4	69.7

Source: Yearbooks of Fishery Statistics, Food and Agriculture Organization of the United Nations.

major fishing countries (Table III). Japan, the U.S.S.R., China, Peru, the U.S.A., and Norway accounted for over half the world catch in 1975. Only 18 countries had catches of 1 million tons or more in 1975, but these 18 countries account for three-quarters of the world catch. These major fishing countries can be divided into four groups by considering the percentage increase in their fisheries from 1955 to 1975:

Over 400%	Over 150%	Over 50%	Under 50%
Peru	Denmark	Japan	Norway
N. Vietnam	U.S.S.R.	Indonesia	U.S.A.
S. Korea	S. Africa	Iceland	Canada
Thailand	Phillipines	Spain	
Chile	India		
	China		

Nor has the contribution of the various groups of fishes, crustaceans, and molluscs been equal. Well over half the landings are of finfish; nearly half the landings come from the herring, cod, and mackerel groups (Table IV).

Continental shelf areas within 200 miles of U.S. shores are about 9 percent of the shelf area of the world, excluding the Antarctic. However, most of the world's marine fishery production comes from temperate and subarctic shelf areas. About 20 percent of these areas lies within 200 miles of U.S. shores. Fish and shellfish stocks off U.S. coasts are an enormous and valuable renewable resource. Total annual catches by U.S. and foreign commercial fleets within 200 miles of the U.S. immediately before the advent of extended jurisdiction were about 6 million metric tons a year. In 1977, the first (partial) year of extended jurisdiction, they were expected to be just under 5 million metric tons. In addition, there is a U.S. recreational catch conservatively estimated as at least 0.7 million metric tons. Assuming a retail value of 50 cents per pound for commercial and recreational catches gives a total estimated retail value for present catches of about $6 billion per year.

Aquaculture, defined as the culture and husbandry of aquatic animals and plants, provides some 10 percent of world aquatic food supplies. Present production of fish, shellfish, and plants amounts to about 6 million metric tons. The majority is produced in mainland China (2-3 million tons) and comprises primarily various species of carp, which are also the major species raised in other parts of Asia, Europe, and the Middle East. Hence, most present aquaculture is conducted in fresh water.

In the United States, private marine aquaculture accounts for some 133,000 metric tons of oysters, and about 450 tons of pen-reared salmon. Salmon catch attributable to public hatcheries, overwhelmingly in the

Table IV
World Marine Fishery Landings, 1975, By Species Groups

Group	landings	million metric tons
Herrings, Sardines, Anchovies, etc.		13.7 (23%)
Peruvian anchovy	3.5	
Atlantic herring	1.5	
Sardinella	1.5	
Sprat	1.0	
Other	6.2	
Cods, Hakes, Haddock, etc.		11.8 (20%)
Alaska Pollock	5.0	
Atlantic cod	2.4	
Other	4.4	
Mackerels, etc.		3.6 (6%)
Chub mackerel	1.9	
Atlantic mackerel	1.1	
Other	0.6	
Salmons, Trouts, etc.		2.8 (5%)
Tunas, Bonitos, Billfishes, etc.		1.9 (3%)
Shrimps, etc.		1.3 (2%)
Squids, etc.		1.2 (2%)
Flounders, etc.		1.1 (2%)
Oysters		0.9 (1%)
Others (more than 30 groups)		21.8
Total		60.1

Source: Food and Agriculture Organization of the United Nations Yearbook of Fishery Statistics, Volume 40.

Columbia River, is estimated at more than 27,000 tons. Fresh-water aquaculture, primarily of catfish and trout, produces about 39,000 tons. Experimental efforts are in progress on various marine and freshwater species.

The only well-documented history of aquaculture in the United States, for oysters, tends not to support the optimistic predictions often made for the future of aquaculture. The U.S. fishery statistics have included for many years the landings of eastern public oysters, eastern private oysters, the Pacific oyster, and the western oyster (see: "Fishery Statistics of the United States" for various years). For the last quarter century the landings of eastern public oysters have been increasing at a moderate rate, while those of the other three categories, largely aquacultured, have been decreasing.

Year	Public Oysters	Aquacultured Oysters
	— — thousand metric tons, whole — —	
1950	160.9	322.9
1955	168.5	313.4
1960	152.4	215.2
1965	156.5	181.0
1970	187.6	127.7
1974	185.7	133.1

The reasons for the production of aquacultured oysters being less than half of what it used to be are many—disease, pollution, competing land and water uses, etc., but they do not change the fact that a reversal of present and past long -term downward trend of production is not in sight.

Major constraints to large-scale development of aquaculture in the United States are principally economic, compounded in some cases by institutional problems. Biological knowledge for many species is now available, but the technology needed for profitable commercial production is most often lacking.

Fish is eighth of nine food groups (sugar, sweets, fats and oils; flour and cereals; fresh vegetables; dairy; meat and poultry; eggs; fresh fruits; fish; processed fruits and vegetables) in the ratio of energy content to energy consumed in production. In the ratio of energy use to protein content, however, fish leads the nine groups and is more efficient than meat and poultry by perhaps one-third. Coastal fishing is reasonably energy-efficient, at about the same level as milk from grass-fed cows. Distant-water fishing, on the other hand, is one of the most inefficient means of food production, and can be compared to feedlot beef production in energy use. As man cultivates marine foods more intensively in aquaculture, the energy cost of production rises.

In summary, then, the prospects for increased food supplies from the sea in the future are not a myth; they are a reality. On the other hand, the prospects are not of unlimited abundance and of catches increasing indefinitely. The most reliable present forecast is for a potential yield of perhaps 120 million tons a year of conventional species. If catches continue to increase exponentially at about 5 percent per year, this limit will be reached around 1990. If, as seems more likely, increases follow a pattern that is more nearly linear, the 120 million ton limit will be reached shortly after the turn of the century.

Bringing into the harvest presently unexploited or underexploited types of food from the sea, e.g., squids, krill, etc., may raise the total that can be taken to as high as 300 million tons a year. A linear increase at the present rate would mean that the 300 million ton level would be reached around the year 2100.

Achievement of these levels is dependent on proper management of resources and fisheries. The sad lessons of past overexploitation and recent extensions of national jurisdictions make the picture more hopeful now than it has been in many years.

Production of food from the sea could be increased without increasing fishing perhaps 50 percent above its present level by technological changes. Principal among these would be the diversion to the direct food market of the roughly one-third of present production that goes into meal and oil. Decreases in the amounts of discard and waste could also make important contributions. These technological changes, as well as the changes that would make exploitation of other than present conventional species practical, are more dependent on economics than on any other single factor. They will not take place unless they offer promise of profit.

Aquaculture may not in the short run make large contributions to production of food from the sea. The problems that now exist are largely economic. We have or can get the biological knowledge to raise almost anything. The problem is to raise it in such a way as to operate a profitable business. Where there are unexploited or underexploited wild stocks of the same or competing species, aquaculture cannot reasonably be expected to be profitable. For the near term these considerations appear to limit practical aquaculture potential to relatively modest amounts of scarce and high-priced species for consumption in the developed countries.

Economic Constraints On Food Production From The Sea

Daniel D. Huppert

U.S. Department of Commerce
National Oceanic and Atmospheric Administration
National Marine Fisheries Service
La Jolla, California

That marine ecological systems are tremendously productive of plant and animal life is an established fact. In assessing the potential for food production from the sea, however, marine scientists have produced quite a range of "estimates" of the sea's productivity. In 1965 Schaefer (1) conservatively estimated that the world fishery production could be increased to 200 million tons "with no radical developments, such as fish farming or far out kinds of fishing gear." This total production was to include all fish, molluscs, and crustaceans supporting traditional fisheries.

Noting that the nutritional value of animal protein is essentially the same whether it comes from the bluefin tuna, the anchovy, or the lowly Antarctic krill, Chapman (2) surmised that any estimate of the sea's potential must assume something about man's tastes and needs. If people need and desire a traditional mix of taste, texture and fragrance, then much of the food must come from the relatively scarce populations of third and fourth-stage carnivores. If, on the other hand, man desires only a balanced mix of amino acids, minerals and vitamins, then food production may rely upon the more abundant lower-stage plants and animals. The potential annual yield of well-balanced, undifferentiated animal protein could, according to Chapman, range up to 2 billion tons. The annual sustainable yield of the more desirable predators would amount to only around 60 million tons.

These estimates refer only to the harvest of wild stocks. More intense cultivation techniques, loosely termed "aquaculture", are estimated to yield over 4 million metric tons worldwide annually (3). Much of this tonnage is derived from fresh and brackish waters. True mariculture is really an infant industry, but Bardach, Ryther and McLarney claim that yields from existing aquaculture installations could increase tenfold over the next three decades if "there were no economic constraints on the upgrading of culture" (3).

All these predictions of physical or technological potential appear somewhat academic in view of the history of world fish catches. World production of fish has leveled off since the post-war boom (see Table I). Whether this is a more-or-less permanent feature of world fisheries is not easy to determine at this early stage. But many of the known, abundant food fish stocks having the "taste, texture and fragrance" to which Western man, at least, has become accustomed, appear to be fully exploited. North Atlantic groundfish stocks have been fully, or nearly-fully exploited for several years (4). It is becoming increasingly clear that the same is true of North Pacific stocks of groundfish and of most northern hemisphere pelagic fish. Certainly, there are several stocks which are relatively lightly fished at present (jack mackerel, anchovies and squid in the Pacific come to mind), and further exploratory fishing in the South Pacific and Indian Ocean could reveal more potential fisheries. Nevertheless, the volume of untapped potential resources is dwindling. The expansion of production of food fish requires that increasingly marginal stocks be exploited or that tastes be altered to accept previously unacceptable fish. It appears that Chapman's estimate of 60 million tons for highly desirable food fish was close to the mark.

Fish caught for reduction to meal and oil accounted for a major part of the expansion in world fish production in the 1960's. Peru, South Africa, Norway and Iceland are responsible for the lion's share of the fish meal

Table I

Total World Fisheries Catches, 1950-1975

(million of metric tons)

Year	Catch	Year	Catch
1950	21..1	1963	48.2
1951	23.5	1964	52.5
1952	25.1	1965	53.3
1953	25.9	1966	56.8
1954	27.9	1967	61.1
1955	28.9	1968	64.3
1956	30.4	1969	62.9
1957	31.5	1970	70.0
1958	33.2	1971	70.9
1959	36.7	1972	66.2
1960	40.0	1973	66.8
1961	43.4	1974	70.5
1962	46.9	1975	69.7

and oil entering world trade, although the United States and Japan produce significant amounts of meat, also. As shown in table II, however, a halt to the expansion in fish caught for reduction paralleled the deceleration in food fish catch. It has been found, at least tentatively, that many of the abundant schooling pelagic fish easily exploited for reduction are either fished to the maximum yield or are only infrequently highly abundant. A few pockets of potential expansion, such as the northern anchovy off the west coast of North America, are well known. But the few hundred thousand tons of annual yield which could be afforded by addition of these under-exploited stocks to the world fisheries would not change the world situation significantly.

Table II

Disposition of World Catch, 1970-1975

Year	1970	1971	1972	1973	1974	1975
			(millions of metric tons)			
Total world catch	70.0	70.9	66.2	66.8	70.5	69.7
For human consumption	43.5	45.4	45.8	48.2	49.5	48.7
Marketed fresh	19.5	20.1	19.8	20.5	21.3	20.7
Freezing	9.7	10.7	11.2	12.5	12.9	12.7
Curing	8.1	8.0	8.0	8.0	8.1	8.1
Canning	6.2	6.6	6.8	6.8	7.2	7.2
For other purposes	26.5	25.5	20.4	18.6	21.0	21.0
Reduction[1]	25.5	19.4	19.4	17.6	20.0	20.0
Miscellaneous	1.0	1.0	1.0	1.0	1.0	1.0

[1]Includes only whole fish destined for the manufacture of oils and meals.

Source: FAO, Yearbook of Fishery Statistics, 1975. (Rome 1976).

In comparison to Schaefer's 200 million ton estimate of annual yield, or to Chapman's 2 billion ton estimate, the limited world production revealed by this casual review of fisheries is disappointing. To some extent the sea's potential may yet succumb to relatively straightforward application of technology, exploration and capital investment. Nevertheless, there are some fundamental economic conditions which must be met before any extensive fishery development efforts can pass unscathed through the crucible of economic reality.

Among the pertinent economic conditions are:

(i)   Prices of seafood products must cover all costs of production while being low enough to compete with alternative sources of food; and

(ii) economic waste inherent in over-fishing and overcapitalization must be discouraged in marine fisheries.

These two conditions and likely constraints to their achievement are discussed in the following sections.

Prices and Costs

It is widely recognized that for any productive activity to be economically successful the unit cost of production must be kept below the price at which consumers will buy significant quantities of the product. Individual fishermen and aquaculturists obviously understand this principle and make daily decisions based upon cost and price considerations. The economists' task is to extend and generalize this idea and to apply it to overall supply and demand situations.

Demand analysis begins with the notion that the needs and desires of consumers can be satisfied by a variety of products, and that actual purchases are determined, in part, by the array of prices confronting consumers and by the amount of income available to the consuming public. Thus, given a desire for both an adequate nutritional balance and for special tastes and textures, the typical consumer will allocate his available income over the available foods in a way that is most beneficial to him. Prices have a crucial part to play in the consumer's choices. Obviously, if seafoods, for instance, are more expensive per unit of nutrition and "taste", and if the supplies of alternative foods are expanding at lower prices, then demand for sea food cannot be expected to grow rapidly. The demand for sea food in the United States should be sensitive to price because there are so many red meat and poultry products available in great quantities and at reasonably low prices.

Given this very general conclusion, the retail price indices listed in table III are revealing. During the period 1955-1976, per capita consumption of red meat rose from 128 pounds to 213 pounds; per capita consumption of poultry rose from 27 pounds to 53 pounds; while per capita consumption of fish increased from 10 to 13 pounds. During the same period meat prices have risen at about the same rate as food prices in general; poultry prices have fallen relative to meat and food prices. As a class, fish has become relatively more expensive than the principal alternative high-protein foods. It is probably only the rising trend in per capita income that has helped to maintain the increasing consumption of fish in

Table III

Price Indices for Fish and Competitive Agricultural Products in the United States.
(1956-1958 = 100)

	Retail price indices for:			Wholesale price indices for:		
Year	Meat	Poultry	Fish	All food	Soybean meal	U.S. fish meal
1955	87.7	121.5	93.9	94.0	1.11	1.00
1956	84.8	106.5	93.8	94.7	1.00	0.99
1957	94.2	103.8	95.0	97.8	0.92	0.99
1958	104.9	102.6	101.6	101.9	1.09	1.02
1959	101.0	93.5	103.4	100.3	1.10	0.99
1960	99.2	95.0	103.5	101.4	1.03	0.70
1961	100.5	85.8	105.8	102.6	1.29	0.85
1962	102.5	90.7	110.2	103.6	1.29	0.91
1963	100.9	89.3	110.0	105.1	1.41	0.89
1964	99.4	87.3	107.4	106.4	1.35	0.95
1965	106.9	90.0	110.6	108.8	1.39	1.17
1966	116.8	94.9	117.8	114.2	1.63	1.13
1967	113.8	88.9	121.8	115.2	1.49	0.94
1968	116.5	91.7	123.8	119.4	1.51	0.95
1969	126.8	96.9	130.6	125.5	1.45	1.17
1970	133.9	96.4	143.7	132.4	1.54	1.38
1971	132.9	96.9	158.6	136.4	1.51	1.18
1972	147.1	98.2	172.9	142.3	2.04	1.30
1973	183.4	137.7	198.3	162.9	4.63	3.41
1974	186.8	130.7	228.7	186.3	1.74	2.09
1975	202.7	144.4	247.7	202.1	2.41	1.79
1976	202.7	136.9	276.9	208.3	3.16	2.49

the United States. Assuming that the price trend revealed by the retail price index for fish is the result of increasing costs of production relative to those of the other foods, these figures may reflect a relatively poor performance of the U.S. fisheries relative to U.S. agriculture. Another interpretation of the retail price trend is that the fisheries have operated at least cost but have been unable to expand production to meet the increasing demand due to constraints on the available fish stocks. With increasing demand and steady or sluggish supply, prices will rise. With either interpretation, it is clear that the domestic sea food industry is not demonstrating a capability for expanding production in tandem with land-based food industries. Furthermore, because much of the sea food consumed domestically is imported, it may be inferred that our foreign trading partners are subject to the same limitations. Yet the biological potential of the oceans, if we are to believe Chapman (5) and Schaefer (1), has hardly been exhausted. The increasing cost and sluggish supply is probably due to the full or over-exploitation of traditionally important fish stocks, accompanied by the inability of the industry to supplement traditional fisheries with new species or product forms from the unused or under-developed fish stocks. From an economic viewpoint the ocean's potential is well developed.

Available biological productivity does not imply economic productivity unless the biological products are both desired by consumers and cheaply produced. The most stringent economic constraint upon further expansion of food fish harvests appears to be the meager demand for most of the unused species at prices covering the unit production costs and providing a reasonable expectation of profit to the producers.

The market for industrial fishery products is quite similar to that for food fish, but with a twist. Because fish meal and oil enter the production processes for other goods as relatively undifferentiated inputs (i.e. not species-specific nor required to have subtle qualities to be acceptable), the market potential is not so severely constrained by tradition, culture or the biological productivity of popular fish stocks. In the case of fish meal the need for high protein supplements in poultry and livestock feed can be met by vegetable protein meals such as soybean meal. In table III it is indicated that soybean meal prices have risen relative to fish meal prices during the last two decades. Fish meal producers should, therefore, be in a good position to expand production and increasingly encroach upon the markets for high protein meals.

Contrary to this expectation the production of fish meal has shown the same sluggish tendency as has become expected of food fish production. Apparently, the concentrations of pelagic schooling fish (clupeoids, in particular) which can be caught inexpensively (i.e. at a cost of 25-50 dollars per ton) are an increasing rarity. Thus with fishery reduction products, as with food fish, the biological potential of the sea is barely exploited while the economically useful portion of that potential is largely developed. To expand the fisheries for reduction fish into, for example, "trash" bottomfish would cause an increase in the cost of fish meal due to the harvest costs. Higher raw fish costs must be covered by higher final product prices, but prices cannot be much higher if competitiveness is to be maintained. Any technological advances which increase the availability of fish for reduction at current prices would be useful. This applies equally to food fish production. However, technical innovations in our domestic fisheries are as likely to increase the rate of exploitation on existing fully exploited stocks as they are to help broaden the resource base.

Aquaculture may be a solution to this dilemma. By placing the entire process of production (or, at least, more of the process than is encompassed by the traditional fisheries) within the control of men, aquaculture presents us with the opportunity of applying more scientific methods to the food production process. Instead of hunting wild stocks, we establish specific stocks of favored species selected for genetic characteristics which optimize growth, appearance or whatever else promotes economic value. Under controlled conditions mortality is low and growth is fast. The productivity of the feed lot is applied to marine organisms.

There are isolated instances of reasonable success with aquaculture. Paradoxically, very few of the real successes have been developed through the application of Western technological knowhow in recent years. Oyster and mussel culture, salmon and trout rearing, and pond culture of carps and "milkfish" have all been developed over a much longer period than is spanned by the recent science of aquaculture. Infusions of modern scientific methods have undoubtedly helped to overcome problems of disease control and nutrition. This makes possible more physically productive and economically profitable aquaculture projects, but the amount of food fish produced by aquacultural techniques remains relatively meager.

Current developments in aquaculture seem to focus almost entirely upon high-priced products such as the salmonids, shrimp (6), freshwater prawns (7), and delicacies like lobster and abalone. The major reason for this emphasis is clear—the cost constraint on the production of delicacies is much less severe than on the production of staples. Given the high production costs characteristic of developing technologies, it is not surprising that intensive aquaculture techniques should be applied to high-priced species. High prices, however, dictate low volume.

Furthermore, in assessing the potential for food from the sea, it is not clear that the intensive aquacultural techniques will ever be economic enough to compete with agriculture or even to challenge the primitive hunting of fish with vessels. Ultimately, the cost and availability of requisite inputs such as water, coastal land, labor and technical expertise will determine the extent to which aquaculture will become competitive. Unless it is competitive in price, aquaculture will never contribute significantly to the world food supply. Recent studies (8) seem to be pessimistic about the possibility of great strides in the direction of lower cost aquaculture.

Management of Fish Stocks

Although biological productivity, demand for sea food, and harvest costs encompass the main constraints to food from the sea, a different type of impediment to food production is the institutional convention called "common property" or "free access". So long as oceanic fishery resources are open to exploitation by all without restriction, no fisherman competing vigorously to improve his own lot in life has much incentive to control his take of fish. It has long been recognized that the limited biological productivity of any animal population can be severely reduced through over-fishing by competitive fishermen. The power of government has been invoked in many instances to prevent over-fishing, but existing fishery regulations are often economically irrational and are also too limited in scope to deal with international fishery problems. As more of the world's fishery resource comes under the jurisdiction of coastal States, and as more of the oceanic fish stocks of real importance are brought under international management conventions, prospects for conservation of biological productivity will improve. Even if overfishing in the biological sense is prevented, however, the economic costs associated with sea food harvests may be unnecessarily high due to excessive competition for the limited harvests allowed under biologically oriented fishery management.

The importance of economic issues in fishery management was first analysed rigorously by Gordon (9). His conclusions are still appropriate today. Under fishery regulations which do not restrain the number of men and the capital equipment in the fishery, normal economic incentives of competitive fishermen will drive them to apply more and more economic inputs to the fishery until no net economic return can be earned. Thus over-capitalization (that is, investment of excessive amounts of capital equipment) occurs even when over-fishing is prevented. Strictly speaking, over-capitalization does not specifically result in a reduction in harvest of any managed fish stock. The use of enormous amounts of fishing vessels over short fishing seasons can result, however, in a shortage of capital for use in other fishing ventures which would otherwise attract investment funds. Thus the overall impact of free access may be to lessen the world harvest of sea foods.

This economic view of fisheries exploitation has some important ramifications. For one thing, application of advanced technology to ocean fish stocks will not necessarily result in greater harvests but may instead simply lead to more sophisticated and costly over-capitalization. I would certainly hesitate to argue that technological innovation is unimportant to the further development of world fisheries, but I would emphasize that progress would be more rapid if there were institutional safeguards to prevent over-capitalization and to assure at least moderate operating profits in existing fisheries.

Progress toward greater food production would be much facilitated by a re-direction of innovative expertise and capital investment. Rather than emphasizing cost reduction in already heavily-exploited fisheries, investment activities could be devoted to developing new products and new fisheries. Institutions are needed which restrain over-capitalization and encourage the use of the resulting economic profits for fishery development elsewhere. Currently, no such institutions exist. Thus there are as many problems with over-development as there are with under-development in fisheries. The north Atlantic and north Pacific fisheries are coming under increasingly strong harvesting restraints, while potentially profitable fisheries in the Indian Ocean remain underdeveloped largely for lack of investment capital (10). Any field of resource development must reconcile limited availability of capital and innovative expertise with seemingly unlimited opportunities. Under current institutions, the world fisheries must operate under the further constraint that much of the available capital and technology is wasted on duplicate efforts in over-capitalized fisheries. In the long run, the inability of international fishing conventions to deal effectively with the inherent economic inefficiency of common property fisheries may be the most effective constraint to full development of the sea's potential for food production.

That there are economic constraints to the production of food from the sea should come as no surprise. The required relationship of cost to price retards the economic development of many biologically productive fish and shellfish populations due to excessive harvest costs or to lack of consumer demand for reasonable rates of harvest. The same considerations of cost and price limit the current potential for aquacultural developments. And the irrational over-capitalization of many of the world's fisheries squanders an important source of funds for investment and technological development in new fisheries and products. These are real constraints which can prove troublesome to any plans for further rapid development of food from the sea. At the same time, economic constraints should not be accepted with great pessimism, for cautious and deliberate effort to remove or relax the constraints should prove both feasible and beneficial.

References

1. Schaefer, M.B. (1965). The Potential Harvest of the Sea. *Trans. Am. Fish.Soc.* **94**, 123.
2. Chapman, W.M. (1973). Food from the sea and public policy. In *Ocean Resources and Public Policy.*Ed. T.S. English. University of Washington Press,Seattle.
3. Bardach, J.E., Ryther J.H. and McLarney W.O. (1972). *Aquaculture, the Farming and Husbandry of Freshwater and Marine Organisms.* Wiley-Interscience, New York. p. 24.

4. Crutchfield, J.A. (1973). Resources from the Sea. In *Ocean Resources and Public Policy.* Ed. T.S. English. University of Washington Press, Seattle. p. 110.

5. Chapman, W.M. (1966). Ocean Fisheries: Status and Outlook. Exploiting the Ocean, Transactions of the Second Annual Meeting of the Marine Technology Society: p. 15.

6. Anderson, Lee G. (1973). An Economist Looks at Mariculture. *Mar. Tech. Soc. Jour.* **7**, 9.

7. Shang, Y.C. and Fujimura T. (1977). The Production Economics of Freshwater Prawn (*Macrobrachium rosenbergii*) Farming in Hawaii. *Aquaculture* **11**, 99.

8. Weatherby, A.H. and Cogger B.M.G. (1977). Fish Culture: Problems and Prospects. *Science* **197**, 427.

9. Gordon, H.S. (1954). The Economic Theory of a Common-property Resource: the Fishery. *J. Polit. Econ.,* **62**, 124.

10. Marr, J.C. (1972). Indian Ocean Fishery Development. In *World Fisheries Management.* Ed. B.J. Rothschild. University of Washington Press, Seattle.

Public Health Constraints
On Food Production From The Sea

F. Raymond Fields

U.S. Department of Commerce
National Oceanic and Atmospheric Administration
National Marine Fisheries Service
Pascagoula, Mississippi

The public health aspect of land-based animal food products is extensive, has been in place for a number of years, has a well-defined reporting system, and is fairly well coordinated at the national level. It starts with the practicing veterinarian who is involved with a state livestock health board and a federal animal health agency located within each state. As the animals move from production centers to slaughter and processing into food products, there is a formalized system of inspection by both the Federal and state governments. For technical and scientific support of inspection services, there are well equipped and staffed diagnostic laboratories to examine animal diseases in depth. There are also public health laboratories at the state level which receive samples and reports from sanitarians operating on both the county and city levels. City, county, state, and federal personnel inspect and sample products for health purposes at the manufacturing, wholesale, and, in some cases, retail levels.

Some of the above-mentioned agencies deal with seafood in a monitoring and testing capacity. Because of its life as a free and wild organism and its coldblooded nature, the seafood-producing animal is not generally scrutinized critically until human handling causes a degradation of the product. Agencies that were in existence before the effects of industrial and municipal effluents upon the marine environment became apparent have extended their responsibilities; and new agencies have emerged. The federal Environmental Protection Agency is involved heavily in this regard. Additionally the National Oceanic and Atmospheric Administration (NOAA), primarily through the National Marine Fisheries Service laboratories on the Atlantic, Pacific, and Gulf coasts, is committed to in-depth studies of both coastal areas and the associated fishery resources. Although in most cases the technology exists to halt the destruction of marine ecosystems, the social change necessary to implement the technology, in my judgment, is not yet at hand. Part of the destruction of the ecosystem results from contamination of the rivers, marshes, estuaries, bays, and even oceans where these wild fishery resources live and reproduce. Study of the populations of marine organisms is a basic necessity to ensure not only continued production as food, but often the survival of the species as a naturally reproducing entity.

Innovative thinkers within the scientific community, spurred on by the industries whose primary income is derived from marine sources, have helped create mechanisms to examine the resource species and its habitat. The social change which will, perhaps, protect the habitat has had some positive effect. But old ideas die slowly; the notion is still strong, in my opinion, with many individuals concerned with waste disposal that one can make a garbage dump of the aquatic part of the world. Because of the worldwide presence of domestic and industrial waste, we are faced with a number of potential public health problems which limit the utilization of fishery resources. In addition, there are problems indigenous to the environment or to the fishery resources themselves which limit utilization. For this discussion, these factors are called public health constraints.

Those constraints which are present while the animal is living are environmental hazards; those which occur as the organism is manufactured into foodstuffs are processed-induced hazards; and those which occur when it is stored, transported, cooked, and served are food service hazards.

Environmental Hazards

Several marine toxins are sometimes found in seafood. Some are due to a concentration of substances elaborated by algae. As the toxin progresses up the food chain, it eventually becomes concentrated enough so that the food organism is injurious to the human consumer. Paralytic shellfish poison found in mollusks from the Northwest and Alaska, elaborated by the alga *Gonyaulax catanella* serves as an example. Another toxin is that associated with puffer fish which is apparently indigenous to the fish itself. Ciguatera toxin is usually found in grouper, jack fishes, barracuda, snappers, and surgeonfish in an area between 30° north and south latitude. The mechanism of ciguatera toxin production is not fully understood.

The metals of most importance in effluents discharging into the marine environment are mercury, cadmium, lead, and arsenic. Others which can occur in significant concentration are chromium and copper.

Toxic organic substances of public health significance which enter the marine environment may be divided into: pesticides such as DDT and its analogs, dieldrin, and Endrin; herbicides such as 2,4-D, 2,4,5-T, and Herbicide Orange; industrial solvents and chemicals such as polychlorinated biphenyls, polybrominated biphenyls, and dioxin (a recent report on the Housatonic River in Connecticut estimates the dumping of 500,000 pounds of PCB in the last 20 years from one electrical plant alone); and petroleum compounds such as diesel oils, crankcase oil, and crude oil.

Another class of compounds which may pose future problems through expanded usage is the polychlorinated phenols. Pentachlorophenol, for example, is used as a substitute for creosote in wood preservation, and is gaining acceptance as a pesticide. A newer class of compounds, the polycycloaromatics, is coming into prominence. The benzopyrenes are an example.

Microbiological contaminants which are often found are *Vibrio parahaemolyticus* and *Vibrio cholerae, Salmonella* and *Shigella* sp., *Erysipelas* sp., *Pseudomonas* sp., *Clostridium* spp., and the enteropathogenic coliforms. *Vibrio parahaemolyticus* was first discovered to be a human pathogen in seafoods by the Japanese and is thought to occur in harbor and inshore waters worldwide. Although these micro organisms do not usually limit the use of seafoods, they do limit the way in which the food may be processed and used. The same is true of the viral and nematode diseases such as Hepatitis B and Anisakiasis. Other helminth infestations limit the use of otherwise acceptable fish by the unesthetic appearance due to the presence of the worm in the flesh itself. Such is common in large drum from the Gulf of Mexico. Larvel forms can also occur in the flesh of other seafoods. *Sulcascaris* sp. larvae (final host is the sea turtle) are found in drum; *Thynnascaris* sp., *Cucullanus* sp., *Scolex polymorphus* in mullet; and *Porocaecum* sp. in scallops.

Process-Induced Hazards

The process-induced hazards are most commonly bacteria, toxins, and chemicals. One limiting factor is simply basic spoilage of the catch due to lack of refrigeration or poor handling practices. It has been impossible to establish a percentage figure of the total world production, but the U.S. Food and Drug Administration reports that of the imported shrimp sampled, about 10 percent is rejected due to decomposition. If this rejection rate is true, the potential limitation of resource utilization could be as much as 23 million pounds, when one considers that the U.S. imports annually 230 million pounds of shrimp. Food Technologist and Inspector Donald R. Maher of the National Marine Fisheries Service, points out that some years ago only five percent of the red snapper from the Gulf of Mexico reaching the Chicago market had a shelf life of five days. British and FAO studies in the tropics indicate that due to lack of refrigeration, preservation by sun drying and salting is widely utilized. But losses are high due to rancidity formation in the fats.

Some of the more common toxins induced are bacteriological—such as those of *Clostridium botulinum* and *C. perfringens* which develop because improper processing steps allow toxin elaboration in the foodstuff. In terms of process-induced chemicals, nitrosamines serve as examples of those which may be formed by the combining of nitrites used as preservatives with the amines of the flesh. Histamines and related toxins are formed by the breakdown of proteins following the death of scombroid fishes—tuna and mackerel.

Additionally, accidental contamination of the seafood products by pesticides, cleaning compounds and sanitizers can further limit product utilization.

Food Service Hazards

Other factors limiting utilization are conditions during transportation, storage, and preparation which lead to thawing, dehydration, and outright spoilage. Retail storage has been guilty of product mishandling due to poor freezer case maintenance, and to the fact that the purchasing public mishandles the product. In order to give some feeling for the extent of this potential problem, I would point out that of the cases of food-borne disease outbreaks reported to CDC in 1974, only 63 were due to seafood while 1,300 were found to be due to other sources.

Finally, much of the seafood product is wasted, made inedible, or spoiled by poor preparation in both commercial and non-commercial food establishments and in the home.

It has neither been my intention nor purpose to trot out the Horsemen of the Apocalypse in a parade of possible public health problems confronting the utilization of fishery resources. Rather, I have merely addressed a few of the issues public health scientists are dealing with in the utilization and consumption of fishery products. In my judgment, the public health issues associated with fishery products are not nearly as profound nor as intricately complex as those associated with other animal protein products such as red meat and poultry. One of the more confusingly complex public health issues confronting contemporary seafood utilization deals with the differing opinion about true public health relevance by public health administrators. The lowly frog serves as an example. Due to environmental harvesting conditions, frog legs possess a high contamination level of *Salmonella*. Thorough cooking prior to consumption destroys the pathogens; however, the possibility of cross-contamination in the kitchen with other foodstuffs which are not cooked causes concern. Many public health professionals in the U.S. believe that contaminated frog legs should not be allowed to be offered for sale. Others believe that consumer education in terms of proper food preparation is the real answer. Nonetheless, frog legs are currently discriminated against due to *Salmonella* contamination. Contrast this with fresh poultry, which has roughly the same degree of *Salmonella* contamination, is consumed in greater volume by a wider susceptible population at risk, and currently receives little regulatory activity from a *Salmonella* monitoring point of view. One of the seldom recognized problems in seafood utilization is the divergent points of view by public health administrators. Surely this matter needs resolution.

For fishery products, only by a constant effort to educate the public (which, after all, makes up governmental bodies and the personnel of industry and municipalities) to the value of maintaining both the resource and the environment in a high state of production can we hope to increase seafood production and consumption.

I see the educational effort as a necessity in foreign relations, such as the negotiations concerned with inspection and monitoring of growing areas and processing operations in other countries. This is due to the fact that 65 to 70 percent of our U.S. seafood consumption is from imported sources. The Department of Commerce supports the passage of legislation to bring about mandatory surveillance inspection of all fishery products, whether of foreign or domestic origin.

Obviously, research into ways and means to improve water quality worldwide is imperative. In this country, molluscs, crustaceans, and high quality fish such as snapper, haddock, cod, halibut, and salmon are rapidly becoming luxury gourmet items. The high mercury content of swordfish has restricted its interstate use for some years. Unless we are able to remove the public health constraints which not only affect us as consumers but even affect the production of the fishery resource itself, nearly every class of seafood may become not a basic part of our nutrition but a luxury item only.

Physical Upper Limits On Fisheries Production

Julien R. Goulet, Jr.

U.S. Department of Commerce
National Oceanic and Atmospheric Administration
National Marine Fisheries Service
Washington, D.C.

The Marine Fisheries Production System is a limited system. It is not open ended, nor does it provide an infinite cornucopia of fishery products. Rather, as with all natural systems, the Marine Fisheries Production System has limits that need to be considered only when demand for fishery products is a large fraction of the system's potential production.

I consider only system limits, that is, limits that are a property of the Marine Fisheries Production System, and not external limits such as the price of landed products, the extent of fleet capitalization, consumer demand for selected products, the ban on taking of marine mammals, etc. I do not consider technologic limits, nor economic limits, and I assume that we have the technology and capital to exploit all that can be exploited. I consider only the limits to that exploitation imposed by the nature of the Marine Fisheries Production System, or rather by the nature of the model selected to understand the system.

Fisheries Production System

The Marine Fisheries Production System can be defined by its inputs, its outputs, and the internal transformations which convert input to output. The input to the system is primary production. The outputs from the system are man's harvest and waste matter. Detritus is recycled; it is both an input and an output. This is an extreme simplification—river runoff brings in organic matter, birds harvest from the system, some biomass is stored in sediments, etc.

Biomass is continually recycled within the system, losing a large fraction at each cycle. Whether or not there is any harvest by man, the total output equals the total input over the long term. Man's harvest just removes some of the transformed input before it can be completely transformed into waste matter. In that sense, man is in competition with high trophic level predators. Short term fluctuations in the total biomass of the system are not considered, and the difference between short term and long term, whether it is years or geologic epochs, is left undefined.

The internal transformations which take place within the system can be represented by the food chain equation: $F = P f C E^l$
where F is the fisheries production, P is the primary carbon production, f is the exploitable fraction, C is the biomass to carbon ratio, E is the efficiency of trophic transfer, and l is the trophic level.

Four limits to Marine Fisheries Production are represented in this equation: The primary carbon production or input (since the system cannot transform more biomass than it receives); the trophic level at which we harvest from the system; the trophic transfer efficiency; and the exploitable fraction. The exploitable fraction is the maximum fraction of production that can be harvested considering all the biomass in the ocean, not just the presently exploited stocks, or the presently desirable stocks. It is therefore an index of our ability to compete with high trophic level predators. It ignores technical and economic feasibility, assuming any necessary technology is available. It implies that we may have to harvest sculpins, dogfish, or chaetognaths if we wish to reach the full potential of the Marine Fisheries Production System.

There are at least three approaches to refining this food chain model in order to obtain more precise estimates of fisheries production. Ryther (1) partitioned the world oceans into three regimes—upwelling, coastal, and open ocean. In each regime he identified a typical food chain and average annual primary production and estimated 120 million metric tons of world fisheries production.

A second approach is the elaboration of a complete system of dynamic equations, specifying the change in biomass in each component of the system as a function of transfers from other components. This approach can provide detailed analysis of small closed ecosystems. For application to larger ecosystems or to the world's fisheries production system, it is difficult to specify every necessary component—should there be a separate component for *Physalia* or *Janthina*? The system of equations may be incomplete unless one component is labelled "other"; and the component labelled "other" may be significant unless the total number of components reaches intolerable levels—even for modern computers.

The third approach (2) is to consider the Marine Fisheries Production System as an unstructured food web, in which all heterotrophs are treated at the same average trophic position. Lange and Hurley (3) expanded this work and provided a rigorous mathematical treatment. They developed a matrix of transfer coefficients between four components: source or primary production, irretrievable dead matter or waste matter, retrievable dead matter or recyclable detritus, and fish standing stock. Conceptually, if a fifth component, man's harvest, is added, the matrix is solved and the equation which expresses potential harvest as a function of primary production is extracted, the original food chain equation is retrieved. However, all parameters have average values representative of the average system. The food chain equation is expressed in its exponential form because trophic position can be a non-integer.

Because the exploitable fraction is most likely a function of regime—the exploitable fraction would be much reduced for open ocean fisheries as compared to upwelling regime fisheries—the exploitable fraction is included with the primary production and the equation expresses an "Exploitable Primary Production". The transfer efficiency for herbivores and carnivores can be different, and the revised food chain equation is: $F = P C E_h \exp[(p-1) \ln E_c]$

where F is the fisheries production, P is the exploitable primary carbon production, C is the biomass to carbon ration, E_h is the herbivore trophic efficiency, exp is the exponential function or antilog, P is the trophic position of the harvest, ln is the natural logarithm, and E_c is the carnivore trophic efficiency.

Estimates

According to the literature, the carnivore efficiency seems to range from 1 percent to 50 percent. Parsons and Takahashi (4) stated that its most likely value is between 10 percent and 15 percent. They also stated that herbivore efficiency is most likely greater than 20 percent.

I used data from Parsons and Takahashi (4) to estimate the biomass to carbon ratio. To estimate exploitable primary production, I used the regimes and productivities tabulated by Moiseev (5). The world has 36.7 million square kilometers of sea surface; the U.S. has less than 1 percent of that (2.06 million square kilometers) in its 200 mile Fisheries Conservation Zone. The five regimes are upwelling, coastal, divergent, intermediate, and central water regimes. I have included highly productive estuarine waters in the upwelling regime. Forty percent of the world's waters are central waters, of lowest productivity; while 80 percent of the U.S. waters are coastal, of second highest productivity (Table I).

The total world primary production is 22.1 billion tons of carbon estimated per year; the U.S. production is about 1 percent of that—less than 276 million tons of carbon per year. One quarter of U.S. primary production comes from upwelling areas and 3/4 comes from the coastal areas. The primary production of the world oceans is pretty evenly distributed among the 5 regimes (Table I).

The exploitable fraction in each regime is a bit of a problem. Ryther (1) estimated 0.5 for a single species fisheries—a short lived, low trophic level stock in an upwelling regime. Moiseev (5) estimated 0.25 for general coastal fisheries. For a first approximation, I used 0.5 for upwelling

Table I
Primary Production and Exploitable Production for U.S. and World Surface Waters

Regime[1]	Productivity[2]			Exploitable Fraction[3]			Area[4]	Primary Production[5]			Exploitable Prim. Prod.[5]		
	low	med	high	low	med	high		low	med	high	low	med	high
U.S. Waters													
Upwelling	182	273	365	.45	.5	.55	.22	40.0	60.1	80.3	18.0	30.1	44.2
Coastal	91	124	183	.225	.25	.275	.165	150.1	204.6	302.0	33.8	51.2	83.1
Divergent	55	73	91	.113	.125	.130	.09	5.0	6.6	8.2	0.6	0.8	1.1
Intermediate	37	51	55	.057	.063	.069	.10	3.7	5.1	5.5	0.2	0.3	0.4
TOTAL							2.06	198.8	276.4	396.0	52.6	82.4	128.8
World Waters													
Upwelling	182	273	365	.45	.5	.55	10.7	1947	2921	3906	876	1461	2148
Coastal	91	124	183	.225	.25	.275	38.7	3522	4799	7082	792	1200	1948
Divergent	55	73	91	.113	.125	.130	86.5	4758	6315	7872	535	789	1082
Intermediate	37	51	55	.057	.063	.069	82.8	3064	4223	4554	174	266	316
Central	18	26	37	.028	.031	.034	148.3	2669	3856	5487	74	120	187
TOTAL							367.0	15960	22114	28902	2451	3836	5681

1. See table 40, p. 107 of Moiseev (1969)
2. Units are mtC/km²·yr. See table 40, p. 107 of Moiseev (1969)
3. See text. Rang of ± 10% assumed.
4. Units are 10⁶ km². See table 16 and 18, pp. 27,29 of Moiseev (1969) for U.S. area and table 40, p. 107 for world area .
5. Units are 10⁶ mtC/yr.

regimes, 0.25 for coastal regimes. 0.125 for divergent regimes, etc.—halving the exploitable fraction for each succeeding regime.

The world's annual exploitable primary production is estimated as 3.84 billion tons of carbon. The U.S. has about 2 percent of that (82.4 million tons of carbon). One-third of the U.S. exploitable primary production comes from upwelling waters, and two-thirds comes from coastal waters. One-third of the world's exploitable primary production comes from upwelling waters, one-third from coastal waters, and the remaining primarily from divergent waters. While the central waters are 40 percent of surface waters, they provide only 3 percent of exploitable primary production (Table I).

To determine the average trophic position of the harvest, I partitioned the catch into seven categories: Grazers, Detritivores, Planktivores, Omnivores, Small Predators, Medium Predators, and Large Predators (Table II). The Planktivores include krill, planktivorous crustaceans and planktivorous fish. The following equation was used to calculate the average trophic position of harvest and also of each category using food ratios: $P = \ln(\sum \exp p_i / \sum B_i)$,

where P is the trophic position of harvest, B_i is the biomass of the i th component of harvest, and P_i is the trophic position of the i th component of the harvest.

Table II—Trophic Categories

CATEGORY	FEEDS ON	RATIOr_i	p_i	P[1]
Grazers	algae	1.0	1.0	1.0
Planktivores	phytoplankton	0.5	1.0	
	zooplankton	0.5	2.0	1.62
Detritivores	detritus	0.5	0.0	
	phyloplankton	0.1	1.0	
	zooplankton	0.4	2.0	1.316
Small predators	planktivores	1.0	2.62	2.62
Medium predators	sm. pred.	0.4	3.62	
	planktivores	0.2	2.62	
	detritivores	0.4	2.316	3.079
Large predators	sm. pred.	0.4	3.62	
	med. pred.	0.4	4.079	
	detritivores	0.2	2.316	3.704
Omnivores	planktivores	0.4	2.62	
	sm. pred.	0.2	3.62	
	detritivores	0.4	2.316	2.834

[1]TROPHIC POSITION: $p = \ln(\sum r_i \exp p_i)$

The present (1975) world catch of fisheries products totals 58 million tons (Table III). The catch in U.S. waters is 11 percent of that or 6.6 million tons, which includes 2.6 million tons of U.S. commercial catch, 0.7 million of U.S. sport catch, and 3.3 million of foreign catch. One third of the world catch is of planktivores; only 5 percent is of large predators. The largest fraction of the U.S. catch is of medium predators, followed by planktivores. The average trophic position of the U.S. catch is 2.818 while the trophic position of the world catch is slightly lower, 2.642.

For all the parameters—exploitable primary production, biomass to carbon ratio, herbivore efficiency, carnivore efficiency, and trophic position—I estimated low, mid, and high values. I then calculated potential fisheries production, and two ranges. The outer range is given by the worst and best cases, all parameters at their low or high values; and the most likely range is given by having one parameter low or high at a time while all other parameters are at their mid value.

The mid value potential marine fisheries production for U.S. waters is 9.6 million tons; and 642 million tons for the world (Table IV). This com-

Table III—Trophic Positions

TROPHIC CATEGORY	TROPHIC POSITION	U.S.[1] HARVEST	WORLD[2] HARVEST
Grazers	1.0	—	17,100
Planktivores	1.62	1,409,396	19,345,084
Detritivores	1.316	623,438	3,047,214
Sm. Pred.	2.62	539,784	3,301,744
Med. Pred.	3.079	2,551,703	12,697,615
Large Pred.	3.704	558,702	3,182,666
Omnivores	2.834	595,164	8,053,966
Unclassified		272,384	8,477,326
TOTAL		6,550,571	58,122,715
Trophic position[3]		2.818	2.642

1. Units are metric tons. Includes U.S. commercial catch for 1971-1975 (Robinson 1977), U.S. sport catch for 1970 (Deuel 1973), and foreign catch for 1975 (unpublished tabulation, Fisheries Assessment Division, NMFS, Washington, D.C. 20235).
2. Units are metric tons. Average 1970-1974 world catch (FAO 1975).
3. $p = \ln(\sum B_i \exp p_i \sum B_i)$

Table IV
Estimates of all Parameters and of Fisheries Production

PARAMETER	U.S.				WORLD			
	low	med	high	Units	low	med	high	Units
P	52.6	82.4	128.8	10^6mtC	2451	3836	5681	10^6mtC
C'	13.4	22.6	31.8		13.4	22.6	31.8	"
E_h[2]	0.2	0.225	0.25		0.2	0.225	0.25	"
E_c[2]	0.1	0.125	0.15		0.1	0.125	0.15	"
p[3]	3.00	2.818	2.59		2.984	2.642	2.433	"
F[4]	1.41	9.56	50.15	10^6mt	68	642	2979	10^6mt
F(P)[5]	6.10		14.94	"	410		951	"
F(C)[5]	5.67		13.45	"	381		903	"
F(E_h)[5]	8.50		10.62	"	571		713	"
F(E_c)[5]	6.37		13.32	"	445		866	"
F(p)[5]	6.55		15.36	"	315		991	"
Limiting Parameter	C		p		p		p	
Present harvest		6.55		10^6mt		58.1		10^6mt

1. Calculated from Table 12, p. 49 of Parson and Takahashi (1973)
2. Estimated from Parsons and Takahashi (1973, p. 124)
3. Range determined by sequentially deleting one entire category
4. Low estimate is worst case (all variables low); high estimate is best case (all variables high).
5. Variable in parentheses is only variable low or high, others have mid value. Underlined values are extremes.

pares to the present catch of 6.6 million tons from U.S. waters and 58.1 million tons worldwide. The worst case-best case ranges are 1.4 million to 50.1 million tons for U.S. waters and 68 million to 2.98 billion tons worldwide. The most likely ranges are 5.7 to 15.4 million tons for U.S. waters; and 315 to 991 million tons worldwide.

Discussion

Why does this analysis indicate that the U.S. is presently harvesting over half of its potential marine fisheries production, while the world is harvesting only one-tenth? The most likely range of potential fisheries production for U.S. waters, 5.7 to 15.4 million tons, is slightly lower than conventional estimates of 10 to 20 million tons, while the estimate of world fisheries production of 315 to 991 million tons seems unreasonably high.

The answer lies in the inclusion of vast expanses of central ocean waters. If we tried to exploit these central waters, we could not do so at the present average trophic position.

Remember that the basic assumption of this analysis was that technologic and economic constraints did not exist. Practically, this vast potential has limits; but those limits, technologic and economic, are not system limits.

Let us examine the Marine Fisheries Production System in a slightly different manner. Let us consider a three component world fishery—planktivores, large predators, and all others (which I'll call coastal fisheries). The planktivores are harvested at a trophic position of 1.620; the large predators are harvested at a trophic position of 3.704; and the coastal fisheries are harvested at a trophic position of 2.852 (determined by recalculation with the other two categories removed).

I determined the exploitable primary production needed to support the present world fisheries in these three categories and determined the surplus exploitable primary production (Table V). We are presently, worldwide, catching 3.2 million tons of large predators, 35.6 million of coastal fisheries, and 19.3 million of planktivores.

These 58.1 million tons of fisheries products represent 516 million tons of carbon, or less than 15 percent of the exploitable primary production. The surplus exploitable, primary production, 3.32 billion tons of carbon, could be harvested as 61 million tons of large predators, or 359 million tons of coastal fisheries, or 4.65 billion tons of planktivores.

Recognizing that we cannot harvest all of this surplus as coastal fisheries because the shelf areas are less than 5 percent of the surface area, we assume that only a proportional amount of coastal fisheries could be harvested. That harvest, proportional to shelf areas, is 15.5

Table V
Calculations of Surplus Primary Productions and Potential Fish Products

Pattition present catch as follows:

Category	Trophic position	Catch		exploitable primary production needed[2]	
Planktivores	1.62	19.345	10^6mt	13.8	10^6mtC
Coastal fisheries[1]	2.852	35.568	10^6mt	329.1	10^6mtC
Large predators	3.704	3.183	10^6mt	173.2	10^6mtC
TOTAL				516.1	

Surplus exploitable primary Production (3836-516)	3320	10^6mtC
% exploited	13.5%	
If surplus exploitable as plankitivores	4651	10^6mt
If surplus exploitable as large predators	61	10^6mt
If surplus exploitable as coastal fisheries	359	10^6mt
If surplus exploitable as coastal fisheries is proportional to shelf areas (3320 X 15.78 / 367)[3]		143 x 10^6mtC
as coastal fisheries		15.5 x 10^6mt
Revised surplus (3320-143)		3177 x 10^6mtC
If exploited as planktivores		4450 x 10^6mtC
If exploited as large predators		58 x 10^6mtC

planktivores = 4450 — 76.724 x large predators.

[1]Total catch including planktivores and large predators and including unclassified as average. See Table 3.
[2]Inverse of fish production equation: $P = F/CE_h$ except $(p-1) \ln E_c$
[3]Shelf areas of world, 15.78 x 10^6km^2, excluding Artic and Antarctic from table 20, p35 of Moiseev (1969)

million tons of coastal fisheries representing 143 million tons of carbon. The remaining surplus exploitable primary carbon, 3.18 billion tons, can be harvested as 58 million tons of large predators or 4.45 billion tons of planktivores.

The trade off between planktivores and large predators has a ratio of 76.7 tons of planktivores to one ton of large predators. We thus have 58.1 million tons of present world catch, and an estimated coastal fisheries surplus of 15.5 million tons, for a total of 73.6 million tons. The remaining open ocean surplus can be exploited as large predators, or planktivores, or some combination of the two, for a fisheries production ranging from 132 million to 4.52 billion tons.

Summary

If we exclude harvesting from the vast open ocean area, the best estimate of marine fisheries production is approximately 74 million tons—58 million of present catch plus 16 million of additional coastal fisheries. This figure can be increased slightly because present technologic and economic considerations allow the harvesting of some Antarctic krill, a planktivore, and a slight increase in harvesting of open ocean large predators, such as tuna, by expansion into under-exploited areas.

This analysis is a coarse first cut. It would be easy to quibble with many details. Certainly changing the estimates of some of the variables, especially those variables with exponential relations, can change the estimates of fisheries production tremendously. While this is an extremely simplified model for the Marine Fisheries Production System, it turns out to be a data hungry model. The estimated output limit is a strong function of the estimated input limits: the exploitable primary production, the trophic efficiency, and especially the trophic level of harvest.

I would also like to caution that the model is an integrative model. It does not concern itself with the way the marine fisheries ecosystem expresses itself. Certainly we cannot, at our option, trade off between harvesting Antarctic krill and harvesting Alaska tanner crab. We cannot trade off between harvesting Chesapeake Bay oysters and harvesting Eastern Pacific yellowfin tuna. But we may have already forced a trade off between harvesting blue whales and harvesting Antarctic krill, or between harvesting George's Bank haddock and harvesting dogfish.

References

1. Ryther, J.H. (1969). Photosynthesis and Fish Production in the Sea. *Science* **166**, 72.
2. Isaacs, J.D. (1972). Unstructured Marine Food Webs and Pollutant Analogues. *Fish. Bull.* **70**, 1053.
3. Lange, G.D. and Hurlev, A.C. (1975). A Theoretical Treatment of Unstructured Food Webs. *Fish. Bull.* **73**, 378.
4. Parsons, T.R. and Takahashi, M. (1973). *Biological Oceanographic Processes.* Pergamon Press, New York. p. 186
5. Moiseev, P.A. (1969). *The Living Resources of the World Ocean.* Translated 1971. Israel program for Scientific Translations, Jerusalem, p. 334.

INDEX

Genera, Species and Common Names

INDEX[1]

[1]Genus, species and common names.